THERMOELASTICITY

A. D. Kovalenko

Thermoelasticity

Basic Theory and Applications

Translated from the Russian

by D. B. Macvean

Lecturer Engineering Laboratories University of Glasgow

With an appendix on Thermoelastic Stability

by J. B. Alblas

Professor of Mechanics Technical University Eindhoven

ΙͶͰͲΝΙ

WOLTERS-NOORDHOFF PUBLISHING GRONINGEN 1969

THE NETHERLANDS

Catal. card nr. 72-90849

ACADEMY OF SCIENCES OF THE UKRANIAN SSR
INSTITUTE OF MECHANICS

This book contains a summary of the theory of thermoelasticity, in particular, the basic laws and methods of thermoelasticity that are necessary for the study of thermal stresses in structural components produced by steady and unsteady temperature fields. The solutions are given for a series of static and quasi–static problems concerning thermal stresses in disks, plates, shells, and bodies of revolution. Not only dynamic problems of thermoelasticity, but thermoelastic effects evoked by deformation processes are considered. The material is intended for scientists working in the field of thermoelasticity. It can also be used by students in applied mathematics departments of universities where emphasis is placed on continuum mechanics.

TABLE OF CONTENTS

Chapter III

Basic Laws and Problems of Heat Conduction   51

Chapter IV

The Plane Problem in Thermoelasticity   82

Chapter V

Thermoelastic Behaviour of Shells of Revolution   113

Chapter VI

Axisymmetric Problem of Thermoelasticity

Chapter VII

Appendix . . . .

PREFACE

This book is based on a special course of thermoelasticity that the author has been teaching for some years to the students of the applied mathematics department at the Shevchenko State University, Kiev.

The reader will find an account of the basic principles and methods of thermoelasticity including heat conduction, thermal stresses arising as the result of heat exchange with the surroundings, and thermal effects evoked by deformation processes.

The contents of the book has been arranged in the following order: first attention is given to the thermodynamics underlying thermoelasticity and the problem of thermoelasticity is formulated in its most general form taking account not only of the interaction between the strain and temperature fields but also of dynamic effects during unsteady processes of deformation; then the quasi–static problem of thermoelasticity is formulated and the theory of heat conduction is developed to the extent necessary for the study of temperature fields; further, an examination is made of the basic class of thermoelastic problems in the quasi–static formulation (the plane problem, shells of revolution, and the axisymmetric problem); in the last chapter the dynamics and related problems of thermoelasticity are discussed.

The book makes use of results of research by the author and his co–workers in the field of quasi–static thermoelasticity and heat conduction.

INTRODUCTION

Recently, thermodynamics has undergone marked development in connection with important problems arising during the design of steam and gas turbines, jet motors, rockets, high—speed aircraft, nuclear reactors, etc.

Heat flow from the gas stream in heat engines, aerodynamic heating in high—speed aircraft, the heat given out by nuclear reactors, etc. all lead to the fact that the components in these machines operate under conditions of non—uniform, unsteady heating which change the physical and mechanical properties of the materials. There are then temperature gradients accompanying the non—uniform temperature distribution throughout the various components.

Because of constraints, a non—uniform temperature distribution in a component having a complex shape usually gives rise to thermal stresses. It is essential to know the magnitude and effect of these thermal stresses when carrying out a rigorous design of such components.

The thermal stresses alone and in combination with the mechanical stresses produced by the external forces can give rise to cracks and rupture in components containing brittle materials.

Some materials become brittle when thermal stresses appear quickly as the result of a high temperature gradient in an unsteady temperature field; it is said that they cannot withstand thermal shock. The repeated action of thermal stresses leads to thermal fatigue in machine parts. Thermal stresses can cause considerable plastic strains leading to complete or progressive destruction of the structure. Such stresses can also lead to thermal buckling in thin—walled structures.

In the general case, the change in temperature of a body is caused not only by heat transport from the surroundings but also by the process of deformation. When the rate of deformation is finite, thermo—mechanical effects of another nature are of importance, namely the generation and flow of heat within the body, the occurrence of associated elastic and thermal waves, thermoelastic dissipation of energy, etc.

The present book is devoted to the theory of thermoelasticity based on the application of thermodynamic principles to the processes of deformation. The book does not contain an exhaustive treatment of the foundations of thermoelasticity but aims rather at giving a brief treatment of the basic principles and methods of thermoelasticity embraced in the following fields: heat conduction, thermoelastic stresses and strains caused by heat flow from the surroundings, and thermoelastic effects arising from the deformation processes.

The book is divided into seven chapters.

Chapter I is devoted to the thermodynamic foundations of thermoelasticity. The treatment begins with the basic laws of classical thermodynamics. In formulating the second law of thermodynamics preference has been given to the more recent formulation developed by Shiller (1897–1901) at Kiev University, Carathéodory (1901) in Germany, and Afanassjewa–Ehrenfest (1925–1928). This formulation establishes a general empirical principle concerning the impossibility of certain processes. Known as the principle of adiabatic inaccessibility, it enables one to express the second law of thermodynamics in mathematical terms when the thermodynamic state of a system is described by a large number of independent variables, as is the case with deformable solids.

The theory of irreversible processes has been explained to the extent necessary for the study of the thermodynamics of an ideally elastic, homogeneous, isotropic body that is deformed under the action of non–uniform heating. The method of thermodynamic functions, which was developed by Gibbs in the eighteen–seventies, has been used to deduce the stress–strain relations, the expressions for the entropy, and the associated heat flow equation.

The derivation of the basic equations, the formulation of the problem, and the representation of the solution of the thermoelastic problem has been carried out in full generality, i.e. account has been taken of (1) the relation between the strain and temperature fields implied by the laws of thermodynamics and (2) the inertia forces due to either unsteady heating or external forces.

In deriving a heat conduction equation with terms depending on the strain, use has been made of the thermodynamics of linear irreversible processes, which is valid provided the thermodynamic system deviates only slightly from the equilibrium state.

Chapter I dealing with the thermodynamics of linear irreversible processes closes with the treatment of a variational principle for the coupled problem of thermoelasticity. This principle enables one to construct approximate solutions for problems in elasto—dynamics and unsteady heat conduction.

Chapter II is devoted to the quasi—static formulation of thermoelasticity. Here the coupling terms in the heat conduction equation and the inertia terms in the equations of motion are neglected. A special chapter is reserved for the quasi—static problem because of its great practical importance. Under normal conditions of heat exchange, the heat flux produced by the deformations and dynamic effects give rise to unsteady heating which is so small that the corresponding terms in the equations can be discarded. Then the system of equations reduces to the usual heat conduction equation and the equations describing the static thermoelastic problem for the stresses with prescribed temperature field, which is due to the external heat sources alone. When dealing with quasi—static thermoelastic problems, we will use the general representation for the displacements in the form derived by Papkovich in the period 1932—1937. In this representation, the solution of the homogeneous equation for the displacement vector contains a vector and a scalar both of which are arbitrary harmonic functions. The particular solution of the corresponding nonhomogeneous equation taking account of the prescribed temperature field is determined by a scalar function that satisfies the Poisson equation. This scalar function is called the *thermoelastic displacement potential*.

The formulation of the quasi—static thermoelastic problem has been given not only for a simply connected body but also for a multiply connected one. In Chapter II a study has also been made of the analogy between thermoelastic problems and the corresponding problems in the isotropic theory of elasticity with fictitious body and surface forces. These forces are determined by thermoelastic variational principles which are generalizations of the Lagrange variational equation and the Castigliano variational principle for the isotropic theory of elasticity. We also present the generalization, due to Maizel' (1941), of the Betti—Maxwell theorem to the case of thermoelastic problems. Chapter III contains those basic results in the theory of the conduction of heat necessary for the study of temperature fields and the corresponding thermal stresses in the quasi—static theory. The free transfer of heat at the surface of the body has been considered, the basic equations of steady and unsteady heat conduction without and with heat sources have been deduced, idealized boundary conditions have been formulated, and certain problems concerning steady and unsteady temperature fields in plates, disks, and cylinders have been studied. Apart from being of practical importance, these problems illustrate how the basic methods of the theory of thermoelasticity are applied.

Chapters IV, V, and VI are devoted to various classes of quasi—static thermoelastic problems.

Chapter IV treats the general formulation of thermoelasticity for plane strains and for plane stresses. In this connection, special attention has been paid to the formulation of the thermoelastic problem for plane states of stress in multiply—connected regions with a view to studying thermal stresses in multiply—connected bodies. Here specific conditions are deduced for the uniqueness of the displacements and angles of rotation. The relation between the lack of such uniqueness and dislocations is explained. An analogy is also made between plane thermoelastic problems for multiply—connected bodies with a steady temperature field and the corresponding plane problem of the isotropic theory of elasticity with dislocations as laid down by Muskhelishvili in 1916.

As examples illustrating the application of the methods of solution of plane thermoelastic problems, we have treated the determination of the thermal stresses in a disk and a cylinder for (1) plane axisymmetric (steady and unsteady) temperature field and (2) a plane non—axisymmetric steady temperature field.

Chapter IV culminates in the exact solution of the problem of the axisymmetric stretching and bending of a circular plate as the result of a steady axisymmetric temperature field. In deducing this solution, use is made of the analogy between the problem of the axisymmetric plane states of stress and the problem of axisymmetric bending of a circular plate.

Chapter V is devoted to the thermoelasticity of shells of revolution and contains a treatment of the general theory of shells of revolution with a temperature field which is symmetric with respect to the axis of the shell but which varies in an arbitrary manner along the meridian and through the thickness. Here use has been made of the isotropic theory of shells as contained in the well—known textbooks of Gol'denveizer, Lur'e, and Novozhilov, etc. In the case of shells of revolution with constant meridian curvature, the problem can be made manageable with the aid of an analogy between statics and geometry. By writing the shell equations in complex notation, the solution can be expressed in terms of complex functions that satisfy a second—order differential equation. In the case of conical and spherical shells with force, moment, and displacement boundary conditions, special functions have been used to deduce general solutions that enable one to calculate the thermal stresses.

In Chapter VI the Papkovich–Neuber stress functions have been used for the study of axisymmetric thermoelastic problems relating to cylinders and solid spheres with prescribed temperature fields (steady and unsteady). The functional arbitrariness in the above representation of the general solution is exploited in order to simplify the fulfillment of the boundary conditions. In the case of a cylinder of finite length, the solutions for the infinite cylinder and that for a slab are superimposed. The fulfillment of the boundary conditions on the curved surface and on the end faces of the cylinder leads to an infinite system of algebraic equations that can best be solved by the Koyalovich method.

In the case of the sphere, the determination of the functions appearing in the representation of the general solution leads to the solution of the vector form of Laplace's equation which, unlike the equation in cartesian or cylindrical coordinates, does not reduce to separate equations for the respective components of the vector. When the temperature field is arbitrary, the solution of the thermal stress problem in a sphere leads to the solution of a system of algebraic equations each of which contains four equations.

Finally Chapter VII deals with dynamic thermoelastic problems concerning dynamic effects in bodies subjected to the action of impulsive heat fluxes. Consideration is also given to the related thermoelastic problems of the vibrational processes accompanying the extraction of heat, the propagation of coupled elastic and thermal waves, and the thermoelastic dissipation of energy. Both of the above classes of thermoelastic problems lead to the study of wave equations.

As a fundamental dynamic problem we have chosen the problem of thermal shock on the surface of a half–space, first studied by Danilovskaya in 1950 using operational calculus. This problem has a comparatively simple solution and embraces the features of the propagation of dynamic thermal stresses that are typical for such problems (thermal shock on the surface of cylinder, sphere, etc.). The problem of the vibrations of a rectangular plate as the result of thermal shock on the surface has also been solved. This problem is of importance in connection with thin–walled structures.

As a typical coupled problem in thermoelasticity, we have treated the propagation of plane harmonic compressional waves in an infinite continuum. Here the elastic waves are modified by the action of the heat. Expressions been derived for the consequent change in phase velocity, attenuation of amplitude, and the relative energy dissipation.

The last problem relating to thermoelastic coupling is that of longitudinal waves in an infinite solid cylinder. In order to derive the solution it is necessary to use both the irrational part and the solenoidal part of the general solution.

Chapter I

THERMODYNAMIC FOUNDATIONS OF THERMOELASTICITY

1.1. Preliminaries. Notation

Thermoelasticity is concerned with questions of equilibrium of bodies treated as thermodynamic systems whose interaction with the environment is confined to mechanical work, external forces, and heat exchange.

As in the classical theory of elasticity, the bodies will be treated as ideal elastic, homogeneous, isotropic material continua.

Thermoelasticity makes use of several laws of continuum mechanics already familiar in the linear theory of elasticity. These will be explained briefly in Section 1.2.

The state of a thermodynamic system is defined by a finite number of independent variables, namely macroscopic quantities known as the *thermodynamic variables* or the *state variables*.

One of these independent macroscopic variables of a thermodynamic system is the temperature, which is non—mechanical and serves as a measure of the intensity of the thermal motion.

A temperature change in a body can be due either to heat supplied from an external source or it can result directly from the process of deformation.

The relation between the strains and the temperature can be established with the aid of the laws of thermodynamics.

The direct applications of the laws of classical thermodynamics to the study of the deformation of a body is possible only for reversible processes.

Strictly speaking, the actual process of thermoelastic deformation of a body is a non—equilibrium process, whose irreversibility is due to the temperature gradient.

The theory of irreversible processes developed in recent years enables us to formulate the problem of irreversible deformations in a more rigorous manner.

Since the thermodynamics of irreversible processes is based on a generalization of classical thermodynamics, Section 1.3 will be devoted to the fundamental aspects of the thermodynamics of reversible processes. Then, in Section 1.4 we shall turn to the principles of the thermodynamics of irreversible processes.

Section 1.5 indicates the thermodynamic approach to deriving the temperature—dependent, stress—strain relations. On the other hand, within the framework of the thermodynamics of linear irreversible processes, a strain—dependent heat conduction equation is derived. The system of equations thus obtained describes the so—called *coupled problem of thermoelasticity* in which the temperature and strain fields are treated as mutually interacting.

The formulation and the representation of the general solution of the coupled problem of thermoelasticity is treated in Section 1.6.

In the general case, the derivation of exact solutions of coupled problems in thermoelasticity is a combination of elastodynamics and unsteady heat flow, and is a formidable mathematical problem.

The variational principle in Section 1.7, which is based on the thermodynamics of irreversible processes, enables us to develop approximate methods of solution of these problems. In this and the following chapters, the equations have been simplified by using the index notation and the summation convention of tensor analysis.

The cartesian coordinates x, y, z will be denoted by x_1, x_2, x_3 and the more compact expression x_i ($i = 1, 2, 3$). The vector $\mathbf{a}$ with components a_1, a_2, a_3 will be denoted by a_i. In the same sense, the displacement vector u_i in an elastic body denotes the vector with components u_1, u_2, u_3. The states of stress and strain in an elastic body are defined by the corresponding second—order tensors σ_{ij} and ϵ_{ij} ($i, j = 1, 2, 3$). The symbols σ_{ij} and ϵ_{ij} denote quantities with nine components.

The indices are indicates by small Latin letters. The repeated indices are called *dummy indices*. Indices that are not repeated are called *free indices*. The following two rules will always be understood:

1. Repeated indices indicate summation from 1 to 3. For example, the scalar product of two vector $\mathbf{a}$ and $\mathbf{b}$ is

$$\mathbf{a} \cdot \mathbf{b} = a_i \cdot b_i = a_1 b_1 + a_2 b_2 + a_3 b_3, \qquad (1.1.1)$$

and the first invariant of the stress tensor is

$$\sigma_{ii} = \sigma_{11} + \sigma_{22} + \sigma_{33}. \qquad (1.1.2)$$

No special index is necessary for the repeated indices. As convenience requires any lower case Latin letter can be used.

8

2. The free indices run through the values 1 to 3. For example, the symbol σ_{ij} denotes any one of the nine components of the array

$$\left\{ \begin{array}{ccc} \sigma_{11} & \sigma_{12} & \sigma_{13} \\ \sigma_{21} & \sigma_{22} & \sigma_{23} \\ \sigma_{31} & \sigma_{32} & \sigma_{33} \end{array} \right\}. \tag{1.1.3}$$

The antisymmetric third—order unit tensor will be denoted by e_{ijk}. It is antisymmetric with respect to the three indices, i.e. interchange of any pair of indices changes the sign, but not the magnitude, of the component. Only six of its 27 components are non—zero; these have indices that are the permutations of the numbers 1, 2, and 3. The components have only three possible values, namely 0 when a pair of indices is equal, +1 when ijk is an even permutation of 1, 2, 3, and -1 when ijk is an odd permutation of 1, 2, 3. Thus we have

$$e_{123} = e_{231} = e_{312} = 1, \quad e_{132} = e_{213} = e_{321} = -1. \tag{1.1.4}$$

If we form the contraction of two third—order tensors with respect to any two indices k and n (i.e. form an inner product), we obtain the fourth—order unit tensor

$$e_{ijk} e_{lmk},$$

the components of which have the following values:

0 when $i = j$ or $l = m$,

+1 when ij and lm are the same rearrangement of two numbers ($i = l$, and $j = m$, but $i \neq j$),

-1 when ij and lm are the opposite arrangement of the same two numbers ($i = m$, and $j = l$, but $i \neq j$).

This result can be written in the form

$$e_{ijk} e_{lmk} = \delta_{il} \delta_{jm} - \delta_{im} \delta_{jl} \tag{1.1.5}$$

where δ_{ij} is the Kronecker delta described by the follc ig properties

$$\delta_{11} = \delta_{22} = \delta_{33} = 1, \quad \delta_{ij} = 0 \ (i \neq j). \tag{1.1.6}$$

The unit tensor e_{ijk} can be used to represent the vector product of two vectors. For instance, the vector product $\mathbf{a} \times \mathbf{b}$ is a vector $\mathbf{c}$ with the components

$$c_i = e_{ijk}a_j b_k \qquad (1.1.7)$$

or written out in full

$$c_1 = a_2 b_3 - a_3 b_2, \quad c_2 = a_3 b_1, \quad c_3 = a_1 b_2 - a_2 b_1.$$

Differentiation with respect to a certain coordinate is denoted by a comma after the component indices followed by an index indicating the coordinate concerned, e.g.

$$u_{i,j} = \frac{\partial u_i}{\partial x_j} \quad (i,j = 1, 2, 3), \qquad (1.1.8)$$

$$\epsilon_{ij,\,kl} = \frac{\partial^2 \epsilon_{ij}}{\partial x_k \partial x_l} \quad (i,j,k,l = 1,2,3). \qquad (1.1.9)$$

Partial derivatives with respect to time are indicated by superimposed dots, e.g.

$$\ddot{u}_i = \frac{\partial^2 u_i}{\partial t^2}. \qquad (1.1.10)$$

From Chapter III onwards, the index notation and the summation convention will be dropped. All formulae will be written in expanded form. The coordinates x_1, x_2, x_3 will then be denoted by x, y, and z. The latter symbols will even be used as indices for the stress and strain tensors. For example, instead of σ_{11}, ..., σ_{12}, ..., ϵ_{11}, ..., ϵ_{12}, ..., we will write σ_x, ..., σ_{xy}, ..., ϵ_x, ..., ϵ_{xy}, ..., respectively. The components u_1, u_2, u_3 of the displacement vector will be denoted by u, v, w. The remaining notation will be introduced in the course of the development of the material.

1.2. Strains. Equations of equilibrium (motion). Work of external forces

This Section will be devoted to a brief consideration of those basic principles of continuum mechanics [20, 36, 44] which are encountered in the linear theory of elasticity and which are used in thermoelasticity.

10

It will be assumed that the displacements and their derivatives are small. Differentiating the vector u_i with respect to the variables x_j, we obtain the second–order tensor $u_{i,\,j}$, which can be written as the sum of the symmetric tensor e_{ij} and the antisymmetric tensor ω_{ij}, namely

$$u_{i,j} = \frac{1}{2}(u_{i,j} + u_{j,i}) + \frac{1}{2}(u_{i,j} - u_{j,i}) = \epsilon_{ij} + \omega_{ij}, \qquad (1.2.1)$$

The symmetric tensor ϵ_{ij} is called the *strain tensor*. Between the components of strain and the displacement components we have the kinematic relations

$$\epsilon_{ij} = \frac{1}{2}(u_{i,j} + u_{j,i}), \qquad (1.2.2)$$

where $\epsilon_{ij} = \epsilon_{ji}$.

The antisymmetric tensor ω_{ij} is characterized by the relations

$$\omega_{ij} = \frac{1}{2}(u_{i,j} - u_{j,i}) = -\omega_{ji} \qquad (i,j = 1,2,3).$$

The matrix of this tensor is

$$\left\{ \begin{array}{ccc} 0 & -\omega_3 & \omega_2 \\ \omega_3 & 0 & -\omega_1 \\ -\omega_2 & \omega_1 & 0 \end{array} \right\}, \qquad (1.2.3)$$

i.e. the tensor is determined by three components ω_k $(k = 1, 2, 3)$, which are the components of an axial vector.

The vector $\boldsymbol{\omega}$ is called the *rotation vector*. Its magnitude is equal to the mean value of the angle of rotation of the volume element, and in a right–handed system of axes its direction is given by the right–hand screw rule.

By means of the unit tensor e_{ijk} (see Section 1.1), the following relation can be established between the rotation vector ω_k and the antisymmetric tensor ω_{ij}.

$$\omega_k = \frac{1}{2} e_{kji} \omega_{ij}. \qquad (1.2.4)$$

Multiplying both sides of equation (1.2.4) by the unit tensor and making use of identity (1.1.5), one obtains

$$\omega_{sr} = e_{rsk} \omega_k. \qquad (1.2.5)$$

Let us consider the elastic body with volume V and surface Ω as shown in

11

Fig. 1. The point P is on the surface Ω, and $d\Omega$ is an element of surface containing point P. The orientation of the surface element $d\Omega$ is given by the unit vector **n** directed normal to and outward from the surface $d\Omega$. The volume under consideration is subjected to external forces that are subdivided into surface forces, or tractions, and volume forces.

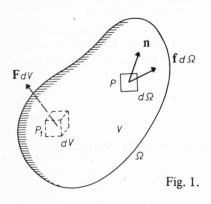

The surface element $d\Omega$ at P with outward normal **n** is subjected to traction $\mathbf{f}\,d\Omega$, where **f** is the stress vector. The magnitude of **f** is called the *stress*.

The volume element dV at P_1 is subjected to the volume force $\mathbf{F}\,dV$, where **F** is the specific volume force.

If the volume element at P_1 is travelling with acceleration $\ddot{\mathbf{u}}$, then, in addition to the force $\mathbf{F}\,dV$, it is subjected to the inertia force $-\rho\ddot{\mathbf{u}}dV$,

Fig. 1.

where ρ is the mass density of the body at point P_1, and $-\rho\ddot{\mathbf{u}}$ is the specific inertia force.

Let us choose the volume element at P in the form of an infinitesimally small tetrahedron with three faces parallel to the coordinate planes and the fourth coinciding with $d\Omega$ corresponding to the outward normal **n** (see Fig.2).

The equilibrium of all the forces acting on the tetrahedron is expressed by equations

$$\mathbf{f} = \mathbf{f}_j n_j \ (j = 1,2,3) \quad (1.2.6)$$

where $\mathbf{f}_j$ are the stresses on the surface elements perpendicular to the axes x_j, and the components n_j of the unit vector **n** are the direction cosines of **n** with respect to the axes x_j (the volume forces are not considered because they are of

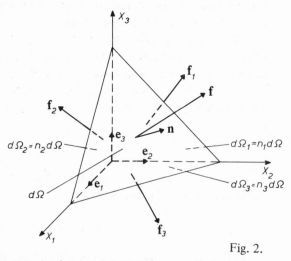

Fig. 2.

12

a higher order of smallness).

Let the resolution of the vectors **f** and **f**$_j$ with respect to the unit vectors e_1, e_2, and e_3 (see Fig. 2) be given by the expressions

$$\mathbf{f} = \mathbf{e}_i f_i, \quad \mathbf{f}_j = \mathbf{e}_i \sigma_{ji}. \tag{1.2.7}$$

Then, in view of (1.2.16), the vector equation (1.2.6) can be replaced by the three scalar equations

$$f_i = \sigma_{ij} n_j \quad (i, j = 1, 2, 3), \tag{1.2.8}$$

where f_i are the components of the stress vector, and σ_{ij} are the components of the stress tensor.

When the coordinates are cartesian, the stress tensor is determined by the matrix (1.1.3) of its components. The diagonal elements of matrix (1.1.3) are calle᠁ the *normal stresses* on the respective surfaces, and the off—diagonal elements are called the *shear stresses* (see Fig. 3).

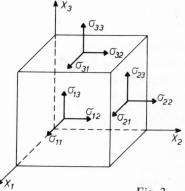

Let us consider the equilibrium of an arbitrary volume V of a body bounded by the surface Ω. Equilibrium requires that the resultant force and the resultant moment (with respect to an arbitrary point) of the external volume and surface forces should vanish. According to d'Alembert's principle, the case of a moving body can be covered by equations of the same form by adding the inertia forces to the volume forces. The above conditions then become

Fig. 3.

$$\int_V (F_i - \rho \ddot{u}_i) dV + \int_\Omega f_i d\Omega = 0, \tag{1.2.9}$$

$$\int_V e_{ijk} x_j (F_k - \rho \ddot{u}_k) dV + \int_\Omega e_{ijk} x_j f_k d\Omega = 0, \tag{1.2.10}$$

where x_j are the coordinates of the points of application of the forces.

13

When we replace f_i in (1.2.9) and (1.2.10) by the expression (1.2.8) and apply the divergence theorem, the surface integrals yield

$$\int_\Omega f_i d\Omega = \int_\Omega \sigma_{ij} n_j d\Omega = \int_V \sigma_{ij,j} dV, \qquad (1.2.11)$$

$$\int_\Omega e_{ijk} x_j f_k \, d\Omega = \int_\Omega e_{ijk} x_j \sigma_{kl} n_l d\Omega =$$

$$= \int_V (e_{ijk} x_j \sigma_{kl})_{,l} dV = \int_V e_{ijk} \sigma_{kj} dV + \int_V e_{ijk} x_j \sigma_{kl,l} dV = 0. \quad (1.2.12)$$

In deducing result (1.2.12), use has been made of relations $x_{j,l} = \delta_{jl}$ and $\delta_{jl}\sigma_{kl} = \sigma_{kj}$, where δ_{jl} is the Kronecker delta.

Substituting (1.2.11) into (1.2.9) and (1.2.12) into (1.2.10), we obtain

$$\int_V (\sigma_{ij,j} + F_i - \rho \ddot{u}_i) dV = 0, \qquad (1.2.13)$$

$$\int_V e_{ijk}[\sigma_{kj} + x_j (\sigma_{kl,l} + F_k - \rho \ddot{u}_k)] dV = 0. \qquad (1.2.14)$$

Since volume V is arbitrary, equation (1.2.13) yields the following three equations of motion

$$\sigma_{ij,j} + F_i = \rho \ddot{u}_i \qquad (i = 1, 2, 3). \qquad (1.2.15)$$

In view of (1.2.15), it follows from (1.2.14) that

$$\int_V e_{ijk} \sigma_{kj} dV = 0$$

or

$$\sigma_{kj} = \sigma_{jk}, \qquad (1.2.16)$$

i.e. the stress tensor is symmetric.

To conclude this section we now consider the rate of work of the external forces during the deformation of an elastic body of volume V, namely

14

$$\dot{L} = \int\limits_V (F_i - \rho \ddot{u}_i)\, \dot{u}_i dV + \int\limits_\Omega f_i \dot{u}_i d\Omega. \qquad (1.2.17)$$

Substitution of expression (1.2.8) for f_i into (1.2.17) and transformation of the surface integral into a volume integral by means of the divergence theorem yields

$$\dot{L} = \int\limits_V \dot{W}\, dV = \int\limits_V [(\sigma_{ij,j} + F_i - \rho \ddot{u}_i)\, \dot{u}_i + \sigma_{ij} \dot{u}_{i,j}] dV. \qquad (1.2.18)$$

Taking account of equation (1.2.15) and identity (1.2.1), we find that the rate of work of the external forces per unit volume is

$$\dot{W} = \sigma_{ij}\, (\dot{\epsilon}_{ij} + \dot{\omega}_{ij}) = \sigma_{ij} \dot{\epsilon}_{ij}. \qquad (1.2.19)$$

In deducing this expression we have made use of the fact that $\sigma_{ij}\omega_{ij} = 0$, since σ_{ij} is symmetric and ω_{ij} is antisymmetric.

1.3. Basic laws of classical thermodynamics

Here we will recall some of the basic ideas of thermodynamics [3, 24].

Any material body that consists of a large number of particles and inter- acts with the environment is called a *thermodynamic system.*

The state of a thermodynamic system is characterized by a number of macroscopic quantities called the (thermodynamic) *state variables.*

The latter are divided into *external variables* that characterize the external conditions to which the thermodynamic system is subjected, and the *internal variables* that depend on the motion and the mutual interactions of the micro—particles (molecules) in the system. In this sense the strains in an elastic body are external variables. On the other hand, mass density, internal energy, etc. are internal variables.

A complete set of independent thermodynamic variables completely de- fines the state of the system. Other quantities determined by the state of the system at a given instant are *state functions.*

A thermodynamic system left to itself under constant external conditions passes into a state of equilibrium in which all parameters become constant and there is no macroscopic movement. Such a state of the system is called *thermodynamic equilibrium.*

The notion of temperate is closely connected with the concept of thermodynamic equilibrium.

Experiment shows that if each of two systems are in a state of thermal equilibrium when brought into contact with a third system, then these two will be in a state of equilibrium amongst themselves irrespective of whether the respective external parameters are equal or not. (Thermal equilibrium is a transitive relationship.) Hence it follows that the state of thermodynamic equilibrium of a system is determined not only by the external parameters but also by a quantity describing the internal state. This quantity which has the same value for all systems that are mutually in a state of equilibrium is called the *temperature.*

The statement that there is such a temperature which characterizes the equilibrium state of a system is called the *zeroth law of thermodynamics.*

During thermodynamic equilibrium, all the internal parameters of a system are functions of the external parameters and the temperature.

When the macroscopic properties of a system change with time, it is said that a *process* is taking place in the system.

When all variables of a system change so extremely slowly that each instant the system is in state of thermodynamic equilibrium, one speaks of an *equilibrium process*[1].

An equilibrium process is *reversible,* i.e., it is a process that can take place in the reverse direction without any change in the environment.

A process accompanied by a departure from the equilibrium is called *non–static.* The basic property of such a process is its irreversibility, i.e., the impossibility of returning the system to the initial state without some change taking place in the environment. From this point of view, the process of heat conduction with a finite temperature difference is irreversible.

The *total energy* of a system consists of the external energy connected with the motion of the system as a whole (the kinetic energy of the system and the change in its potential energy), and the *internal energy* which comprises the energy of all forms of motion and of the interactions of the micro–particles making up the system.

---

1) In [3, 24] such processes are also called *quasi–static.* In the present book, we have preferred the above name in order to avoid confusion with the *quasi–static problem of thermoelasticity* in Chapter II.

The internal energy U is a state function, and in an equilibrium process it is determined by the external parameters and the temperature.

The interaction of a thermodynamic system with the environment consists in the exchange of energy between the environment and the system through the execution of work or the exchange of heat. Work is a way of transmitting the energy associated with the external variables. The amount of energy received by a system in this way is also called *work* and is denoted by W.

When a change in temperature leads to an exchange of energy while the external variables are constant, the process is called *heat exchange*. The amount of energy supplied to the system in this case is called the *heat* and is denoted by Q.

Neither work nor heat is a state function of the system. They are meaningful only when the process is completed and the state of the system has changed.

If the state of the system changes only in virtue of a change in the external parameters, there is no exchange with the environment of energy in the form of heat. Such a system is said to be *adiabatically isolated* or *adiabatic*.

In an adiabatic system, the work is independent of the path from one state to another and depends only on the initial and final states of the system; during an adiabatic process work is done only in virtue of a change of energy of the system. The energy of a system is additive, i.e., the energy of a system is equal to the sum of the energies of its parts.

In the general case of a system that is not adiabatically isolated, changes of energy are caused not only by macroscopic work but also by heat exchange.

Being an expression of the conservation of energy, the *first law of thermodynamics* expresses the balance of energy during mechanical and thermal processes (either reversible or irreversible). For a finite process, the first law of thermodynamics asserts that

$$U_2 - U_1 = Q + W, \tag{1.3.1}$$

where $U_2 - U_1$ is the change of internal energy when the system passes from state 1 to state 2, the heat Q is that received by the system, and W is the external work done on the system.

For an infinitesimal process, the first law of thermodynamics reads

$$dQ = dU + dW', \tag{1.3.2}$$

17

where $dW' = -dW$.

In this form, equation (1.3.2) states that the heat supplied to the system goes into internal energy and work performed by the system.

It is proved in thermodynamics that when the process is reversible the expression for the elementary heat can be represented as a Pfaffian form:

$$dQ = X_1 dx_1 + X_2 dx_2 + \ldots + X_n dx_n, \qquad (1.3.3)$$

where x_i $(i = 1, \ldots, n)$ are independent state variables, and X_i $(i = 1, \ldots, n)$ are functions of these variables.

The *second law of thermodynamics* is a generalization of experimental data and asserts that it is impossible to have a *perpetuum mobile* of the second kind, i.e., it is impossible to construct a machine that would convert heat into work using a single heat reservoir at a constant temperature.

In the more recent statement of the second law, appeal is made to a more general empirical principle concerning the impossibility of certain processes. This leads to a simplification of the mathematical formulation of the second law.

The first of such formulations of the second law was given in 1898 by N.N. Shiller at the University of Kiev [50, 51]. He deduced a result concerning the integrating factor for dQ in agreement with the result of the German—born Greek mathematician Carathéodory. In 1909, Carathéodory made use of the theory of Pfaffian forms to develop this formulation of the second law [56], which has now become known as the *Carathéodory principle of adiabatic inaccessibility*.

In critically reviewing Carathéodory's paper [56], T.A. Afanassjewa—Ehrenfest in [2, 60] was the first to prove that the second law of thermodynamics comprises two independent statements, the first of which refers to reversible processes and the second to irreversible processes. He also clarified the distinction between (1) the notion of the adiabatic inaccessibility of a given state from another state by means of a reversible transition and (2) the notion of the irreversibility of a thermodynamic process.

At the present time the statement of the principle of adiabatic inaccessibility consists of the following two parts (see [3, 28, 55, etc]):

1) in the vicinity of each state of a thermodynamic system there are states that are inaccessible by means of an adiabatic reversible process;

2) in the vicinity of each state of a thermodynamic system there are states that are inaccessible by means of an *arbitrary* adiabatic irreversible process.

The first part of the statement of the inaccessibility principle leads to the existence of a new single–valued state function, namely the *entropy S*. Of course, when the system is adiabatic and the process reversible, the Pfaffian form (1.3.3) goes over into the Pfaffian equation

$$dQ = X_1 dx_1 + X_2 dx_2 + ... + X_n dx_n = 0, \qquad (1.3.4)$$

in which the parameters x_i $(i = 1, ..., n)$ can be regarded as coordinates of a point in n–dimensional space.

In the theory of Pfaffian equations with n variables one has the following theorem [28]: when the Pfaffian equation (1.3.4) is integrable (i.e. an integrating factor exists), it is impossible to reach every point in the vicinity of a prescribed point $P(x_i)$ by passing along the integral curves through this point.

Carathéodory proved the validity of the converse theorem: If in the vicinity of a given state with variables x_i there is a state with variables x_i' that is inaccessible along paths compatible with equation (1.3.4), it follows that this equation is integrable. However, since the presence of inaccessible points in the case of an adiabatic, reversible process described by equation (1.3.4) has been established experimentally, it follows that this equation is integrable.

The integrability of (1.3.4) is then used in thermodynamics to prove the existence of the total differential

$$dS = \frac{dQ}{T}, \qquad (1.3.5)$$

where S is the entropy, and T the absolute temperature.

The second part of the statement of the inaccessibility principle leads to the asserted positive definiteness of the entropy increment during adiabatic irreversible processes, namely

$$dS > 0. \qquad (1.3.6)$$

1.4. Basic thermodynamic laws of irreversible processes associated with thermoelastic strains in unevenly heated bodies

In order to study the actual process of thermoelastic deformation of a body under the action of external forces and non–uniform heating, it is necessary to appeal to the thermodynamics of irreversible processes.

The central ideas of the thermodynamics of irreversible processes embrace the notions of local equilibrium and slow processes.

The values of the thermodynamic variables are defined for suddenly extracted macroscopically small parts of the body, which can be considered to be in states of local equilibrium.

This generalization of classical thermodynamics is based on the assumption that the global state of equilibrium is preceded by equilibrium in the macroscopically small parts of the system.

Thermodynamic equilibrium throughout the whole volume as the result of heat conduction sets in very much slower.

The thermodynamics of irreversible processes postulates that the basic equations of the thermodynamics of reversible processes, (1.3.2) and (1.3.5), remain valid for the macroscopically small parts of the system in local equilibrium [3, 10].

The energy balance for an element of the body leads to the equation

$$-q_{i,i} = \dot{Q} \tag{1.4.1}$$

connecting the components q_i of the heat flux vector $\mathbf{q}$ with the rate of specific heat influx. (Here and henceforth 'specific' will mean 'per unit volume'.) Now recalling expression (1.2.19) for the rate of specific work of a body:

$$\dot{W}' = -\dot{W} = -\sigma_{ij}\dot{\epsilon}_{ij}, \tag{1.4.2}$$

we can combine the first and second laws of thermodynamics into the relation

$$-q_{i,i} = T\dot{S} = \dot{U} - \sigma_{ij}\dot{\epsilon}_{ij}, \tag{1.4.3}$$

where S is the *specific entropy* and U is the *specific internal energy*.

Equation (1.4.3) must be supplemented with a phenomenological equation describing the irreversible process of heat conduction. This is known as the *Fourier law of heat conduction*, which relates the heat flux to the temperature gradient:

$$q_i = -\lambda_T T_{,i}, \tag{1.4.4}$$

where λ_T is the *coefficient of thermal conductivity*.

The fact that the entropy is a positive—definite quantity is one of the most important principles in the thermodynamics of irreversible processes.

From equations (1.4.3) and (1.4.4) it follows that

$$\dot{S} = -\frac{q_{i,i}}{T} = \dot{S}_{\mathrm{I}} + \dot{S}_{\mathrm{II}}, \tag{1.4.5}$$

where

$$\dot{S}_{\mathrm{I}} = -\left(\frac{q_i}{T}\right)_{,i} \tag{1.4.6}$$

is the change of entropy as the result of the flow of heat from the environment, and

$$\dot{S}_{\mathrm{II}} = -\frac{1}{T^2} q_i T_{,i} = \frac{1}{T^2} \frac{q_i q_i}{\lambda_{\mathrm{T}}} > 0 \tag{1.4.7}$$

is the local rate of entropy production caused by the temperature gradient.

1.5. Thermodynamic functions. Equations of state. Heat conduction equation

When studying the thermodynamics of deformation, it is found advantageous to introduce, in addition to the specific internal energy U and the specific entropy S, the following two state functions:
the (specific) *free energy*

$$F = U - TS \tag{1.5.1}$$

and *Gibbs thermodynamic potential*

$$G = F - \sigma_{ij}\epsilon_{ij}. \tag{1.5.2}$$

The functions U, F, G are *state functions*, i.e., their increments during a change of state of the elastic body are total differentials. These functions are also called *thermodynamic potentials*.

Starting with the expression for the total differential of the specific internal energy:

$$dU = TdS + \sigma_{ij}d\epsilon_{ij}, \tag{1.5.3}$$

with the aid of (1.5.1) and (1.5.2) we find

21

$$dF = -SdT + \sigma_{ij}d\epsilon_{ij}, \tag{1.5.4}$$

$$dG = -SdT - \epsilon_{ij}d\sigma_{ij}. \tag{1.5.5}$$

Since dU, dF, and dG are total differentials, it follows that

$$\frac{\partial U}{\partial S} = T, \qquad \frac{\partial U}{\partial \epsilon_{ij}} = \sigma_{ij}, \tag{1.5.6}$$

$$\frac{\partial F}{\partial T} = -S, \qquad \frac{\partial F}{\partial \epsilon_{ij}} = \sigma_{ij}, \tag{1.5.7}$$

$$\frac{\partial G}{\partial T} = -S, \qquad \frac{\partial G}{\partial \sigma_{ij}} = -\epsilon_{ij}, \tag{1.5.8}$$

The knowledge of at least one thermodynamic potential enables one to determine all state variables, i.e. the absolute temperature, the stress tensor the strain tensor, and the entropy.

Now let us recall the physical meaning of the thermodynamic potentials.

It is clear from (1.5.3) and (1.5.4) that during an isothermal process ($T =$ const) the elementary work coincides with the change in free energy F, whereas in an adiabatic process ($S =$ const) the elementary work coincides with the increment of internal energy U.

From (1.5.4) and (1.5.5) it follows that during an isothermal process the complementary work on the elastic body is equal to the increase of the Gibbs thermodynamic potential, whereas for the same process the elementary work is equal to the decrease in free energy.

In order to derive the stress–strain relation it is necessary to formulate the expression for the specific free energy F as a function of the components of the strain tensor and of the temperature T.

Taking account of the smallness of the strains and assuming that the purely thermal strain corresponding to the temperature difference $T - T_0$ (where T_0 is the temperature of the body in the unstrained state) is of first–order smallness compared with the strain components, we will truncate the expansion of F in ϵ_{ij} and T after the second–order terms, i.e., we will retain only quadratic terms in ϵ_{ij} and products of ϵ_{ij} with the purely thermal strain.

Being a scalar quantity, the specific free energy does not depend on the choice of coordinates and can thus be expressed in terms of the invariants of the strain tensor and the temperature.

In tensor analysis it is proved that the symmetric strain tensor has the linear invariant ϵ_{kk} and the two second order invariants ϵ_{kk}^2 and $\epsilon_{ij}\epsilon_{ij}$. Thus we have the following expression for the free energy [20]:

$$F = \frac{\lambda}{2}\epsilon_{kk}^2 + \mu\epsilon_{ij}\epsilon_{ij} - (3\lambda + 2\mu)\alpha_T(T - T_0)\epsilon_{kk} + F_0, \quad (1.5.9)$$

where λ, μ, α_T are constants, and F_0 is a function of T.

On the basis of (1.5.7), the specific entropy is found to be

$$S = (3\lambda + 2\mu)\alpha_T\epsilon_{kk} - \frac{dF_0}{dT} \quad (1.5.10)$$

and the stress–strain relation is

$$\sigma_{ij} = \lambda\epsilon_{kk}\delta_{ij} + 2\mu\epsilon_{ij} - (3\lambda + 2\mu)\alpha_T(T - T_0)\delta_{ij}. \quad (1.5.11)$$

When differentiating F with respect to ϵ_{ij} it is to be recalled that $\partial\epsilon_{kk}/\partial\epsilon_{ij} = \delta_{ij}$, where δ_{ij} is the Kronecker delta.

The coefficients λ and μ in (1.5.11) are the well–known *Lamé constants* for isothermal deformation.

The *volumetric dilatation* (the first invariant of the strain tensor) is obtained from (1.5.11) by setting $i = j = 1, 2, 3$ and adding. Since $\delta_{kk} = 3$, we find

$$\epsilon_{kk} = \frac{\sigma_{kk}}{3\lambda + 2\mu} + 3\alpha_T(T - T_0), \quad (1.5.12)$$

By setting σ_{kk} in (1.5.12) equal to zero, we obtain the volumetric dilatation during purely thermal expansion.

Thus, the factor α_T introduced in (1.5.9) is the *coefficient of thermal expansion*.

Substituting expression (1.5.12) for ϵ_{kk} into (1.5.11) and solving the latter for ϵ_{ij}, one obtains the stress–strain relation in the form

$$\epsilon_{ij} = \frac{(1 + \nu)\sigma_{ij}}{E} - \frac{\nu\sigma_{kk}}{E}\delta_{ij} + \alpha_T(T - T_0)\delta_{ij}. \quad (1.5.13)$$

where E is *Young's modulus* and ν is *Poisson's ratio*, which are related to the Lamé constants through the equations

$$\lambda = \frac{\nu E}{(1 + \nu)(1 - 2\nu)}, \quad \mu = \frac{E}{2(1 + \nu)}. \quad (1.5.14)$$

23

From (1.5.13) it is seen that the total strain ϵ_{ij} at every point in an elastic body is the sum of two components:
1) the strains

$$\epsilon'_{ij} = \frac{1}{E}[(1 + \nu)\sigma_{ij} - \nu\sigma_{kk}\delta_{ij}], \tag{1.5.15}$$

arising either from the action of the external loads or from the action of the stresses maintaining the continuity of the body under non–uniform heating. These strains are related to the stresses through the familiar generalization of Hooke's law; and
2) the strains

$$\epsilon''_{ij} = \alpha_T(T - T_0)\delta_{ij}, \tag{1.5.16}$$

corresponding to the free thermal expansion of an elastic body under a temperature increase $T - T_0$. In the case of an isotropic body, these strains are represented by a spherical tensor, i.e. a scalar multiple of the unit tensor.

Substituting expression (1.5.9) into (1.5.2) and replacing ϵ_{ij} by means of (1.5.13), we obtain the following expression for Gibbs thermodynamic potential:

$$G = -\frac{1 + \nu}{2E}\sigma_{ij}\sigma_{ij} + \frac{\nu}{2E}\sigma_{kk}^2 - \alpha_T(T - T_0)\sigma_{kk} -$$

$$-\frac{3E}{2(1 - 2\nu)}\alpha_T^2(T - T_0)^2 + F_0. \tag{1.5.17}$$

Now the first formula in (1.5.8) yields the following expression for specific entropy

$$S = \alpha_T\sigma_{kk} + \frac{3E\alpha_T^2}{1 - 2\nu}(T - T_0) - \frac{dF_0}{dT}. \tag{1.5.18}$$

Expression (1.5.10) or (1.5.18) can be used for determining the *specific heat at constant strain* c_ϵ and the *specific heat at constant stress* c_σ, respectively. Thus we find

$$c_\epsilon = T\frac{\partial S(\epsilon_{kk}, T)}{\partial T} = -T\frac{d^2F_0}{dT^2},$$

$$c_\sigma = T\frac{\partial S(\sigma_{kk}, T)}{\partial T} = \frac{3E\alpha_T^2T}{1 - 2\nu} - T\frac{d^2F_0}{dT^2}, \tag{1.5.19}$$

24

and hence

$$c_\sigma - c_\epsilon = \frac{3E\alpha_T^2 T}{1 - 2\nu} = 3(3\lambda + 2\mu)\alpha_T^2 T. \qquad (1.5.20)$$

By the specific heat c_ϵ we will mean the specific heat at zero strain. Then, from the first of equations (1.5.19) it follows that

$$F_0 = -\int_{T_0}^{T} \int_{T_0}^{T} \frac{c_\epsilon}{T}\, dT dT, \qquad (1.5.21)$$

where the constants of integration are chosen so that $F = 0$ and $S = 0$ when $\epsilon_{ij} = 0$ and $T = T_0$.

In the following it will be assumed that the specific heat c_ϵ and the coefficient of thermal conductivity λ_T are independent of temperature.

Substitution of relation (1.5.21) for F_0 into expression (1.5.10) for the specific entropy yields

$$S = (3\lambda + 2\mu)\alpha_T \epsilon_{kk} + c_\epsilon \ln \frac{T}{T_0}. \qquad (1.5.22)$$

We are now in a position to add the heat conduction equation to the well–known linear equations of elasticity in Section 1.2 and the stress–strain relations (1.5.11) or (1.5.13).

Substituting expression (1.4.4) for the heat flux and expression (1.5.22) for the specific entropy S into equation (1.4.3), and taking account of the result

$$(3\lambda + 2\mu)\alpha_T T = \frac{c_\sigma - c_\epsilon}{3\alpha_T}, \qquad (1.5.23)$$

from (1.5.20), we find the following *heat conduction equation:*

$$\lambda_T T_{,ii} = c_\epsilon \dot{T} + \frac{c_\sigma - c_\epsilon}{3\alpha_T} \dot{\epsilon}_{kk}. \qquad (1.5.24)$$

The above system contains the coupling term $\dfrac{c_\sigma - c_\epsilon}{3\alpha_T} \dot{\epsilon}_{kk}$ in (1.5.24) and the terms $(3\lambda + 2\mu)\,\alpha_T(T - T_0)\,\delta_{ij}$ in (1.5.11) or $\alpha_T(T - T_0)\,\delta_{ij}$ in (1.5.13).

Let us consider the case where $(T - T_0)/T \approx 0$. Then $\ln (T/T_0)$ in (1.5.22) can be replaced by $(T - T_0)/T_0$, and T in (1.5.23) by T_0. The respective linearized forms of (1.5.22) and (1.5.24) become

$$S = (3\lambda + 2\mu)\alpha_T \epsilon_{kk} + c_\epsilon \frac{T - T_0}{T_0},$$ (1.5.25)

$$\lambda_T T_{,ii} = c_\epsilon \dot{T} + T_0 (3\lambda + 2\mu)\alpha_T \dot{\epsilon}_{kk}.$$ (1.5.26)

It is to be noted that for an adiabatic deformation (when S = const.), equation (1.5.25), which satisfies the condition

$$S = 0 \quad \text{when} \quad T = T_0 \quad \text{and} \quad \epsilon_{kk} = 0,$$

yields

$$T - T_0 = -\frac{(3\lambda + 2\mu)\alpha_T T_0}{c_\epsilon} \epsilon_{kk}.$$ (1.5.27)

Substitution of (1.5.27) into (1.5.11) leads to

$$\sigma_{ij} = \lambda_a \epsilon_{kk} \delta_{ij} + 2\mu \epsilon_{ij},$$ (1.5.28)

where λ_a is the Lamé constant for adiabatic strain, namely

$$\lambda_a = \lambda + \frac{(3\lambda + 2\mu)^2 \alpha_T^2 T_0}{c_\epsilon},$$ (1.5.29)

The second Lamé constant μ is unaltered.

1.6. Formulation of the thermoelastic problem and representation of general solution

In the general case, the thermoelastic problem is formulated as follows:

There are sixteen unknown functions of position x_k and time t, namely six stress components σ_{ij}, six strain components ϵ_{ij}, three components u_i of the displacement vector, and the temperature T. The four sets of equations governing these quantities are

1) three equations of motion

$$\sigma_{ij,j} = \rho \ddot{u}_i;$$ (1.6.1)

26

2) the heat conduction equation

$$T_{,ii} - \frac{1}{a}\dot{T} - \frac{T_0(3\lambda + 2\mu)\alpha_T}{\lambda_T}\dot{\epsilon}_{kk} = 0, \qquad (1.6.2)$$

where $a = \lambda_T/c_\epsilon$ is called the *thermal diffusivity;*

3) the six stress–strain relations

$$\sigma_{ij} = 2\mu\epsilon_{ij} + [\lambda\epsilon_{kk} - (3\lambda + 2\mu)\alpha_T(T - T_0)]\delta_{ij}; \qquad (1.6.3)$$

4) the six strain–deformation relations

$$\epsilon_{ij} = \frac{1}{2}(u_{i,j} + u_{i,j}). \qquad (1.6.4)$$

Typical initial and boundary conditions in terms of the displacements u_i and the temperature T are

1) initial conditions (for $t = 0$)

$$u_i = g_i^{(1)}(x_k), \quad \dot{u}_i = g_i^{(2)}(x_k), \quad T = G^{(1)}(x_k); \qquad (1.6.5)$$

2) boundary conditions (for $t > 0$)

$$u_i = g_i^{(3)}(x_k, t), \quad T = G^{(2)}(x_k, t). \qquad (1.6.6)$$

Here and henceforth the notation $g(x_k)$, $G(x_k)$ etc. denotes functions of all the coordinates x_k ($k = 1, 2, 3$).

A uniqueness theorem for the above problem has been derived in [69].

Let us now work out the equations of motion in terms of the displacements. The stress–strain relations (1.6.3) can be used to eliminate the stresses from (1.6.1). Since the terms ϵ_{kk} and T occur only when $i = j$, this yields*

$$2\mu\epsilon_{ij,j} + \lambda\epsilon_{kk,i} - (3\lambda + 2\mu)\alpha_T T_{,i} - \rho\ddot{u}_i = 0.$$

Now the strain–displacement relations (1.6.4) will be used to eliminate the strains. Replacing the dummy index j by k and noting that $u_{k,ik} = u_{k,ki}$, we obtain

$$\mu u_{i,kk} + (\lambda + \mu)u_{k,ki} - (3\lambda + 2\mu)\alpha_T T_{,i} = \rho\ddot{u}_i. \qquad (1.6.7)$$

---

* Here and in the following the term T_0 will be omitted when $T - T_0$ is differentiated.

27

Together with the fourth equation (1.6.2) and the initial and boundary conditions, the three equations (1.6.7) suffice for the determination of the time–dependent displacement and temperature fields. In vector form these equations read

$$\mu \nabla^2 \mathbf{u} + (\lambda + \mu) \operatorname{grad} \operatorname{div} \mathbf{u} - (3\lambda + 2\mu) a_T \operatorname{grad} T = \rho \ddot{\mathbf{u}},$$

$$\nabla^2 T - \frac{1}{a} \dot{T} - \frac{T_0 (3\lambda + 2\mu)\alpha_T}{\lambda_T} \operatorname{div} \ddot{\mathbf{u}} = 0. \tag{1.6.8}$$

The displacement vector **u** can be resolved into the sum of an irrotational and a solenoidal part:

$$\mathbf{u} = \operatorname{grad} \Phi + \operatorname{rot} \mathbf{A}, \tag{1.6.9}$$

where Φ is the scalar potential and $\mathbf{A}$ is the vector potential.

Substitution of expression (1.6.9) into (1.6.8) leads to a set of equations that can be split up in the following way [35, 59, 65]:

$$\nabla^2 \Phi - \frac{1}{c_1^2} \ddot{\Phi} - \frac{(3\lambda + 2\mu)\alpha_T}{\lambda + 2\mu} (T - T_0) = 0, \tag{1.6.10}$$

$$\nabla^2 \mathbf{A} - \frac{1}{c_2^2} \ddot{\mathbf{A}} = 0, \tag{1.6.11}$$

$$\nabla^2 T - \frac{1}{a} \dot{T} - \frac{T_0 (3\lambda + 2\mu)\alpha_T}{\lambda_T} \nabla^2 \dot{\Phi} = 0, \tag{1.6.12}$$

$$c_1^2 = \frac{\lambda + 2\mu}{\rho}, \quad c_2^2 = \frac{\mu}{\rho},$$

where c_1 is speed of propagation of dilatational waves, c_2 is the speed of propagation of shear waves, which are characterized by change of shape without change of volume, and T_0 is the temperature of the body in the unstressed state when $\Phi = 0$.

Eliminating T from equations (1.6.10) and (1.6.12), we obtain one equation for Φ, namely

$$\left(\nabla^2 - \frac{1}{a} \frac{\partial}{\partial t} \right) \left(\nabla^2 - \frac{1}{c_1^2} \frac{\partial^2}{\partial t^2} \right) \Phi - \frac{T_0 (3\lambda + 2\mu)^2 \alpha_T^2}{(\lambda + 2\mu) a c_\epsilon} \nabla^2 \dot{\Phi} = 0. \tag{1.6.13}$$

If the coupling between the strain and temperature fields is neglected, we

28

obtain a representation of the general solution (1.6.9) of the dynamic thermo-elastic problem in which the scalar potential Φ and the vector potential $\mathbf{A}$ are determined from the equations

$$\square_1^2 \Phi = \frac{(3\lambda + 2\mu)\alpha_T}{\lambda + 2\mu} (T - T_0) = \frac{1 + \nu}{1 - \nu} \alpha_T (T - T_0), \qquad (1.6.14)$$

$$\square_2^2 \mathbf{A} = 0, \qquad (1.6.15)$$

where $\square_n^2 = \nabla^2 - \dfrac{1}{c_n^2} \dfrac{\partial^2}{\partial t^2}$, $n = 1, 2$.

The solution of the coupled thermoelastic problem in the general case presents great mathematical difficulties. Variational methods are best suited to obtaining approximate solutions of this problem.

1.7. Variational principles for coupled thermoelastic problems

Starting with the basic thermodynamic laws of irreversible processes, Biot [52] has set up a variational principle for the coupled problem of thermo-elasticity. The treatment given here will differ somewhat from that given by Biot.

Limiting consideration to small deviations of the thermodynamic system from the state of equilibrium ($T \approx T_0$), we will consider (1) the vector field of displacements $\mathbf{u}$, and (2) the vector field of entropy flux $\mathbf{s}$. The *entropy flux* $\mathbf{s}$ is defined as the rate of heat flow divided by the absolute temperature in the direction indicated by vector $\mathbf{s}$. It is related to the heat flux $\mathbf{q}$ through the equation

$$\mathbf{q} = T\dot{\mathbf{s}} \approx T_0 \dot{\mathbf{s}},$$

or

$$q_i \approx T_0 \dot{s}_i, \qquad (1.7.1)$$

where s_i are the components of the entropy flux.

In view of equations (1.4.1) and (1.4.7), we have

$$-\dot{s}_{i,i} = \frac{\dot{Q}}{T_0} = \dot{S}, \qquad (1.7.2)$$

29

$$\dot{S}_{\mathrm{II}} = \frac{1}{\lambda_{\mathrm{T}}} \dot{s}_i \dot{s}_i, \tag{1.7.3}$$

where S is the specific entropy.

Let the components u_i of the displacement vector and the components s_i of the entropy flux undergo the six independent variations δu_i, δs_i ($i = 1, 2, 3$). On the basis of equations (1.6.1), (1.4.4), and (1.7.1), we can set up the following fairly obvious identity

$$\int\limits_V (\sigma_{ij,j} - \rho \ddot{u}_i) \delta u_i dV - \int\limits_V \left(T_{,i} + \frac{T_0 \dot{s}_i}{\lambda_{\mathrm{T}}} \right) \delta s_i dV = 0, \tag{1.7.4}$$

where the integration extends over the volume of the body.

After applying the divergence theorem to (1.7.4), we have

$$\int\limits_\Omega \sigma_{ij} n_j \delta u_i d\Omega + \int\limits_V (-\rho \ddot{u}_i) \delta u_i dV - \int\limits_V \sigma_{ij} \delta \epsilon_{ij} dV -$$

$$- \int\limits_\Omega (T - T_0) n_i \delta s_i d\Omega + \int\limits_V (T - T_0) \delta s_{i,i} dV - \int\limits_V \frac{T_0 \dot{s}_i}{\lambda_{\mathrm{T}}} \delta s_i dV = 0. \tag{1.7.5}$$

Equations (1.6.3), (1.7.2), and (1.5.25) enable us to transform the third and fourth integrals in (1.7.5) as follows

$$\int\limits_V \sigma_{ij} \delta \epsilon_{ij} dV = \delta \int\limits_V \left(\frac{\lambda}{2} \epsilon_{kk}^2 + \mu \epsilon_{ij} \epsilon_{ij} \right) dV -$$

$$- \int\limits_V (3\lambda + 2\mu) \alpha_{\mathrm{T}} (T - T_0) \delta \epsilon_{kk} dV, \tag{1.7.6}$$

$$\int\limits_V (T - T_0) \delta s_{i,i} dV = - \int\limits_V (T - T_0) \delta S dV =$$

$$= -\delta \int\limits_V \frac{c_\epsilon (T - T_0)^2}{2T_0} dV - \int\limits_V (3\lambda + 2\mu) \alpha_{\mathrm{T}} (T - T_0) \delta \epsilon_{kk} dV. \tag{1.7.7}$$

30

When transforming integrals (1.7.6) and (1.7.7), use has been made of the fact that $\delta_{ij}\epsilon_{ij} = \epsilon_{kk}$. After substituting these integrals into (1.7.5) and taking account of boundary condition (1.2.8), we can formulate the *variational principle for the coupled problem of thermoelasticity* as follows

$$\delta V_B + \delta D = \int_\Omega [f_i \delta u_i - (T - T_0) n_i \delta s_i]\, d\Omega + \int_V (-\rho \ddot{u}_i) \delta u_i dV, \quad (1.7.8)$$

where

$$V_B = \int_V \left[\frac{\lambda}{2} \epsilon_{kk}^2 + \mu \epsilon_{ij} \epsilon_{ij} + \frac{c_\epsilon (T - T_0)^2}{2T_0} \right] dV, \quad (1.7.9)$$

$$D = \frac{1}{2} \int_V \frac{T_0 \dot{s}_i \dot{s}_i}{\lambda_T}\, dV. \quad (1.7.10)$$

The scalar invariant V_B is called the *Biot thermoelastic potential,* and the scalar invariant D is called the *dissipation function.*

As is evident from equality (1.7.3), the scalar invariant D is proportional to the rate of entropy production in the whole body.

The right–hand side of equation (1.7.8) can be interpreted as a generalized virtual work. Moreover, the quantity $-(T - T_0) n_i$, where n_i is the unit outward normal on the boundary, is analogous to a force, and δs_i is analogous to a virtual displacement.

In uncoupled thermoelastic problems, only the displacements u_i are subjected to variations. Then, when the coupling term

$$\int_V (3\lambda + 2\mu)\, \alpha_T\, (T - T_0)\, \delta \epsilon_{kk} dV$$ is omitted from (1.7.7), the variational

principle (1.7.5) yields the Lagrange variational equation for the case of thermoelastic equilibrium (cf. Section 2.3). If, on the other hand, the mechanical terms in (1.7.8) are set equal to zero, we obtain the *variational equation for heat conduction:*

$$\delta V_B + \delta D = - \int_\Omega (T - T_0) n_i \delta s_i d\Omega, \quad (1.7.11)$$

31

where

$$V_B = \frac{1}{2} \int\limits_V \frac{c_\epsilon (T - T_0)^2}{T_0} \, dV, \qquad (1.7.12)$$

$$D = \frac{1}{2} \int\limits_V \frac{T_0 \dot{s}_i \dot{s}_i}{\lambda_T} \, dV, \quad \dot{s}_i = \frac{q_i}{T_0}. \qquad (1.7.13)$$

Chapter II

QUASI–STATIC THERMOELASTIC PROBLEM. BASIC EQUATION

2.1. General remarks

Certain simplifying assumptions concerning the conditions for heat conduction can be made in connection with the formulation of the coupled thermoelastic problem in Section 1.6.

When the external heat sources cause non–uniform heating, it can be assumed that the temperature field is independent of the strains caused by it. Then the mechanical coupling term $-\dfrac{T_0 \, (3\lambda + 2\mu) \, \alpha_T}{\lambda_T} \, \dot{\epsilon}_{kk}$ in the heat conduction equation (1.6.2) can be omitted. If, however, the temperature changes in the elastic body are not producted by an external heat source but are due to the strains, the irreversible process is accompanied by thermoelastic energy dissipation and the mechanical coupling term must be retained in equation (1.6.2). Moreover, in view of the small temperature changes associated with the deformations caused by the external forces, it is possible to omit the terms $-(3\lambda + 2\mu) \, \alpha_T \, (T - T_0) \, \delta_{ij}$ in equations (1.6.3). In either of these cases the thermoelastic problem is uncoupled; the field of deformations is independent of the temperature field.

Under usual conditions of heat exchange, the rate of temperature change is small in comparison with the speed of sound in the material. Thus, at any given instant, the thermal stresses in an elastic body can be determined on the basis of the instantaneous values of the temperature field (irrespective of whether it is time dependent or not). Thus, there is no need to consider the inertia forces corresponding to the motion of the particles during the varying thermal expansion, i.e., the inertia term $-\rho\ddot{u}$ in (1.6.1) can be disregarded.

When the mechanical coupling terms in the heat conduction equation and the inertia terms in the equations of motion are disregarded, the formulation of the *thermoelastic problem* is said to be *quasi–static*.

The first stage in the solution of the quasi–static problem consists in finding the temperature field T. It involves the solution of equation (1.6.2) after omitting the terms depending on the strains. The initial conditions are determined by the temperature distribution at time $t = 0$, and the boundary conditions depend on the law of heat conduction between the environment and the surface of the body (see Chapter III).

After finding the temperature field, we determine the corresponding field of thermal stresses. Since the inertia terms in the thermoelastic equations are omitted, the time plays the role of a parameter.

The problem consists in determining the 15 quantities $\sigma_{ij}, \epsilon_{ij}, u_i$ that satisfy (1) the equilibrium equations

$$\sigma_{ij,j} + F_i = 0. \tag{2.1.1}$$

in which the static body forces are considered, (2) the six stress–strain relations (1.5.11) or (1.5.13), and (3) the six strain–displacement equations (1.2.2). On part Ω_1 of the surface of the body the boundary conditions may be formulated in terms of the displacements

$$u_i = g_i(x_k), \tag{2.1.2}$$

and on the remainder Ω_2 in terms of the stresses

$$\sigma_{ij}n_j = f_i(x_k), \tag{2.1.3}$$

where $\Omega_1 + \Omega_2 = \Omega$.

When solving specific thermoelastic problems it is convenient to choose either the displacements u_i or the stresses σ_{ij} as dependent variables. Correspondingly, we have first the thermoelastic problem in terms of the displacements (Section 2.2) where all other unknowns are determined in terms of the u_i, and second the thermoelastic problem in terms of the stresses (Section 2.3) in which the first step is the determination of the stresses σ_{ij}.

The general solution of the thermoelastic problem in terms of the displacements will be taken in the form given by Papkovich [40]. This is a most convenient form, since it contains functions governed by relatively simple differential equations. Moreover, it has a certain functional redundancy which can be exploited when satisfying the boundary conditions.

The formulation of the thermoelastic problem in terms of the stresses is explained in Section 2.3. Not only simply connected but also doubly connected regions are considered. Conditions are formulated for the uniqueness of the displacements and the rotations.

In general it is very difficult to determine the thermal displacements and stresses by direct integration of the appropriate differential equations and satisfaction of the nonhomogeneous boundary conditions. For this reason there is great interest in the variational principles of thermoelasticity as explained in Section 2.4. These principles enable one to derive approximate solutions of thermoelastic problems in a way similar to the variational method for isotropic elasticity [23] namely

1) methods based on a generalization to the thermoelastic problem of the Lagrange variational equations and the expressions approximating the virtual displacements, and

2) methods based on a generalization to the thermoelastic problem of the principle of minimum strain energy and expressions approximating the virtual stresses.

One of these direct methods of solution of the thermoelastic problem, the method of Maizel' [29], is based on a generalization of the Betti–Maxwell reciprocity theorem explained in Section 2.5.

2.2. Displacement formulation of thermoelastic problem. Representation of general solution

The first of equations (1.6.8) can be used to formulate the thermoelastic problem in terms of the displacements. Omitting the inertia term and introducing the body force $\mathbf{F}$, we obtain the following basic equation

$$\mu \nabla^2 \mathbf{u} + (\lambda + \mu) \operatorname{grad} \operatorname{div} \mathbf{u} - (3\lambda + 2\mu)\alpha_T \operatorname{grad} T + \mathbf{F} = 0. \quad (2.2.1)$$

The function T in this equation is assumed to be known from the solution of the corresponding heat conduction problem.

The boundary conditions in the displacements (2.1.2) can be used as they stand. By means of relations (1.5.11), the boundary conditions in the stresses (2.1.3) can also be expressed in terms of the displacements

$$\left\{ \mu(u_{i,j} + u_{j,i}) + [\lambda u_{k,k} - (3\lambda + 2\mu)\alpha_T (T - T_0)] \delta_{ij} \right\} n_j = f_i (x_1). \quad (2.2.2)$$

The general solution of equation (2.2.1) has the form

$$\mathbf{u} = \mathbf{u}^* + \mathbf{u}^{(T)} + \mathbf{u}^{(F)}, \quad (2.2.3)$$

where $\mathbf{u}^*$ is the general solution of the homogeneous form of equation (2.2.1), $\mathbf{u}^{(T)}$ is a particular solution of (2.2.1) corresponding to $\mathbf{F} = 0$, and $\mathbf{u}^{(F)}$ is a particular solution of the nonhomogeneous equation (2.2.1) corresponding to $T - T_0 = 0$.

The general solution $\mathbf{u}^*$ of the homogeneous equation was given by Papkovich [38] in the form

$$\mathbf{u}^* = 4\,(1 - \nu)\,\mathbf{B} - \mathrm{grad}\,(\mathbf{B} \cdot \mathbf{r} + B_0), \tag{2.2.4}$$

where $\mathbf{B}$ is a harmonic vector satisfying the equation

$$\nabla^2 \mathbf{B} = 0, \tag{2.2.5}$$

and B_0 is a harmonic scalar satisfying the equation

$$\nabla^2 B_0 = 0, \tag{2.2.6}$$

where $\mathbf{r}$ is the position vector.

We recall that the harmonic scalar B_0 in solution (2.2.4) can be omitted without restricting the generality. However, its retention leads to simplification in a number of cases.

The particular solution $\mathbf{u}^{(F)}$ has been studied in the theory of elasticity. Here we limit consideration to the particular solution $\mathbf{u}^{(T)}$. This solution, which was derived by Papkovich [39] and Goddier [61], has the form

$$\mathbf{u}^{(T)} = \mathrm{grad}\,\Phi, \tag{2.2.7}$$

where the scalar function Φ satisfies the Poisson equation

$$\nabla^2 \Phi = \frac{1 + \nu}{1 - \nu} \alpha_T \,(T - T_0). \tag{2.2.8}$$

The function Φ is known as the thermoelastic displacement potential.

In the works of Melan and Parkus [31], Nowacki [35], and others, the determination of the thermoelastic displacement potential Φ is the basic step in the study of thermal stresses. In these works, the following method of solution of concrete quasi–static problems of thermoelasticity is adopted:

With a known temperature field, they first find the particular solution of equation (2.2.8) for the thermoelastic potential Φ whose first spatial derivatives determine the respective particular solutions for the displacements.

Then the thermoelastic stresses corresponding to this potential are calculated. In general these stresses do not satisfy the prescribed conditions on boundaries.

On this solution they next superimpose the solution corresponding to the boundary—value problem of the isotropic theory of elasticity. This solution contains a sufficient number of constants of integration in order to satisfy the boundary conditions.

We recall that solution (2.2.7) is the final step only when the body has infinite extent.

The above formulation and representation of the solution of the quasi—static thermoelastic problem in terms of the displacements is valid not only for simply—connected but also for multiply—connected bodies. Moreover the displacements must be single—valued functions having continuous derivatives up to the second order inclusively.

In concluding this Section we will mention the analogy between the quasi—static problem of thermoelasticity and the problem of the isotropic theory of elasticity with fictitious body and surface forces.

When equations (2.2.1) and (2.2.2) are compared with the corresponding equations in the isotropic theory of elasticity, one sees that the quasi—static thermoelastic problem is equivalent to a problem in isotropic elasticity in which the body force $\mathbf{F}$ has the value $-(3\lambda + 2\mu)\alpha_T$ grad T and the prescribed surface forces f_i are augmented by a normal component equal to $(3\lambda + 2\mu)\alpha_T (T - T_0)$. This analogy has been used extensively in the study of thermal stresses in the book of Timoshenko [47] and others.

2.3. Stress formulation of thermoelastic problem

When solving a thermoelastic problem with the stress conditions (2.1.3), it is advantageous to start with equations governing the stresses. These are obtained by eliminating the strains and displacements from equations (2.1.1), relations (1.5.11) or (1.5.13), and (1.2.2). Then the six stress components σ_{ij} are used as dependent variables.

Let us first consider this problem for a simply—connected body.

The equilibrium equations (2.1.1) and the boundary conditions (2.1.3) are already expressed in the stresses.

For the complete formulation of the thermoelastic problem in the stresses, it is necessary to use relations (1.2.2) to determine the displacements u_i in terms of the known components of the strain tensor ϵ_{ij}.

In view of equation (1.2.5), identity (1.2.1) can be written as

$$u_{i,j} = \epsilon_{ij} + e_{jik}\omega_k. \tag{2.3.1}$$

37

The integrability conditions for (2.3.1) are

$$e_{pmj}(\epsilon_{ij} + e_{jik}\omega_k)_{,m} = e_{pmj}\epsilon_{ij,m} + e_{pmj}e_{jik}\omega_{k,m} = 0. \quad (2.3.2)$$

Relation (1.1.5) can be used to transform the second term on the right—hand side of (2.3.2) into

$$e_{pmj}e_{jik}\omega_{k,m} = (\delta_{pi}\delta_{mk} - \delta_{pk}\delta_{mi})\,\omega_{k,m} = \delta_{pi}\omega_{k,k} - \omega_{p,i}. \quad (2.3.3)$$

Substituting expression (2.3.3) into (2.3.2) and noting that $\omega_{k,k} = 0$, we obtain

$$\omega_{p,i} + e_{pmj}\epsilon_{ij,m} = 0. \quad (2.3.4)$$

Application of the integrability conditions to (2.3.4) now yields

$$e_{qni}e_{pmj}\epsilon_{ij,mn} = 0. \quad (2.3.5)$$

Relation (2.3.5) has two free indices p and q and is symmetric with respect to them. Thus, we have six equations which are called the *compatibility conditions* for the strains.

Setting

$$p = 3, \quad q = 3, \quad n = m = 1, \quad i = j = 2$$

and

$$p = 2, \quad q = 3, \quad m = 3, \quad n = 1, \quad i = 2, \quad j = 1,$$

we find the following two typical types of compatibility equations

$$\epsilon_{11,22} + \epsilon_{22,11} = 2\epsilon_{12,12},$$

$$\epsilon_{11,23} + \epsilon_{23,11} = \epsilon_{12,13} + \epsilon_{13,12}.$$

The remaining four equations are obtained directly by cyclic interchange of the indices.

When conditions (2.3.5) are satisfied, the expressions

$$du_i = u_{i,j}dx_j,$$

$$d\omega_i = \omega_{i,j}dx_j$$

are total differentials.

By integrating expressions (2.3.1) and (2.3.4) for $u_{i,j}$ and $\omega_{i,j}$, we obtain the following components u_i of the displacement vector and ω_i of the rotation vector at point P

$$u_i = u_i^0 + \int_{P_0}^{P} (\epsilon_{ij} + e_{jik}\omega_k)\,dx_j, \quad (2.3.6)$$

$$\omega_k = \omega_k^0 + \int_{P_0}^{P} e_{kmn}\,\epsilon_{ln,m}\,dx_l, \qquad (2.3.7)$$

where the integration is performed over an arbitrary path from P_0 to P in region V, and u_i^0, ω_i^0 are the corresponding components at point P_0.

Integral (2.3.6) can also be written in the form [1]

$$u_i = u_i^0 - e_{jik}\,(x_j^0 - x_j)\,\omega_k^0 +$$

$$+ \int_{P_0}^{P} [\epsilon_{il} + e_{jik}e_{kmn}\,(x_j - x_j')\,\epsilon_{ln,m}]\,dx_l'. \qquad (2.3.8)$$

When the region is simply connected, integrals (2.3.6) and (2.3.7) are independent of the path of integration. Then they represent a single–valued function. Moreover, the displacements must have continuous derivatives up to the third order.

Now we will derive the compatibility equations in terms of the stresses. Let us write relation (2.3.5) in the form

$$\epsilon_{ij,mn} - \epsilon_{im,jn} - \epsilon_{nj,mi} + \epsilon_{nm,ji} = 0. \qquad (2.3.9)$$

When $m = n$, we have

$$\epsilon_{ij,nn} - \epsilon_{in,jn} - \epsilon_{nj,ni} + \epsilon_{nn,ji} = 0. \qquad (2.3.10)$$

The strains in equation (2.3.10) will now be expressed in terms of the stresses by means of equation (1.5.13). Since it follows from (2.1.1) that $\sigma_{in,jn}$ and $\sigma_{nj,ni}$ are equal to $-F_{i,j}$ and $-F_{j,i}$, respectively, we thus find

$$(1 + \nu)\,\sigma_{ij,nn} - \nu\sigma_{kk,nn}\delta_{ij} + \sigma_{nn,ij} + (1 + \nu)\,(F_{i,j} + F_{j,i}) +$$

$$+ E\alpha_T\,(T_{,nn}\delta_{ij} + T_{,ij}) = 0. \qquad (2.3.11)$$

When $i = j$, equation (2.3.11) becomes

$$\text{'} \quad (1 - \nu)\,\sigma_{kk,nn} + (1 + \nu)\,F_{i,i} + 2E\alpha_T T_{,nn} = 0. \qquad (2.3.12)$$

where use was made of the fact that

$$\sigma_{ii,nn} = \sigma_{nn,ii} = \sigma_{kk,nn}, \quad T_{,ii} = T_{,nn}.$$

---

1) The equivalence of (2.3.6) and (2.3.8) can be seen by integrating (2.3.8) by parts and taking account of (2.3.4).

Finally, substituting the expression for $\sigma_{kk,nn}$ found from (2.3.12) into equation (2.3.11) we arrive at the following *compatibility equations in terms of the stresses*

$$(1 + \nu)\,\sigma_{ij,nn} + \sigma_{nn,ij} + \frac{\nu\,(1 + \nu)}{1 - \nu} F_{n,n}\delta_{ij} + (1 + \nu)\,(F_{i,j} + F_{j,i}) +$$

$$+ E\alpha_T\,\left(\frac{1 + \nu}{1 - \nu} T_{,nn}\delta_{ij} + T_{,ij}\right) = 0. \tag{2.3.13}$$

Setting $i = j = 1$ and $i = 1, j = 2$ we obtain the following two typical types

$$(1 + \nu)\,\sigma_{11,nn} + \sigma_{nn,11} + \frac{1 + \nu}{1 - \nu}[(2 - \nu)\,F_{1,1} + \nu\,(F_{2,2} + F_{3,3})] +$$

$$+ E\alpha_T\,\left(\frac{1 + \nu}{1 - \nu} T_{,nn} + T_{,11}\right) = 0. \tag{2.3.14}$$

$$(1 + \nu)\,\sigma_{12,nn} + \sigma_{nn,12} + (1 + \nu)\,(F_{1,2} + F_{2,1}) + E\alpha_T T_{,12} = 0. \tag{2.3.15}$$

The remaining four equations can be obtained by cyclic permutation of the indices.

The stress formulation of the thermoelastic problem involves the determination of six functions σ_{ij} that satisfy (a) the three equilibrium equations (2.1.1), (b) the six compatibility equations (2.3.13), and (c) the three boundary conditions (2.1.3).

When the stresses are known, the strains can be determined from (1.5.13), and then the displacements from (2.3.6).

When the region under consideration is multiply connected, the functions u_i and ω_k determined from equations (2.3.6) and (2.3.7) may be many−valued.

Additional conditions for the one−valuedness of the functions u_i and ω_k determined from their total differential in a multiply connected region have been established in [34].

Let us consider an $(N+1)$−fold multiply connected region and imagine that it has been rendered simply connected by N cuts (internal surfaces), as indicated in Fig. 4.

In order that u_i is single−valued, it is necessary and sufficient that (1) the equations (2.3.13) are satisfied, and (2) that $N+1$ integrals should vanish, namely the integrals (2.3.8) over each contour L_K ($K = 1, ..., N$) which encloses just the K-th hole, i.e.

$$\int_{L_K} [\epsilon_{il} + e_{jik}e_{kmn} (x_j - x_j') \epsilon_{ln,m}] dx_l' = 0, \qquad (2.3.16)$$
$$(K = 1, ..., N).$$

There are similar conditions for the single-valuedness of the function ω_k defined by equation (2.3.7).

Since the quantities

$$x_j \int_{L_K} e_{jik}e_{kmn}\epsilon_{ln,m}dx_l$$

in equations (2.3.16) should vanish when ω_k is to be one-valued, the conditions for the one-valuedness of u_i and ω_k can be written in the form

$$\int_{L_K} (\epsilon_{il} - e_{jik}e_{kmn}x_j\epsilon_{ln,m}) \, dx_l = 0,$$

$$(K = 1, ..., N), \qquad (2.3.17)$$

$$\int_{L_K} e_{kmn}\epsilon_{ln,m}dx_l = 0, \qquad (2.3.18)$$

$$(K = 1, ..., N).$$

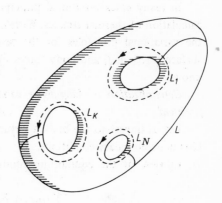

Fig. 4.

With the aid of relation (1.5.13), the above result can be expressed in terms of the stresses as follows

$$\frac{1 + \nu}{E} \int_{L_K} (\sigma_{il} - e_{jik}e_{kmn}x_j\sigma_{ln,m}) \, dx_l -$$

$$- \frac{\nu}{E} \int_{L_K} (\sigma_{pp}\delta_{il} - e_{jik}e_{kml}x_j\sigma_{pp,m}) \, dx_l +$$

$$+ a_T \int_{L_K} [(T - T_0) \, \delta_{il} - e_{jik}e_{kml}x_jT_{,m}] \, dx_l = 0, \qquad (2.3.19)$$

$$(K = 1, ..., N),$$

41

$$\frac{1+\nu}{E} \int\limits_{L_K} e_{kmn}\sigma_{ln,m}dx_l - \frac{\nu}{E} \int\limits_{L_K} e_{kml}\sigma_{pp,m}dx_l +$$

$$+\alpha_T \int\limits_{L_K} e_{kml}T_{,m}dx_l = 0, \qquad (2.3.20)$$

$$(K = 1, ..., N).$$

2.4. Variational principles

In many cases variational principles are well suited for the approximate calculation of thermal stresses. With this application in mind, let us consider the variational principles for the case where the body is subjected to the surface tractions f_i and body forces F_i, and the temperature field $T(x_k, t)$ is known.

Generalization of Lagrange's variational equation to the thermoelastic problem.

Let us impart to the body a virtual displacement δu_i that satisfies all the kinematic boundary conditions.

In view of the equilibrium conditions, we have the following identity

$$\int\limits_V (\sigma_{ij,j} + F_i)\, \delta u_i dV = 0, \qquad (2.4.1)$$

where the integration extends over the whole of volume V of the body.

Application of the divergence theorem yields

$$\int\limits_\Omega \sigma_{ij}n_j\delta u_i d\Omega + \int\limits_V F_i\delta u_i dV - \int\limits_V \sigma_{ij}\delta\epsilon_{ij}dV = 0, \qquad (2.4.2)$$

where Ω is the surface enclosing volume V.

Taking formulae (1.5.7) and boundary conditions (1.2.8) into account and bearing in mind that the temperature field is assumed to remain constant during virtual displacements, we find

$$\delta \left[\int\limits_V FdV - \int\limits_V F_iu_i dV - \int\limits_\Omega f_iu_i d\Omega \right] = 0, \qquad (2.4.3)$$

where F is the specific free energy, and f_i are the components of the surface traction.

42

Equation (2.4.3) is a generalization of Lagrange's well–known principle of virtual displacements for the case of elastic equilibrium [23]. The role of the specific strain energy is here replaced by the specific free energy [62].

Generalization of the principle of minimum potential energy to the thermoelastic problem.

Let us subject the state of stress σ_{ij} of the body to an arbitrary statistically admissible variation $\delta\sigma_{ij}$. A statistically admissible variation is one that satisfies the equilibrium equations (2.1.1), i.e. we have

$$\delta\sigma_{ij,j} = 0. \tag{2.4.4}$$

In order that the boundary conditions (2.1.3) are satisfied, the variations of the surface tractions must satisfy the condition

$$\delta f_i = \delta\sigma_{ij} n_j. \tag{2.4.5}$$

Such variations of the state of stress must of course be compatible with the geometric constraints.

In virtue of equation (1.5.8), we have the following identity

$$\int_V \left(\epsilon_{ij} + \frac{\partial G}{\partial \sigma_{ij}} \right) \delta\sigma_{ij} dV = 0. \tag{2.4.6}$$

Here we will express the strains ϵ_{ij} in terms of the displacements u_i by means of (1.2.2) and then apply the divergence theorem. Remembering that i and j are dummy suffices, we find

$$\int_\Omega u_i \delta\sigma_{ij} n_j d\Omega - \int_V u_i \delta\sigma_{ij,j} dV + \int_V \delta G dV = 0. \tag{2.4.7}$$

On the basis of (2.4.4) and (2.4.5) we finally obtain

$$\delta \left(\int_V G dV + \int_\Omega u_i f_i d\Omega \right) = 0. \tag{2.4.8}$$

where the surface integration extends over the entire surface of the body.

Equation (2.4.8) is a generalization of Castigliano's principle [23]. In (2.4.8), the role of the specific strain energy is played by Gibbs thermodynamic potential (per unit volume) multiplied by minus one [62]. When the variation of the state of stress is such that the surface tractions are invariant ($\delta f_i = 0$), we have

$$\delta \int_V G dV = 0. \tag{2.4.9}$$

This formula is a generalization of the familiar principle of minimum strain energy.

2.5. Generalization of Betti–Maxwell reciprocity theorem to thermoelasticity

Consider two states of stress in an elastic body. The first is characterized by the stresses σ_{ij}, the strains ϵ_{ij}, and the displacements u_i produced by the external forces F_i, f_i, and the temperature field T. The second is characterized by the stresses σ_{ij}', the strains ϵ_{ij}', and the displacements u_i' produced by the external forces F_i', f_i', and the temperature field T'.

After applying the divergence theorem, the equilibrium conditions, and the kinematic boundary conditions, the work of the forces in the first state for the displacements in the second state is given by

$$L_{12} = \int_V F_i u_i' dV + \int_{\Omega} f_i u_i' d\Omega = \int_V (\sigma_{ij,j} + F_i) u_i' dV +$$

$$+ \int_V \sigma_{ij} u_{i,j}' dV = \int_V \sigma_{ij} \epsilon_{ij}' dV. \tag{2.5.1}$$

Similarly, the work of the forces in the second state for the displacements in the first state is given by

$$L_{21} = \int_V F_i' u_i dV + \int_{\Omega} f_i' u_i d\Omega = \int_V \sigma_{ij}' \epsilon_{ij} dV. \tag{2.5.2}$$

Subtracting L_{21} from L_{12} and eliminating either the stresses or the strains with the aid of (1.5.11) or (1.5.13), one finds

$$L_{12} - L_{21} = (3\lambda + 2\mu) \alpha_T \int_V [(T' - T_0) \epsilon_{kk} - (T - T_0) \epsilon_{kk}'] dV =$$

$$= \alpha_T \int_V [(T' - T_0) \sigma_{kk} - (T - T_0) \sigma_{kk}'] dV. \tag{2.5.3}$$

This result is a generalization of the Betti–Maxwell theorem to the static or quasi–static problem of thermoelasticity and is due to Maizel' [29, 30].

Let us now apply (2.5.3) to determine the displacements at a prescribed point in a non–uniformly heated body. It will be assumed that $F_i = 0, f_i = 0$, $T' = T_0$. The system of external forces F_i' and f_i' will be assumed equivalent to a concentrated unit force at point x_r^0 in the direction of axis x_i.

The stresses $\sigma_{ij}^* (x_r^0, x_r)$ and the strains $\epsilon_{ij}^* (x_r^0, x_r)$ are those at point x_r due to the action of the unit force at point x_r^0. The Maizel' formula (2.5.3) now yields the following expression for the displacement at point x_r^0 due to the temperature field T

$$u_i (x_r^0) = (3\lambda + 2\mu) \alpha_T \int_V (T - T_0) \, \epsilon_{kk}^* (x_r^0, x_r) \, dV =$$

$$= \alpha_T \int_V (T - T_0) \, \sigma_{kk}^* (x_r^0, x_r) \, dV, \qquad (2.5.4)$$

where $\sigma_{kk}^* (x_r^0, x_r)$ and $\epsilon_{kk}^* (x_r^0, x_r)$ are the sums of the diagonal components (i.e. the traces) of the stress tensor σ_{ij}^* and the strain tensor ϵ_{ij}^*.

Formulae (2.5.4) can be generalized to the case where the elastic modulus E and the Poisson ratio ν (or the Lamé coefficients λ and μ) are temperature dependent and are thus functions of x_r. In this case we have

$$u_i (x_r^0) = \int_V (3\lambda + 2\mu) \alpha_T (T - T_0) \, \epsilon_{kk}^* (x_r^0, x_r) \, dV =$$

$$= \int_V \alpha_T (T - T_0) \, \sigma_{kk}^* (x_r^0, x_r) \, dV. \qquad (2.5.5)$$

Here, $\sigma_{kk}^* (x_r^0, x_r)$ and $\epsilon_{kk}^* (x_r^0, x_r)$ must be interpreted as the traces of the stress tensor σ_{ij}^* and the strain tensor ϵ_{ij}^* corresponding to the action of a unit force on an elastic body in which E and ν vary as functions of positions in a way corresponding to prescribed temperature field T.

Thus, when the reciprocity theorem is used, the problem of determining the state of thermal stresses in an elastic body reduces to a problem in the isothermal theory of elasticity with a concentrated unit force applied.

When the strains are axisymmetric, the problem of thermoelasticity reduces to that of the state of stress of a uniformly heated body under the action of concentrated forces uniformly distributed around the boundary.

It is obvious that the application of this method requires a store of solved problems in isothermal elasticity for bodies under the action of concentrated forces.

2.6. Curvilinear coordinates

Above, the basic principles of thermoelasticity were treated using rectangular cartesian coordinates. However, the use of orthogonal curvilinear coordinates is advantageous in the solution of many thermoelastic problems.

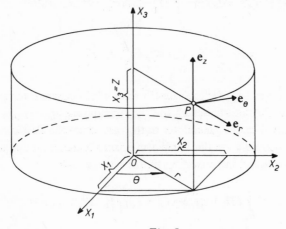

Fig. 5.

We will consider the basic equations in cylindrical and spherical coordinates. Moreover, the summation convention will be dropped when treating curvilinear coordinates.

In cylindrical coordinates the position of a point P is determined by the three coordinates r, θ, z as shown in Fig. 5. The coordinate surfaces are the cylinders r = const., the half—planes θ = const., and the planes z = const.

The cartesian coordinates are related to the cylindrical coordinates through the relations

$$x_1 = r \cos \theta, \qquad x_2 = r \sin \theta, \qquad x_3 = z.$$

Let us consider the trihedral of mutually orthogonal unit vectors e_r, e_θ, and e_z that form a right—handed system. The unit radius vector is e_r, the unit azimuthal vector is e_θ, and the unit axial vector is e_z. Each of these vectors

46

points in the direction in which the corresponding coordinate increases (Fig. 5).

It is well known in vector analysis that the fundamental vector operations in cylindrical polar coordinates are expressed in the form

$$\operatorname{grad} \psi = \mathbf{e}_r \frac{\partial \psi}{\partial r} + \mathbf{e}_\theta \frac{1}{r} \frac{\partial \psi}{\partial \theta} + \mathbf{e}_z \frac{\partial \psi}{\partial z}, \tag{2.6.1}$$

$$\operatorname{div} \mathbf{a} = \frac{1}{r} \frac{\partial (r a_r)}{\partial r} + \frac{1}{r} \frac{\partial a_\theta}{\partial \theta} + \frac{\partial a_z}{\partial z}, \tag{2.6.2}$$

$$\operatorname{rot} \mathbf{a} = \mathbf{e}_r \left(\frac{1}{r} \frac{\partial a_z}{\partial \theta} - \frac{\partial a_\theta}{\partial z} \right) + \mathbf{e}_\theta \left(\frac{\partial a_r}{\partial z} - \frac{\partial a_z}{\partial r} \right) +$$

$$+ \mathbf{e}_z \left[\frac{1}{r} \frac{\partial (r a_\theta)}{\partial r} - \frac{1}{r} \frac{\partial a_r}{\partial \theta} \right], \tag{2.6.3}$$

$$\nabla^2 \psi = \left[\frac{1}{r} \frac{\partial}{\partial r} \left(r \frac{\partial}{\partial r} \right) + \frac{1}{r^2} \frac{\partial^2}{\partial \theta^2} + \frac{\partial^2}{\partial z^2} \right] \psi. \tag{2.6.4}$$

In cylindrical polar coordinates the strain–displacement relations are

$$\epsilon_r = \frac{\partial u_r}{\partial r}, \qquad \epsilon_\theta = \frac{1}{r} \left(\frac{\partial u_\theta}{\partial \theta} + u_r \right), \qquad \epsilon_z = \frac{\partial u_z}{\partial z},$$

$$\epsilon_{r\theta} = \frac{1}{2} \left[\frac{1}{r} \left(\frac{\partial u_r}{\partial \theta} - u_\theta \right) + \frac{\partial u_\theta}{\partial r} \right],$$

$$\epsilon_{\theta z} = \frac{1}{2} \left(\frac{\partial u_\theta}{\partial z} + \frac{1}{r} \frac{\partial u_z}{\partial \theta} \right), \tag{2.6.5}$$

$$\epsilon_{zr} = \frac{1}{2} \left(\frac{\partial u_z}{\partial r} + \frac{\partial u_r}{\partial z} \right).$$

The stress equation are of the form

$$\frac{\partial \sigma_r}{\partial r} + \frac{1}{r} \left(\frac{\partial \sigma_{r\theta}}{\partial \theta} + \sigma_r - \sigma_\theta \right) + \frac{\partial \sigma_{rz}}{\partial z} + F_r = \rho \frac{\partial^2 u_r}{\partial t^2},$$

$$\frac{\partial \sigma_{r\theta}}{\partial r} + \frac{1}{r} \left(\frac{\partial \sigma_\theta}{\partial \theta} + 2\sigma_{r\theta} \right) + \frac{\partial \sigma_{\theta z}}{\partial z} + F_\theta = \rho \frac{\partial^2 u_\theta}{\partial t^2}, \tag{2.6.6}$$

$$\frac{\partial \sigma_{rz}}{\partial r} + \frac{1}{r} \left(\frac{\partial \sigma_{\theta z}}{\partial \theta} + \sigma_{rz} \right) + \frac{\partial \sigma_z}{\partial z} + F_z = \rho \frac{\partial^2 u_z}{\partial t^2},$$

47

where σ_r, σ_θ, σ_z, $\sigma_{r\theta}$, $\sigma_{\theta z}$, σ_{zr} are the components of the stress tensor (see Fig. 6), and F_r, F_θ, F_z are the components of the body force $\mathbf{F}$.

In spherical coordinates the position of a point P is specified by the three coordinates r, φ, θ (Fig. 7). In this case the coordinate surface are the spheres r = const., the cones φ = const., and the half—planes θ = const[1]).

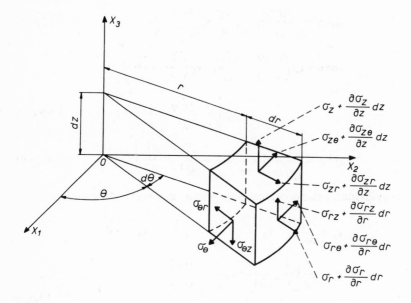

Fig. 6

The transformation formulae between cartesian and spherical coordinates are

$$x_1 = r \cos \theta \sin \varphi, \quad x_2 = r \sin \theta \sin \varphi, \quad x_3 = r \cos \varphi.$$

In terms of the trihedral of mutually orthogonal unit vectors $\mathbf{e}_r$, $\mathbf{e}_\varphi$, $\mathbf{e}_\theta$ (see Fig. 7), the basic vector operators in spherical coordinates assume the

1) For the sake of uniformly within this book, we have departed from general practice in denoting the angle between the plane $x_1 O x_3$ and the meridian plane by θ and the angle between the radius vector and the axis x_3 by φ. The same notation for the angles is used when treating the thermoelasticity of circular discs, plates, shells, and bodies of revolution.

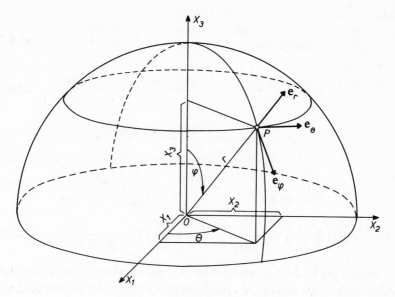

Fig. 7

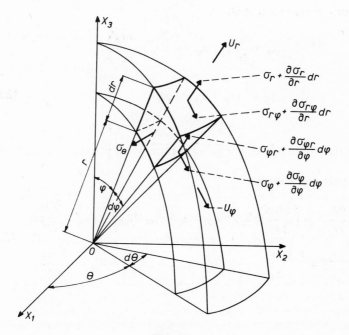

Fig. 8

49

form

$$\text{grad } \psi = \mathbf{e}_r \frac{\partial \psi}{\partial r} + \mathbf{e}_\varphi \frac{1}{r} \frac{\partial \psi}{\partial \varphi} + \mathbf{e}_\theta \frac{1}{r \sin \varphi} \frac{\partial \psi}{\partial \theta}, \tag{2.6.7}$$

$$\text{div } \mathbf{a} = \frac{1}{r^2} \frac{\partial (r^2 a_r)}{\partial r} + \frac{1}{r \sin \varphi} \frac{\partial (\sin \varphi a_\varphi)}{\partial \varphi} + \frac{1}{r \sin \varphi} \frac{\partial a_\theta}{\partial \theta}, \tag{2.6.8}$$

$$\text{rot } \mathbf{a} = \mathbf{e}_r \frac{1}{r \sin \varphi} \left[\frac{\partial (a_\theta \sin \varphi)}{\partial \varphi} - \frac{\partial a_\varphi}{\partial \theta} \right] +$$

$$+ \mathbf{e}_\varphi \left[\frac{1}{r \sin \varphi} \frac{\partial a_r}{\partial \theta} - \frac{1}{r} \frac{\partial (r a_\theta)}{\partial r} \right] + \mathbf{e}_\theta \frac{1}{r} \left[\frac{\partial (r a_\varphi)}{\partial r} - \frac{\partial a_r}{\partial \varphi} \right], \tag{2.6.9}$$

$$\nabla^2 \psi = \frac{1}{r^2} \frac{\partial}{\partial r} \left(r^2 \frac{\partial \psi}{\partial r} \right) + \frac{1}{r^2 \sin \varphi} \frac{\partial}{\partial \varphi} \left(\sin \varphi \frac{\partial \psi}{\partial \varphi} \right) + \frac{1}{r^2 \sin^2 \varphi} \frac{\partial^2 \psi}{\partial \theta^2}. \tag{2.6.10}$$

When consideration is restricted to the case of axisymmetric temperature and stress fields, the strains and stresses are independent of θ and the governing equations in spherical coordinates are (see Fig. 8):
the strain—displacement relations

$$\epsilon_r = \frac{\partial u_r}{\partial r}, \qquad \epsilon_\varphi = \frac{1}{r} \left(u_r + \frac{\partial u_\varphi}{\partial \varphi} \right),$$

$$\epsilon_\theta = \frac{1}{r} (u_r + u_\varphi \, \text{ctg} \, \varphi), \tag{2.6.11}$$

$$\epsilon_{r\varphi} = \frac{1}{2} \left[\frac{\partial u_\varphi}{\partial r} + \frac{1}{r} \left(\frac{\partial u_r}{\partial \varphi} - u_\varphi \right) \right];$$

the equations of motion

$$\frac{\partial \varphi_r}{\partial r} + \frac{1}{r} \left(\frac{\partial \sigma_{r\varphi}}{\partial \varphi} + 2\sigma_r - \sigma_\varphi - \sigma_\theta + \sigma_{r\varphi} \, \text{ctg} \, \varphi \right) + F_r = \rho \frac{\partial^2 u_r}{\partial t^2},$$

$$\frac{\partial \sigma_{r\varphi}}{\partial r} + \frac{1}{r} \left[\frac{\partial \sigma_\varphi}{\partial \varphi} + (\sigma_\varphi - \sigma_\theta) \, \text{ctg} \, \varphi + 3\sigma_{r\varphi} \right] + F_\varphi = \rho \frac{\partial^2 u_\varphi}{\partial t^2}. \tag{2.6.12}$$

Chapter III

BASIC LAWS AND PROBLEMS OF HEAT CONDUCTION

3.1. Preliminaries. Basic equations

The temperature and stress fields in a solid body are (in general) coupled (see Chapter I). However, for the usual heat transfer occurring in an unevenly heated solid body as the result of external heat sources, the influence of the stresses and strains on the temperature distribution can be ignored. This enables us to calculate the temperature distribution in the body on the basis of a well–defined heat transfer without regard to the state of stress.

In a solid the transfer of heat occurs in virtue of heat conduction alone. This has molecular–atomic character and is not accompanied by any macroscopic movement.

Heat transfer at the surface of a body can occur in three ways: heat conduction, convection, or radiation.

In the case of convection the heat exchange occurs by virtue of the motion of non–uniformly heated fluid (or gas) contiguous with the body. Moreover, convective heat exchange is understood to be the sum of the heat carried by the fluid particles and by heat conduction.

Heat exchange by radiation (radiant heat exchange) takes place between bodies separated by a distance (or between different parts of a body) by means of electromagnetic waves.

The equation of heat conduction necessary for the study of temperature fields in elastic bodies can be obtained from the heat–conduction equation (1.5.26) by neglecting the strain–dependent terms in it.

Here we will carry out an independent derivation of this equation. The amount of heat absorbed per unit volume of the body in unit time is equal to $c \, \partial T/\partial t$, where c is the specific heat of the body.

On the other hand, the amount of heat lost per unit volume of the body in unit time is div $\mathbf{q}$, where $\mathbf{q}$ is the *heat flux vector*.

Assuming heat sources in the body that generate q_0 heat per unit volume and unit time, and taking account of equation (1.4.4), the condition for balance of heat furnishes the heat–conduction equation

$$\text{div} (\lambda_T \text{ grad } T) + q_0 = c \frac{\partial T}{\partial t}. \tag{3.1.1}$$

When the coefficient of thermal conductivity λ_T is constant, (3.1.1) reduces to

$$\nabla^2 T + \frac{q_0}{\lambda_T} = \frac{1}{a} \frac{\partial T}{\partial t}. \tag{3.1.2}$$

where $a = \lambda_T/c$ is the *thermal diffusivity*.

In the absence of heat sources ($q_0 = 0$), equation (3.1.2) becomes

$$\nabla^2 T = \frac{1}{a} \frac{\partial T}{\partial t}. \tag{3.1.3}$$

The solution of (3.1.3) determines the unsteady temperature field. For a steady temperature field, equation (3.1.3) reduces to the Laplace equation

$$\nabla^2 T = 0. \tag{3.1.4}$$

In order that the solution of (3.1.2) should be unique, boundary and initial conditions must be added.

The initial conditions consist in a prescribed temperature distribution at a certain instant of time.

The boundary conditions are usually connected with the complex heat exchange on the surface of the body, where all three types of heat transfer can occur simultaneously.

In the theory of heat conduction one adopts the following basic idealized boundary conditions:

1. Prescribed surface temperature

$$T (x_k, t) = f (x_k, t), \tag{3.1.5}$$

where x_k is a point on the surface of the body and $f (x_k, t)$ is a given function.

2. Prescribed heat flux from the body into the surroundings

$$q (x_k, t) = -\lambda_T \frac{\partial T (x_k, t)}{\partial n}, \tag{3.1.6}$$

where n is the outward normal from the surface of the body at point x_k.

In the particular case where $q = 0$, we have the following adiabatic boundary condition for a body isolated from external heat exchange

$$\frac{\partial T\,(x_k,\,t)}{\partial n} = 0. \qquad (3.1.7)$$

3. Prescribed environmental temperature ϑ and a law of convective heat exchange between the surface and the surrounding medium

$$-\lambda_T \frac{\partial T\,(x_k,\,t)}{\partial n} = \alpha\,[T\,(x_k,\,t) - \vartheta], \qquad (3.1.8)$$

where α is the *surface transfer coefficient* (or boundary conductance).

The surface transfer coefficient α depends on the thermal and physical characteristics of the surface and the surrounding medium.

A distinction can be made between *free convection* which arises from the natural motion of the particles of a fluid as a result of the non–uniform density produced by non–uniform heating and *forced convection* which occurs when the motion of the fluid is due to external mechanical effects (such as pumping or the high–speed flow of air past on aircraft, etc). Heat exchange during forced convection is greater than during free convection.

During convective heat exchange an important role is played by the state of the boundary layer. In this region adjoining the surface of the body there are sharp gradients of velocity and temperature (from the velocity and temperature of the free flow to the velocity and temperature of the surface of the body).

The fluid flow in the boundary layer can be either *laminar* in which case the particles flow along stream lines or turbulent in which case the particle motion is irregular. Turbulent flow occurs when the laminar (or streamline) flow becomes unstable. The conditions for the transition from laminar to turbulent flow are determined by a certain (critical) parameter, called the *Reynolds number* $R = \rho v l / \eta$, where ρ is the density, v is the mean stream velocity, l is a typical linear dimension, and η is the coefficient of viscosity.

Heat exchange during laminar flow is primarily a result of thermal conductivity. On the other hand, heat exchange during turbulent flow is mainly due to the macroscopic pulsating motion of the fluid particles.

During turbulent flow the surface transfer coefficient can be many times larger than for laminar flow.

From the above comments it is clear that the coefficient α lies within wide limits and from case to case it must be chosen from experimental data in accordance with the conditions of the convective heat exchange.

When the gas speed is high (as in the case of aerodynamic heating) the

53

free–flow temperature ϑ in (3.1.8) must be replaced by the so–called *adiabatic surface temperature* ϑ_a.

As a result of friction in the boundary layer, the kinetic energy of the free stream is converted into heat. Thus there is a rise of temperature in the boundary layer, and on the thermally insulated surface of the structure there is an adiabatic surface temperature given by the formula

$$\vartheta_a = \vartheta + r \frac{v^2}{2c_p}, \qquad (3.1.9)$$

where ϑ and v are the temperature and speed of the free stream, c_p is the specific heat at constant pressure of the gas, and r is the *recovery coefficient* indicating what fraction of the kinetic energy of the free flow is changed into heat at the surface.

For a given state of the boundary layer, the recovery coefficient r is determined by the *Prandtl number* $\mathrm{Pr} = \eta c_p / \lambda_T$, which for air is practically constant at high temperatures. For instance, $\mathrm{Pr} \doteq 0.72$ to 0.65 in the interval $T = 250$ to $1300°K$.

Theoretical studies have shown that for a flat plate $r = (\mathrm{Pr})^{1/2}$ when the boundary layer is laminar and $r = (\mathrm{Pr})^{1/3}$ when it is turbulent.

In order to solve the partial differential equations (3.1.2) and (3.1.3), use is made of the method of separation of variables, methods based on integral transforms, superposition of solutions for heat sources and of other solutions, numerical methods, etc. They have been described in monographs on heat conduction such as [27, 57] and also in specialized works [1].

A study of the heat conduction equations (parabolic and elliptic types) can be found in works on mathematical physics [43, 46, 49]. Here we will consider heat–conduction problems which have greater practical value and which illustrate the application of the basic methods of heat conduction. The first of these problems is that of unsteady heat exchange in plates or arbitrary profile, the solution of which is of basic importance in connection with the approximation of the temperature in a thin plate by a power law (see Section 3.2). Then in Sections 3.3 and 3.6 we treat the problems of the steady and unsteady axisymmetric plane temperature field in a disk. In Section 3.7 the problem of unsteady axisymmetric heat exchange in a solid cylinder of finite length in a surrounding medium has been studied by means of Laplace transformation and separation of variables.

3.2. Equations for unsteady heat conduction in plates

The cartesian coordinate system xOy lies in the middle surface of the thin plate of thickness h.

We will consider the case where there is an unsteady convective heat exchange on the contour L and on the faces $z = \pm\, h/2$ (see Fig. 9).

When there is a large temperature difference between the surfaces $z = \pm\, h/2$, there is a high temperature gradient through the thickness which gives rise not only to expansion but also to thermal bending.

The determination of the unsteady temperature field in such a plate with constant thermal properties leads to the solution of equation (3.1.3), which in cartesian coordinates has the form

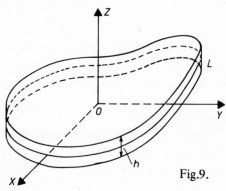

Fig.9.

$$\frac{\partial^2 T}{\partial x^2} + \frac{\partial^2 T}{\partial y^2} + \frac{\partial^2 T}{\partial z^2} = \frac{1}{a}\frac{\partial T}{\partial t}. \tag{3.2.1}$$

The solution of equation (3.2.1) must satisfy the following initial and boundary conditions

$$T = T_0 \quad \text{when} \quad t = 0. \tag{3.2.2}$$

$$\left.
\begin{aligned}
\frac{\partial T}{\partial n} &= -\frac{\alpha_0}{\lambda_T}\,(T - \vartheta_0) \quad \text{on edge } L \text{ of plate} \\[2mm]
\frac{\partial T}{\partial z} &= -\frac{\alpha_3}{\lambda_T}\,(T - \vartheta_3) \quad \text{when } z = \frac{h}{2}, \\[2mm]
\frac{\partial T}{\partial z} &= \frac{\alpha_4}{\lambda_T}(T - \vartheta_4) \quad \text{when } z = -\frac{h}{2}.
\end{aligned}
\right\} \tag{3.2.3}$$

The notation in (3.2.1) to (3.2.3) is as follows. The temperature of the plate is T, T_0 is the initial temperature, $\vartheta_0, \vartheta_3,$ and ϑ_4 are the temperature on the contour, on face $z = +\, h/2$ and on face $z = -\, h/2$, respectively $\alpha_0, \alpha_3,$ and α_4 are the respective surface transfer coefficients, λ_T and a are the coefficient of thermal conductivity and the thermal diffusivity of the material in the plate, and n is the outward normal from the edge of the plate.

We will search for an approximate solution to this problem. By approximating the temperature variation through the thickness of the plate by the power law

$$T = \sum_{i=0}^{m} T^{(i)}(x, y, t) z^i, \qquad (3.2.4)$$

we obtain a two–dimensional problem.

In order to establish the equations governing the functions $T^{(i)}$, we multiply equation (3.2.1) by z^p $(p = 0, 1, \ldots, m)$ and integrate it from $z = -h/2$ to $h/2$. Integration by parts, use of the identity $z^p \dfrac{\partial^2 T}{\partial z^2} = \dfrac{\partial}{\partial z}\left(z^p \dfrac{\partial T}{\partial z} - p z^{p-1} T\right) + p(p-1) z^{p-2} T$, and the boundary conditions (3.2.3) yields

$$\nabla^2 \Theta_p - \frac{h^{p-1}}{2^p}\left\{ 2p\Theta_p + \gamma_3\left[T\left(\frac{h}{2}\right) - \vartheta_3\right] + (-1)^p\gamma_4\left[T\left(-\frac{h}{2}\right) - \vartheta_4\right]\right\} +$$

$$+ p(p-1)\Theta_{p-2} = \frac{1}{a}\frac{\partial\Theta_p}{\partial t} \quad (p = 0, 1, \ldots, m), \qquad (3.2.5)$$

where

$$\left.\begin{array}{l}
\nabla^2 = \dfrac{\partial^2}{\partial x^2} + \dfrac{\partial^2}{\partial y^2}, \\[2mm]
\Theta_p = \displaystyle\int_{-\frac{h}{2}}^{\frac{h}{2}} z^p T dZ, \quad \theta_p = T\left(\dfrac{h}{2}\right) + (-1)^p T\left(-\dfrac{h}{2}\right), \\[3mm]
\gamma_3 = \dfrac{\alpha_3 h}{\lambda_T}, \quad \gamma_4 = \dfrac{\alpha_4 h}{\lambda_T}.
\end{array}\right\}$$

By substituting expression (3.2.4) into both (3.2.2) and the first condition in (3.2.3), we find the initial and boundary conditions for the functions $T^{(i)}$ $(i = 0, 1, \ldots, m)$. When T_0 and ϑ_0 are independent of z, these conditions are

$$\left.\begin{array}{l}
T^{(0)} = T_0, \quad T^{(i)} = 0 \quad (i = 1, \ldots, m) \quad \text{when} \quad t = 0, \\[3mm]
\dfrac{\partial T^{(0)}}{\partial n} = -\dfrac{\alpha_0}{\lambda_T}(T^{(0)} - \vartheta_0), \quad \dfrac{\partial T^{(i)}}{\partial n} = -\dfrac{\alpha_0}{\lambda_T} T^{(i)} \quad \text{on edge } L \text{ of plate} \\[3mm]
(i = 1, \ldots, m).
\end{array}\right\} \quad (3.2.6)$$

Using equation (3.2.5) and conditions (3.2.6) for different values of p, we can establish a necessary system of equations describing the unsteady heat conduction in a plate with different power laws of variation of temperature through the thickness of the plate.

When the temperature does not change with depth

$$T = T^{(0)}. \tag{3.2.7}$$

Then, setting $p = 0$, we obtain the heat conduction equation

$$\nabla^2 T - \frac{2\gamma}{h^2}(T - \vartheta) = \frac{1}{a}\frac{\partial T}{\partial t}, \tag{3.2.8}$$

where

$$\gamma = \frac{(a_3 + a_4)h}{2\lambda_T}, \qquad \vartheta = \frac{\alpha_3 \vartheta_3 + \alpha_4 \vartheta_4}{\alpha_3 + \alpha_4}.$$

The initial and boundary conditions are

$$\left.\begin{array}{c} T = T_0 \quad \text{when} \quad t = 0, \\[2mm] \dfrac{\partial T}{\partial n} = -\dfrac{\alpha_0}{\lambda_T}(T - \vartheta_0) \quad \text{on edge } L \text{ of plate.} \end{array}\right\} \tag{3.2.9}$$

With the linear law of temperature variation with respect to depth

$$T = T^{(0)} + T^{(1)}z, \tag{3.2.10}$$

which corresponds to the values $p = 0, 1$, the two heat conduction equations are

$$\left.\begin{array}{c} \nabla^2 T^{(0)} - \dfrac{2\gamma}{h^2}(T^{(0)} - \vartheta) - \dfrac{\gamma_3 - \gamma_4}{2h}T^{(1)} = \dfrac{1}{a}\dfrac{\partial T^{(0)}}{\partial t}, \\[4mm] \nabla^2 T^{(1)} - \dfrac{6(\gamma_3 - \gamma_4)}{h^3}T^{(0)} - \dfrac{6(2+\gamma)}{h^2}(T^{(1)} - \mu) = \dfrac{1}{a}\dfrac{\partial T^{(1)}}{\partial t}, \end{array}\right\} \tag{3.2.11}$$

where

$$\mu = \frac{\gamma_3 \vartheta_3 - \gamma_4 \vartheta_4}{(2+\gamma)h}.$$

The initial and boundary conditions are

$$T^{(0)} = T_0, \quad T^{(1)} = 0 \quad \text{when } t = 0,$$

$$\left.\begin{array}{cc} \dfrac{\partial T^{(0)}}{\partial n} = -\dfrac{\alpha_0}{\lambda_T}(T^{(0)} - \vartheta_0), & \dfrac{\partial T^{(1)}}{\partial n} = -\dfrac{\alpha_0}{\lambda_T}T^{(1)} \quad \text{on edge } L \text{ of plate.} \end{array}\right\}$$

$$\tag{3.2.12}$$

In the case of quadratic temperature variation through the thickness, i.e.

$$T = T^{(0)} + T^{(1)}z + T^{(2)}z^2, \tag{3.2.13}$$

corresponding to the values $p = 0, 1,$ and 2, we find the following system of three heat conduction equations

$$\nabla^2 T^{(0)} + \frac{3\gamma}{h^2}(T^{(0)} - \vartheta) + \frac{3(\gamma_3 - \gamma_4)}{4h} T^{(1)} + \frac{3\gamma + 20}{4} T^{(2)} = \frac{1}{a}\frac{\partial T^{(0)}}{\partial t},$$

$$\nabla^2 T^{(1)} - \frac{6(2+\gamma)}{h^2}(T^{(1)} - \mu) - \frac{6(\gamma_3 - \gamma_4)}{h^3}\left(T^{(0)} + \frac{h^2 T^{(2)}}{4}\right) = \frac{1}{a}\frac{\partial T^{(1)}}{\partial t}, \tag{3.2.14}$$

$$\nabla^2 T^{(2)} - \frac{60\gamma}{h^4}(T^{(0)} - \vartheta) - \frac{15(\gamma_3 - \gamma_4)}{h^3} T^{(1)} - \frac{15(4+\gamma)}{h^2} T^{(2)} = \frac{1}{a}\frac{\partial T^{(2)}}{\partial t}.$$

The initial and boundary conditions are

$$\left.\begin{array}{c} T^{(0)} = T_0, \quad T^{(1)} = T^{(2)} = 0 \quad \text{when} \quad t = 0, \quad \text{and} \\[2mm] \dfrac{\partial T^{(0)}}{\partial n} = -\dfrac{\alpha_0}{\lambda_T}(T^{(0)} - \vartheta_0), \quad \dfrac{\partial T^{(1)}}{\partial n} = -\dfrac{\alpha_0 T^{(1)}}{\lambda_T}, \quad \dfrac{\partial T^{(2)}}{\partial n} = -\dfrac{\alpha_0 T^{(2)}}{\lambda_T} \end{array}\right\} \tag{3.2.15}$$

on edge L of plate.

In the case where the surface transfer coefficients are equal ($\alpha_3 = \alpha_4 = a$), which means that $\gamma_3 = \gamma_4 = \gamma$, equations (3.2.11) and (3.2.14) reduce to

$$\nabla^2 T^{(0)} - \frac{2\gamma}{h^2}(T^{(0)} - \vartheta) = \frac{1}{a}\frac{\partial T^{(0)}}{\partial t},$$

$$\nabla^2 T^{(1)} - \frac{6(2+\gamma)}{h^2}(T^{(1)} - \mu) = \frac{1}{a}\frac{\partial T^{(1)}}{\partial t}. \tag{3.2.16}$$

$$\nabla^2 T^{(0)} + \frac{3\gamma}{h^2}(T^{(0)} - \vartheta) + \frac{3\gamma + 20}{4} T^{(2)} = \frac{1}{a}\frac{\partial T^{(0)}}{\partial t},$$

$$\nabla^2 T^{(1)} - \frac{6(2+\gamma)}{h^2}(T^{(1)} - \mu) = \frac{1}{a}\frac{\partial T^{(1)}}{\partial t}, \tag{3.2.17}$$

$$\nabla^2 T^{(2)} - \frac{60\gamma}{h^4}(T^{(0)} - \vartheta) - \frac{15(4+\gamma)}{h^2} T^{(2)} = \frac{1}{a}\frac{\partial T^{(2)}}{\partial t}.$$

3.3. Steady, plane, axisymmetric temperature in disks and cylinders

We will determine the steady, plane temperature field in an annular disk of constant thickness h. Let us denote the radius of the outer edge by r_2 and that of the inner edge by r_1 (see Fig. 10).

It will be assumed that there is identical convective heat exchange on the surfaces $z = \pm h/2$.

Changing to polar coordinates and assuming a symmetric temperature field, the heat conduction equation that results from (3.2.8) in this special case is

$$\frac{d^2 T}{dr^2} + \frac{1}{r}\frac{dT}{dr} - \frac{2\gamma}{h^2}(T - \vartheta) = 0, \qquad (3.3.1)$$

where $\gamma = \alpha h/\lambda_T$. Moreover, ϑ and α are the temperature of the medium and the surface transfer coefficient, respectively, at the faces $z = \pm h/2$.

In the present case the boundary conditions (3.2.9) reduce to [1]

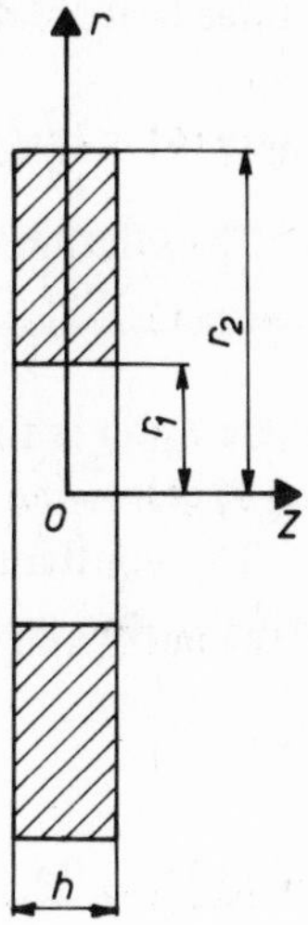

Fig. 10.

$$\left. \begin{array}{ll} \dfrac{dT}{dr} - \dfrac{\alpha_1}{\lambda_T}(T - \vartheta_1) = 0 & \text{when} \quad r = r_1, \\[3mm] \dfrac{dT}{dr} + \dfrac{\alpha_2}{\lambda_T}(T - \vartheta_2) = 0 & \text{when} \quad r = r_2, \end{array} \right\} \qquad (3.3.2)$$

where ϑ_1 and α_1 is the temperature of the surrounding medium and the surface transfer coefficient on the inner edge $r = r_1$, and ϑ_2 and α_2 are the corresponding values on the outer edge $r = r_2$.

When the radius r is replaced by the dimensionless coordinate $\rho = r/r_2$, equations (3.3.1), (3.3.2) become

$$\frac{d^2 T}{d\rho^2} + \frac{1}{\rho}\frac{dT}{d\rho} - \delta^2(T - \vartheta) = 0, \qquad (3.3.3)$$

---

[1] In deducing the first of conditions (3.3.2), account has been taken of the fact that the positive direction of r on the inner edge is opposite to that on the outer edge.

$$\frac{dT}{d\rho} - \gamma_1(T - \vartheta_1) = 0 \quad \text{when} \quad \rho = \rho_1,$$

$$\frac{dT}{d\rho} + \gamma_2(T - \vartheta_2) = 0 \quad \text{when} \quad \rho = 1, \tag{3.3.4}$$

where $\delta^2 = 2\gamma r_2^2/h^2$, $\gamma_1 = \alpha_1 r_2/\lambda_T$, $\gamma_2 = \alpha_2 r_2/\lambda_T$, $\rho_1 = r_1/r_2$.

The solution of (3.3.3) is

$$T = \vartheta + C_1 I_0(\delta\rho) + C_2 K_0(\delta\rho), \tag{3.3.5}$$

where $I_0(x)$ is the modified Bessel function of the first kind and order zero and $K_0(x)$ is the corresponding function of the second kind.

The constants of integration are determined by condition (3.3.4). By virtue of the well–known recurrence formulae

$$\frac{d}{dx} I_0(x) = I_1(x), \quad \frac{d}{dx} K_0(x) = -K_1(x),$$

where $I_1(x)$, $K_1(x)$ are the corresponding functions of order one, the constants are found to be

$$C_1 = \frac{1}{\Delta} [\gamma_1(\vartheta_1 - \vartheta) v_1(\delta) + \gamma_2(\vartheta_2 - \vartheta) v_2(\delta\rho_1)],$$

$$C_2 = \frac{1}{\Delta} [\gamma_1(\vartheta_1 - \vartheta) u_1(\delta) + \gamma_2(\vartheta_2 - \vartheta) u_2(\delta\rho_1)], \tag{3.3.6}$$

where

$$u_1(\delta) = I_1(\delta) + \frac{\gamma_2}{\delta} I_0(\delta),$$

$$u_2(\delta\rho_1) = I_1(\delta\rho_1) - \frac{\gamma_1}{\delta} I_0(\delta\rho_1),$$

$$v_1(\rho) = K_1(\delta) - \frac{\gamma_2}{\delta} K_0(\delta),$$

$$v_2(\delta\rho_1) = K_1(\delta\rho_1) + \frac{\gamma_1}{\delta} K_0(\delta\rho_1),$$

$$\Delta = u_2(\delta\rho_1) [\gamma_2 K_0(\delta) - \delta K_1(\delta)] + v_2(\delta\rho_1) [\gamma_2 I_0(\delta) + \delta I_1(\delta)].$$

When $\gamma_1 = \gamma_2 = \infty$, conditions (3.3.4) become

$$T = \vartheta_1 \quad \text{when} \quad \rho = \rho_1,$$
$$T = \vartheta_2 \quad \text{when} \quad \rho = 1. \tag{3.3.7}$$

Equation (3.3.3) and conditions (3.3.7) describe the problem of an axisymmetric temperature field in a disk for the case of prescribed temperatures ϑ_1 and ϑ_2 on the edges $r = r_1$ and $r = r_2$, respectively, and convective heat exchange on the surfaces $z = \pm h/2$.

The solution of this problem is obtained from (3.3.5) by letting γ_1 and γ_2 tend to infinity. In this way the constants of integration (3.3.6) are found to be

$$C_1 = \frac{-(\vartheta_1 - \vartheta) K_0(\delta) + (\vartheta_2 - \vartheta) K_0(\delta\rho_1)}{I_0(\delta) K_0(\delta\rho_1) - I_0(\delta\rho_1) K_0(\delta)},$$

$$C_2 = \frac{(\vartheta_1 - \vartheta) I_0(\delta) - (\vartheta_2 - \vartheta) I_0(\delta\rho_1)}{I_0(\delta) K_0(\delta\rho_1) - I_0(\delta\rho_1) K_0(\delta)}. \tag{3.3.8}$$

Setting $\delta = 0$ in (3.3.3), which corresponds to zero heat exchange on the surfaces $z = \pm h/2$, we obtain the heat–conduction equation describing the problem of the axisymmetric temperature field of an infinite cylinder with either prescribed convective heat exchange or temperatures on the internal cylindrical surface $r = r_1$ ($\rho = \rho_1$) and on the external cylindrical surface $r = r_2$ ($\rho = 1$). In both cases the temperature field is given by

$$T = C_1 + C_2 \ln \rho. \tag{3.3.9}$$

For the boundary conditions (3.3.4), we have

$$C_1 = \frac{1}{\Delta} [\gamma_2 \vartheta_2 + \gamma_1 \rho_1 (\vartheta_1 - \gamma_2 \vartheta_2 \ln \rho_1)],$$

$$C_2 = \frac{1}{\Delta} [\gamma_1 \gamma_2 \rho_1 (\vartheta_2 - \vartheta_1)], \tag{3.3.10}$$

where

$$\Delta = \gamma_2 + \gamma_1 \rho_1 (1 - \gamma_2 \ln \rho_1).$$

For the boundary condition (3.3.7), we have

$$C_1 = \vartheta_2, \qquad C_2 = \frac{\vartheta_1 - \vartheta_2}{\ln \rho_1}.$$

3.4. Steady axisymmetric temperature field in a circular plate with linear variation of temperature through the thickness

We shall now determine the steady temperature field in an annular plate of constant thickness h. The external radius will be denoted by r_2 and the internal radius (the radius of the central hole) by r_1.

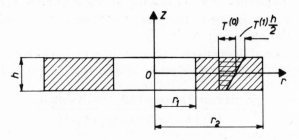

Fig. 11.

The linear law (3.2.10) will be adopted for the temperature variation through the thickness (see Fig. 11). We shall also assume that the transfer coefficient on both faces $z = \pm\, h/2$ is equal to α.

The solution of this problem will be deduced from equations (3.2.11) and boundary conditions (3.2.12). In the present case they assume the form

$$\frac{d^2 T^{(0)}}{d\rho^2} + \frac{1}{\rho}\frac{dT^{(0)}}{d\rho} - \delta^2(T^{(0)} - \vartheta) = 0, \tag{3.4.1}$$

$$\frac{d^2 T^{(1)}}{d\rho^2} + \frac{1}{\rho}\frac{dT^{(1)}}{d\rho} - \delta_1^2(T^{(1)} - \mu) = 0; \tag{3.4.2}$$

$$\left.\begin{array}{ll} \dfrac{dT^{(0)}}{d\rho} - \gamma_1(T^{(0)} - \vartheta_1) = 0 & \text{when} \quad \rho = \rho_1, \\[4mm] \dfrac{dT^{(0)}}{d\rho} + \gamma_2(T^{(0)} - \vartheta_2) = 0 & \text{when} \quad \rho = 1; \end{array}\right\} \tag{3.4.3}$$

$$\left.\begin{array}{ll} \dfrac{dT^{(1)}}{d\rho} - \gamma_1 T^{(1)} = 0 & \text{when} \quad \rho = \rho_1, \\[4mm] \dfrac{dT^{(1)}}{d\rho} + \gamma_2 T^{(1)} = 0 & \text{when} \quad \rho = 1, \end{array}\right\} \tag{3.4.4}$$

where

$$\vartheta = \frac{\vartheta_3 + \vartheta_4}{2}, \quad \mu = \frac{\gamma(\vartheta_3 - \vartheta_4)}{(2+\gamma)h},$$

$$\delta^2 = \frac{2\gamma r_2^2}{h^2}, \quad \delta_1^2 = \frac{6(2+\gamma)r_2^2}{h^2}, \quad \gamma = \frac{\alpha h}{\lambda_T},$$

$$\gamma_1 = \frac{\alpha_1 r_2}{\lambda_T}, \quad \gamma_2 = \frac{\alpha_2 r_2}{\lambda_T}.$$

The solution of equation (3.4.1) with boundary conditions (3.4.3) is determined by expression (3.3.5). Setting $\delta = \delta_1$, $\vartheta = \mu$, $\vartheta_1 = \vartheta_2 = 0$ in this expression, we obtain the solution of equation (3.4.2) with boundary conditions (3.4.4).

Thus, the required temperature field is given by

$$T = \vartheta + z\mu + C_1 I_0(\delta\rho) + C_2 K_0(\delta\rho) + z\mu [C_1' I_0(\delta_1\rho) + C_2' K_0(\delta_1\rho)]. \quad (3.4.5)$$

The constants C_1 and C_2 in this solution have the values (3.3.6), and the constants C_1' and C_2' have the values

$$C_1' = -\frac{1}{\Delta_1} [\gamma_1 v_1(\delta_1) + \gamma_2(\delta_1\rho_1)],$$

$$\hspace{4cm} (3.4.6)$$

$$C_2' = -\frac{1}{\Delta_1} [\gamma_1 u_1(\delta_1) + \gamma_2(\delta_1\rho_1)],$$

where $\Delta_1 = u_2(\delta_1\rho_1)[\gamma_2 K_0(\delta_1) - \delta_1 K_1(\delta_1)] + v_2(\delta_1\rho_1)[\gamma_2 I_0(\delta_1) + \delta_1 I_1(\delta_1)]$.

3.5. Steady, non–axially symmetric, plane temperature field in an infinite cylinder

We shall next determine the steady, plane temperature field in an infinite hollow cylinder when the temperatures ϑ_1 and ϑ_2 of the internal and external cylindrical surfaces, respectively, are functions of the polar angle θ (see Fig. 5). This problem leads to the solution of equation (3.1.4), which in polar coordinates reads

$$\frac{\partial^2 T}{\partial \rho^2} + \frac{1}{\rho}\frac{\partial T}{\partial \delta} + \frac{1}{\rho^2}\frac{\partial^2 T}{\partial \theta^2} = 0. \quad (3.5.1)$$

The solution of equation (3.5.1) must satisfy the boundary conditions

$$
\left.\begin{array}{ll}
\dfrac{\partial T}{\partial \rho} - \gamma_1 (T - \vartheta_1) = 0 & \text{when} \quad \rho = \rho_1, \\[4mm]
\dfrac{\partial T}{\partial \rho} + \gamma_2 (T - \vartheta_2) = 0 & \text{when} \quad \rho = 1,
\end{array}\right\}
\tag{3.5.2}
$$

where

$$
\gamma_1 = \alpha_1 r_2 / \lambda_T, \quad \gamma_2 = \alpha_2 r_2 / \lambda_T,
$$

and ϑ_1, ϑ_2 are periodic functions of θ with period 2π, which can thus be expanded in the Fourier series

$$
\begin{aligned}
\vartheta_1 &= \frac{1}{2} \vartheta_1^{(0)} + \sum_{k=1}^{\infty} \vartheta_1^{(k)} f_k, \\[3mm]
\vartheta_2 &= \frac{1}{2} \vartheta_2^{(0)} + \sum_{k=1}^{\infty} \vartheta_2^{(k)} f_k,
\end{aligned}
\tag{3.5.3}
$$

where

$$
f_k = \begin{cases}
\cos m\theta, & \text{when} \quad k = 2m, \\
\sin m\theta, & \text{when} \quad k = 2m - 1
\end{cases}
\qquad (m = 1, 2, \ldots).
$$

The coefficients in (3.5.3) are given by the formulae

$$
\vartheta_n^{(k)} = \frac{1}{\pi} \int_0^{2\pi} \vartheta_n f_k \, d\theta \quad (n = 1, 2; \quad k = 0, 1, \ldots; \quad f_0 = 1).
\tag{3.5.4}
$$

In view of expressions (3.5.3), the solution of equation (3.5.1) will be sought in the form

$$
T = \frac{1}{2} T^{(0)} + \sum_{k=1}^{\infty} T^{(k)} f_k,
\tag{3.5.5}
$$

64

where $T^{(0)}$ and $T^{(k)}$ are function of ρ.

Substituting solution (3.5.5) into equation (3.5.1) and boundary conditions (3.5.2), we find the following equations for the determination of $T^{(0)}$ and $T^{(k)}$

$$\frac{d^2T^{(0)}}{d\rho^2} + \frac{1}{\rho}\frac{dT^{(0)}}{d\rho} = 0, \tag{3.5.6}$$

$$\frac{d^2T^{(k)}}{d\rho^2} + \frac{1}{\rho}\frac{dT^{(k)}}{d\rho} - \frac{m^2}{\rho^2}\, T^{(k)} = 0, \tag{3.5.7}$$

($m = k/2$ when k is even, and $m = (k + 1)/2$ when k is odd). The boundary conditions are

$$\left.\begin{array}{ll}
\dfrac{dT^{(0)}}{d\rho} - \gamma_1(T^{(0)} - \vartheta_1^{(0)}) = 0 & \text{when} \quad \rho = \rho_1, \\[3mm]
\dfrac{dT^{(0)}}{d\rho} + \gamma_2(T^{(0)} - \vartheta_2^{(0)}) = 0 & \text{when} \quad \rho = 1;
\end{array}\right\} \tag{3.5.8}$$

$$\left.\begin{array}{ll}
\dfrac{dT^{(k)}}{d\rho} - \gamma_1(T^{(k)} - \vartheta_1^{(k)}) = 0 & \text{when} \quad \rho = \rho_1, \\[3mm]
\dfrac{dT^{(k)}}{d\rho} + \gamma_2(T^{(k)} - \vartheta_2^{(k)}) = 0 & \text{when} \quad \rho = 1.
\end{array}\right\} \tag{3.5.9}$$

Equation (3.5.6), with the boundary conditions (3.5.8), is satisfied by the previously found solution (3.3.9) with the coefficients (3.3.10).

Equation (3.5.7) with the boundary conditions (3.5.9) has the following solution

$$T^{(k)} = C_1\rho^m + C_2\rho^{-m}, \tag{3.5.10}$$

where

$$C_1 = \frac{1}{\Delta}[\rho_1\gamma_1(m - \gamma_2)\,\vartheta_1^{(k)} + \rho_1^{-m}\gamma_2(m + \rho_1\gamma_1)\,\vartheta_2^{(k)}],$$

$$C_2 = \frac{1}{\Delta}[\rho_1\gamma_1(m + \gamma_2)\,\vartheta_1^{(k)} + \rho_1^m\gamma_2(m - \rho_1\gamma_1)\,\vartheta_2^{(k)}], \tag{3.5.11}$$

$$\Delta = \rho_1^{-m}(m + \rho_1\gamma_1)(m + \gamma_2) - \rho_1^m(m - \rho_1\gamma_1)(m - \gamma_2).$$

65

3.6. Unsteady, plane, axisymmetric temperature field in a disk

Here we shall determine the unsteady plane temperature field in a solid disk of uniform thickness h and radius r_2 and having a uniform transfer coefficient on the surfaces $z = \pm h/2$.

Expressing equation (3.2.8) in polar coordinates and introducing the dimensionless coordinate $\rho = r/r_2$ and the dimensionless time $\tau = ta/r_2^2$, for the present problem we find the following heat conduction equation

$$\frac{\partial^2 T}{\partial \rho^2} + \frac{1}{\rho}\frac{\partial T}{\partial \rho} - \delta^2(T - \vartheta) = \frac{\partial T}{\partial \tau} \qquad (3.6.1)$$

with the boundary conditions

$$\left.\begin{array}{ll} T = T_0 & \text{when} \quad t = 0, \\[2mm] \dfrac{\partial T}{\partial \rho} + \gamma_2(T - \vartheta_2) = 0 & \text{when} \quad \rho = 1, \end{array}\right\} \qquad (3.6.2)$$

where

$$\delta^2 = \frac{2\gamma r_2^2}{h^2}, \quad \gamma = \frac{\alpha h}{\lambda_T}, \quad \gamma_2 = \frac{\alpha_2 r_2}{\lambda_T}.$$

Here ϑ is the temperature of the surrounding medium and a the transfer coefficient at the surfaces $z = \pm h/2$ of the disk, whereas ϑ_2 is the temperature of the surrounding medium and α_2 the transfer coefficient at the edge $r = r_2$ ($\rho = 1$). Temperature ϑ_2 is a function of τ.

We will solve the heat conduction equation (3.6.1) by using the Laplace transform technique.

The Laplace transform of a function $f(\tau)$ is obtained by multiplying it by $e^{-s\tau}$, where s is a complex quantity, and integrating the product from 0 to ∞. This yield the new function

$$f^*(s) = \int_0^\infty f(\tau)e^{-s\tau}d\tau, \qquad (3.6.3)$$

which is called the transform of $f(\tau)$.

By taking the transform of equation (3.6.1) and taking account of conditions (3.6.2), the partial differential equation for the unknown T is changed into an ordinary differential equation for its transform T^*, namely

$$\frac{d^2 T^*}{d\rho^2} + \frac{1}{\rho}\frac{dT^*}{d\rho} - \epsilon^2 \left(T^* - \frac{\Theta}{s\epsilon^2} \right) = 0 \tag{3.6.4}$$

with the boundary condition

$$\frac{dT^*}{d\rho} + \gamma_2(T^* - \vartheta_2^*) = 0 \quad \text{when} \quad \rho = 1, \tag{3.6.5}$$

where

$$T^* = \int_0^\infty Te^{-s\tau}d\tau, \quad \vartheta_2^* = \int_0^\infty \vartheta_2 e^{-s\tau}d\tau, \tag{3.6.6}$$

$$\Theta = \delta^2\vartheta + sT_0, \quad \epsilon^2 = \delta^2 + s.$$

Equation (3.6.4) has the same form as (3.3.3).

By analogy with the solution of the latter, the solution of equation (3.6.4) with the boundary condition (3.6.5) is

$$T^* = \frac{\Theta}{s\epsilon^2} + C_1 I_0(\epsilon\rho), \tag{3.6.7}$$

where

$$C_1 = \frac{\gamma_2(s\epsilon^2 \vartheta_2^* - \Theta)}{s\epsilon^2 [\gamma_2 I_0(\epsilon) + \epsilon I_1(\epsilon)]}.$$

Let the temperature ϑ_2 of the medium in contact with the exterior edge ($\rho = 1$) of the disk vary with time according to the exponential law

$$\vartheta_2 = \vartheta_{21} + \vartheta_{22}e^{-k\tau}, \tag{3.6.8}$$

where ϑ_{21} and ϑ_{22} are constants.

After calculating the quantity

$$\vartheta_2^* = \frac{\vartheta_{21}}{s} + \frac{\vartheta_{22}}{s+k}$$

and substituting it into the solution (3.6.7), we find the following solution for the transform

$$T^* = \frac{\Theta}{s\epsilon^2} + \frac{\gamma_2 \left\{ \epsilon^2 \left[\vartheta_{21}(s+k) + \vartheta_{22}s\right] - (s+k)\Theta \right\} I_0(\epsilon\rho)}{s(s+k)\epsilon^2 [\gamma_2 I_0(\epsilon) + \epsilon I_1(\epsilon)]}. \tag{3.6.9}$$

Having found the transform, we must now find the original unknown. The transition from the transform to the original function is the major difficulty in the solution of the problem at hand. This transition can be effected with the aid of a well–known expansion theorem in the theory of operational calculus. This theorem was first treated in [4] by Vashchenko–Zakharchenko[1].

The generalized expansion theorem states: If the transform $f^*(s)$ is the ratio of the transcendental functions $\Phi(s)$ and $\psi(s)$, i.e.

$$f^*(s) = \frac{\Phi(s)}{\psi(s)},$$

where the function $\psi(s)$ has only simple roots s_n $(n = 1, 2, \ldots)$, the original function is

$$f(\tau) = \sum_{n=1}^{\infty} \frac{\Phi(s_n)}{\psi'(s_n)} e^{s_n \tau}, \qquad (3.6.10)$$

where

$$\psi'(s_n) = \frac{\partial \psi(s_n)}{\partial s}.$$

There is a similar expansion theorem for the case of repeated roots[2].

---

1) Vashchenko–Zakharchenko was a professor at Kiev University who laid down the fundamentals of operational calculus. In his monograph [4], published in 1862, he gave a systematic treatment of operational calculus and deduced the basic relations for the solution of differential equations by operational methods.

He deduced the expansion theorem not only for simple roots but also for repeated roots.

Later, Heaviside (in his works of 1893 and 1894) applied the method of operational calculus to the solution of certain electrical problems.

2) It should be noted that the transform does not exist for all functions $f(\tau)$. In the general case the inverse Laplace transform is not equal to the original function. The necessary conditions for the transition from the transform to its original, and conversely, are considered in treatises dealing with the fundamentals of operational calculus. The application of the operational calculus to the solution of heat conduction problems has been explained in detail in Lykov's book [27] (Chapter 14). This book also contains an extensive table of Laplace transforms.

In the problems treated in the present book, it will be assumed that the above–mentioned conditions are fulfilled.

In order to apply formula (3.6.10) to the problem of this Section, we must determine the roots of the equation

$$\psi(s) = s(s+k)\,\epsilon^2\,[\gamma_2 I_0(\epsilon) + \epsilon I_1(\epsilon)] = 0. \qquad (3.6.11)$$

The roots of equation (3.6.11) are

$$s_1 = 0, \quad s_2 = -k, \quad s_3 = -\delta^2$$

and the roots β_n of the equation

$$\gamma_2 I_0(\epsilon) + \epsilon I_1(\epsilon) = \gamma_2 J_0(\beta) - \beta J_1(\beta) = 0,$$

where $\beta = i\epsilon$, and $J_0(\beta)$, $J_1(\beta)$ are the Bessel functions of the first kind and of order zero and one, respectively.

Taking these roots into account and carrying out the transition from the transform (3.6.9) to the original with the aid of formula (3.6.10), after certain simplifications we arrive at the following expression for the temperature in the disk

$$T = \vartheta + \frac{\gamma_2(\vartheta_{21} - \vartheta)I_0(\delta\rho)}{\gamma_2 I_0(\delta) + \delta I_1(\delta)} + \frac{\gamma_2 \vartheta_{22} I_0(p\rho)e^{-k\tau}}{\gamma_2 I_0(p) + pI_1(p)} -$$

$$- \sum_{n=1}^{\infty} A_n B_n J_0(\beta_n \rho)e^{-(\delta^2 + \beta_n^2)\tau}, \qquad (3.6.12)$$

where

$$A_n = \frac{2\gamma_2}{(\gamma_2^2 + \beta_n^2)J_0(\beta_n)},$$

$$B_n = \frac{\beta_n^2 \vartheta_{21} + \delta^2 \vartheta}{\beta_n^2 + \delta^2} - T_0 + \frac{\beta_n^2 \vartheta_{22}}{\beta_n^2 + \delta^2 - k},$$

$$p = \sqrt{\delta^2 - k}.$$

In the case of the instantaneous application of a medium with temperature ϑ_2, we find the temperature field from the solution (3.6.12) by setting $\vartheta_{21} = \vartheta_2$ and $\vartheta_{22} = 0$. Thus one obtains

$$T = \vartheta + \frac{\gamma_2(\vartheta_2 - \vartheta)I_0(\delta\rho)}{\gamma_2 I_0(\delta) + \delta I_1(\delta)} - \sum_{n=1}^{\infty} A_n B_n J_0(\beta_n \rho)e^{-(\delta^2 + \beta_n^2)\tau}, \qquad (3.6.13)$$

69

where

$$B_n = \frac{\beta_n^2 \vartheta_2 + \delta^2 \vartheta}{\beta_n^2 + \delta^2} - T_0.$$

3.7. Unsteady axisymmetric temperature field in a finite cylinder

Here we shall determine the unsteady axisymmetric temperature field in a hollow circular cylinder of finite length l with radii r_1 and r_2 (see Fig. 12) which exchanges heat by convection with a surrounding medium.

It will be assumed that the temperature of the medium adjacent to the cylinder is a function of time and position, i.e. that

$$\vartheta_1 = \vartheta_1(z, t), \quad \vartheta_2 = \vartheta_2(z, t),$$

$$\vartheta_3 = \vartheta_3(r, t), \quad \vartheta_4 = \vartheta_4(r, t).$$

The coefficient of thermal conductivity of the material in the cylinder is λ_T and the surface transfer coefficients α_n ($n = 1, 2, 3, 4$) will be assumed constant. The initial temperature of the cylinder T_0 will also be assumed constant.

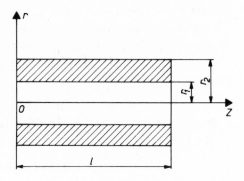

Fig. 12.

This problem is described by equation (3.1.3) with the appropriate initial and boundary conditions.

Introducing the dimensionless coordinates

$$\rho = r/r_2, \quad \rho_1 = r_1/r_2, \quad \zeta = z/r_2, \quad \zeta_1 = l/r_2$$

and the notation

$$\tau = at/r_2^2, \quad \gamma_n = \alpha_n r_2/\lambda_T \quad (n = 1, 2, 3, 4),$$

the present problem reduces to the solution of the equation

70

$$\frac{\partial^2 T}{\partial \rho^2} + \frac{1}{\rho}\frac{\partial T}{\partial \rho} + \frac{\partial^2 T}{\partial \zeta^2} = \frac{\partial T}{\partial \tau} \qquad (3.7.1)$$

with the initial conditions

$$T = T_0 \quad \text{when} \quad t = 0, \qquad (3.7.2)$$

and the boundary conditions

$$
\left.
\begin{aligned}
\frac{\partial T}{\partial \rho} - \gamma_1(T - \vartheta_1) = 0 \quad &\text{when} \quad \rho = \rho_1, \\[2mm]
\frac{\partial T}{\partial \rho} + \gamma_2(T - \vartheta_2) = 0 \quad &\text{when} \quad \rho = 1, \\[2mm]
\frac{\partial T}{\partial \zeta} - \gamma_3(T - \vartheta_3) = 0 \quad &\text{when} \quad \zeta = 0, \\[2mm]
\frac{\partial T}{\partial \zeta} + \gamma_4(T - \vartheta_4) = 0 \quad &\text{when} \quad \zeta = \zeta_1.
\end{aligned}
\right\} \qquad (3.7.3)
$$

Without limiting the generality, we can take $T_0 = 0$.

The solution of equation (3.7.1) will be sought in the form

$$T = T_1 + T_2, \qquad (3.7.4)$$

where function T_1 is the solution of the equation

$$\frac{\partial^2 T_1}{\partial \rho^2} + \frac{1}{\rho}\frac{\partial T_1}{\partial \rho} + \frac{\partial^2 T_1}{\partial \zeta^2} = \frac{\partial T_1}{\partial \tau} \qquad (3.7.5)$$

with the conditions

$$T_1 = 0 \quad \text{when} \quad \tau = 0; \qquad (3.7.6)$$

$$
\left.
\begin{aligned}
\frac{\partial T_1}{\partial \rho} - \gamma_1 T_1 = 0 \quad &\text{when} \quad \rho = \rho_1, \\[2mm]
\frac{\partial T_1}{\partial \rho} + \gamma_2 T_1 = 0 \quad &\text{when} \quad \rho = 1, \\[2mm]
\frac{\partial T_1}{\partial \zeta} - \gamma_3(T_1 - \vartheta_3) = 0 \quad &\text{when} \quad \zeta = 0, \\[2mm]
\frac{\partial T_1}{\partial \zeta} + \gamma_4(T_1 - \vartheta_4) = 0 \quad &\text{when} \quad \zeta = \zeta_1.
\end{aligned}
\right\} \qquad (3.7.7)
$$

71

Function T_2 satisfies the equation

$$\frac{\partial^2 T_2}{\partial \rho} + \frac{1}{\rho}\frac{\partial T_2}{\partial \rho} + \frac{\partial^2 T_2}{\partial \zeta^2} = \frac{\partial T_2}{\partial \tau} \tag{3.7.8}$$

and the conditions

$$T_2 = 0 \quad \text{when} \quad \tau = 0; \tag{3.7.9}$$

$$\left.\begin{array}{lll}
\dfrac{\partial T_2}{\partial \rho} - \gamma_1(T_2 - \vartheta_1) = 0 & \text{when} & \rho = \rho_1, \\[3mm]
\dfrac{\partial T_2}{\partial \rho} + \gamma_2(T_2 - \vartheta_2) = 0 & \text{when} & \rho = 1, \\[3mm]
\dfrac{\partial T_2}{\partial \zeta} - \gamma_3 T_2 = 0 & \text{when} & \zeta = 0, \\[3mm]
\dfrac{\partial T_2}{\partial \rho} + \gamma_4 T_2 = 0 & \text{when} & \zeta = \zeta_1.
\end{array}\right\} \tag{3.7.10}$$

The solution of equations (3.7.5) and (3.7.8) will be found with the aid of the Laplace transform technique and the method of separation of variables. Taking the Laplace transforms of these equations and the corresponding boundary conditions, we arrive at the equation

$$\frac{\partial^2 T_1^*}{\partial \rho^2} + \frac{1}{\rho}\frac{\partial T_1^*}{\partial \rho} + \frac{\partial^2 T_1^*}{\partial \zeta^2} = sT_1^* \tag{3.7.11}$$

with the conditions

$$\left.\begin{array}{lll}
\dfrac{\partial T_1^*}{\partial \rho} - \gamma_1 T_1^* = 0 & \text{when} & \rho = \rho_1, \\[3mm]
\dfrac{\partial T_1^*}{\partial \rho} + \gamma_2 T_1^* = 0 & \text{when} & \rho = 1;
\end{array}\right\} \tag{3.7.12}$$

$$\left.\begin{array}{lll}
\dfrac{\partial T_1^*}{\partial \zeta} - \gamma_3(T_1^* - \vartheta_3^*) = 0 & \text{when} & \zeta = 0, \\[3mm]
\dfrac{\partial T_1^*}{\partial \zeta} + \gamma_4(T_1^* - \vartheta_4^*) = 0 & \text{when} & \zeta = \zeta_1
\end{array}\right\} \tag{3.7.13}$$

and the equation

$$\frac{\partial^2 T_2^*}{\partial \rho^2} + \frac{1}{\rho}\frac{\partial T_2^*}{\partial \rho} + \frac{\partial^2 T_2^*}{\partial \zeta^2} = sT_2^* \qquad (3.7.14)$$

with the conditions

$$\left.\begin{aligned}
\frac{\partial T_2^*}{\partial \rho} - \gamma_1(T_2^* - \vartheta_1^*) = 0 \qquad \text{when} \qquad \rho = \rho_1, \\[2ex]
\frac{\partial T_2^*}{\partial \rho} + \gamma_2(T_2^* - \vartheta_2^*) = 0 \qquad \text{when} \qquad \rho = 1;
\end{aligned}\right\} \qquad (3.7.15)$$

$$\left.\begin{aligned}
\frac{\partial T_2^*}{\partial \zeta} - \gamma_3 T_2^* = 0 \qquad \text{when} \qquad \zeta = 0, \\[2ex]
\frac{\partial T_2^*}{\partial \zeta} + \gamma_4 T_2^* = 0 \qquad \text{when} \qquad \zeta = \zeta_1,
\end{aligned}\right\} \qquad (3.7.16)$$

where

$$\vartheta_n^* = \int_0^\infty \vartheta_n e^{-s\tau} d\tau \qquad (n = 1, 2, 3, 4).$$

We will solve equations (3.7.11) and (3.7.14) by the method of separation of variables. We will discuss this method in detail for the determination of the function T_1^*. Substituting the solution for this function T_1^* in the form

$$T_1^* = F(\rho)\,\Phi(\zeta) \qquad (3.7.17)$$

into equation (3.7.11) and introducing the notation

$$\frac{1}{F}\left(\frac{d^2 F}{d\rho^2} + \frac{1}{\rho}\frac{dF}{d\rho}\right) = -\beta^2,$$

for F and Φ we find the two equations

$$\frac{d^2 F}{d\rho^2} + \frac{1}{\rho}\frac{dF}{d\rho} + \beta^2 F = 0,$$

$$\frac{d^2 \Phi}{d\zeta^2} - (s + \beta^2)\,\Phi = 0,$$

73

the solutions of which are

$$F = A_1 J_0(\beta\rho) + A_2 Y_0(\beta\rho),$$
(3.7.18)

$$\Phi = B_1 \operatorname{ch} \delta\zeta + B_2 \operatorname{sh} \delta\zeta,$$

where $J_0(x)$ and $Y_0(x)$ the zeroth order Bessel functions of the first and second kind, respectively, and $\delta^2 = s + \beta^2$.

Making use of expression (3.7.18), we will represent solution (3.7.17) in the form

$$T_1^* = (C \operatorname{ch} \delta\zeta + D \operatorname{sh} \delta\zeta) [J_0(\beta\rho) + p Y_0(\beta\rho)],$$
(3.7.19)

where $C = A_1 B_1, \quad D = A_1 B_2, \quad p = A_2/A_1$.

Solution (3.7.19) contains four quantities p, β, C, D to be determined by the boundary conditions.

Making use of boundary conditions (3.7.12) and the familiar recurrence relations

$$\frac{d}{dx} J_0(x) = -J_1(x), \quad \frac{d}{dx} Y_0(x) = -Y_1(x),$$

we find

$$T_1^* = \sum_{n=1}^{\infty} (C_n \operatorname{ch} \delta_n\zeta + D_n \operatorname{sh} \delta_n\zeta) u_0(\beta_n\rho),$$
(3.7.20)

where $\delta_n^2 = s + \beta_n^2$.

The quantities β_n are the roots of the transcendental equation

$$\beta u_1(\beta)/u_0(\beta) = \gamma_2,$$
(3.7.21)

and the functions $u_0(\beta\rho)$ and $u_1(\beta\rho)$ are given by

$$u_0(\beta\rho) = \left[Y_1(\beta\rho_1) + \frac{\gamma_1}{\beta} Y_0(\beta\rho_1) \right] J_0(\beta\rho) -$$

$$- \left[J_1(\beta\rho_1) + \frac{\gamma_1}{\beta} J_0(\beta\rho_1) \right] Y_0(\beta\rho),$$

$$u_1(\beta\rho) = \left[Y_1(\beta\rho_1) + \frac{\gamma_1}{\beta} Y_0(\beta\rho_1) \right] J_1(\beta\rho) -$$

$$- \left[J_1(\beta\rho_1) + \frac{\gamma_1}{\beta} J_0(\beta\rho_1) \right] Y_1(\beta\rho).$$
(3.7.22)

74

The constants C_n and D_n are found from the conditions (3.7.13). We will represent the quantities $s\vartheta_3^*$ and $s\vartheta_4^*$ in the form of series of the orthogonal functions $u_0(\beta_n\rho)$[1]

$$s\vartheta_3^* = \sum_{n=1}^{\infty} A_n u_0(\beta_n\rho), \qquad s\vartheta_4^* = \sum_{n=1}^{\infty} B_n u_0(\beta_n\rho), \qquad (3.7.23)$$

where the coefficients in the expansion (3.7.23) have the values

$$A_n = \frac{s}{q_n} \int_{\rho_1}^{1} \vartheta_3^*\rho u_0(\beta_n\rho)d\rho,$$

$$\qquad (3.7.24)$$

$$B_n = \frac{s}{q_n} \int_{\rho_1}^{1} \vartheta_4^*\rho u_0(\beta_n\rho)d\rho;$$

$$q_n = \int_{\rho_1}^{1} \rho u_0^2(\beta_n\rho)d\rho = \frac{1}{2}[u_0^2(\beta_n)+u_1^2(\beta_n)-\rho_1^2 u_0^2(\beta_n\rho_1)-\rho_1^2 u_1^2(\beta_n\rho_1)]. \quad (3.7.25)$$

---

1) The orthogonality property

$$\int_{\rho_1}^{1} \rho u_0(\beta_i\rho) u_0(\beta_j\rho)d\rho = 0 \qquad (i \neq j) \qquad (1)$$

of the functions $u_0(\beta_n\rho)$ can be proved as follows. The functions $u_0(\beta_n\rho)$ $(n = i, j)$ satisfy equation (3.7.26). Multiplying this equation for $n = i$ and $n = j$ by $u_0(\beta_j\rho)$ and $u_0(\beta_i\rho)$, respectively, and subtracting the first product from the second, we find

$$(\beta_i^2 - \beta_j^2) \int_{\rho_1}^{1} \rho u_0(\beta_i\rho) u_0(\beta_j\rho)d\rho = u_0(\beta_i) u_0(\beta_j) \left[\frac{\beta_i u_1(\beta_i)}{u_0(\beta_i)} - \frac{\beta_j u_1(\beta_j)}{u_0(\beta_j)}\right] -$$

$$- \rho_1 u_0(\beta_i\rho_1) u_0(\beta_j\rho_1) \left[\frac{\beta_i u_1(\beta_i\rho_1)}{u_0(\beta_i\rho_1)} - \frac{\beta_j u_1(\beta_j\rho_1)}{u_0(\beta_j\rho_1)}\right]. \qquad (2)$$

In view of equation (3.7.21) and the identity

$$\beta_n u_1(\beta_n\rho_1)/u_0(\beta_n\rho_1) = -\gamma_1$$

we conclude that the right–hand side of (2) is equal to zero, i.e. that the orthogonality condition (1) holds.

75

Integral (3.7.25) can easily be calculated as follows.

Since function $u_0(\beta_n\rho)$ is the solution of

$$\frac{d}{d\rho}\left[\rho\frac{du_0(\beta_n\rho)}{d\rho}\right]+\beta_n^2\rho u_0(\beta_n\rho)=0, \qquad (3.7.26)$$

then

$$\frac{d}{d\rho}\left[\rho\frac{du_0(\beta_n\rho)}{d\rho}\right]^2=-\beta_n^2\rho^2\frac{du_0^2(\beta_n\rho)}{d\rho}$$

or

$$\int_{\rho_1}^{1}\rho^2 du_0^2(\beta_n\rho)=-[\rho^2 u_1^2(\beta_n\rho)]_{\rho_1}^1.$$

Integration by parts yields formula (3.7.25).

Determining the constants C_n and D_n from the boundary conditions (3.7.13) and substituting them into solution (3.7.20), we find

$$T_1^*=\sum_{n=1}^{\infty}\frac{\gamma_3 A_n X_1(\delta_n\varsigma)+\gamma_4 B_n X_2(\delta_n\varsigma)}{s[(\gamma_3+\gamma_4)\delta_n \,\mathrm{ch}\,\delta_n\varsigma_1+(\gamma_3\gamma_4+\delta_n^2)\,\mathrm{sh}\,\delta_n\varsigma_1]}\delta_n u_0(\beta_n\rho), \qquad (3.7.27)$$

where

$$X_1(\delta_n\varsigma)=\mathrm{ch}\,\delta_n(\varsigma_1-\varsigma)+\frac{\gamma_4}{\delta_n}\,\mathrm{sh}\,\delta_n(\varsigma_1-\varsigma),$$

$$\qquad (3.7.28)$$

$$X_2(\delta_n\varsigma)=\mathrm{ch}\,\delta_n\varsigma+\frac{\gamma_3}{\delta_n}\,\mathrm{sh}\,\delta_n\varsigma.$$

The function T_2^* will be determined in a similar manner. We shall seek the solution of equation (3.7.14) in the form

$$T_2^*=F(\rho)\,\Phi(\varsigma). \qquad (3.7.29)$$

Substituting solution (3.7.29) into equation (3.7.14) and introducing the notation

$$\frac{1}{\Phi}\frac{d^2\Phi}{d\varsigma^2}=-\mu^2,$$

for the determination of F and Φ we find the equations

$$\frac{d^2 F}{d\rho^2} + \frac{1}{\rho}\frac{dF}{d\rho} - \epsilon^2 F = 0,$$

$$\frac{d^2\Phi}{d\zeta^2} + \mu^2 \Phi = 0,$$

(3.7.30)

where $\epsilon^2 = s + \mu^2$.

Integrating these equations, substituting the expression for the functions F and Φ into solution (3.7.29), and changing to new constants of integration, we find

$$T_2^* = [AI_0(\epsilon\rho) + BK_0(\epsilon\rho)]\,(\cos\mu\zeta + p\sin\mu\zeta),$$

(3.7.31)

where $I_0(x)$ and $K_0(x)$ are the zeroth order modified Bessel functions of the first and second kind, respectively.

After determining the quantities p and μ from boundary conditions (3.7.16), we find

$$T_2^* = \sum_{j=1}^{\infty} [A_j I_0(\epsilon_j\rho) + B_j K_0(\epsilon_j\rho)]\,Z(\mu_j\zeta),$$

(3.7.32)

where

$$Z(\mu\zeta) = \cos\mu\zeta + \frac{\gamma_3}{\mu}\sin\mu\zeta,$$

(3.7.33)

and μ_j are the roots of the equation

$$\operatorname{tg}\mu\zeta_1 = \frac{\gamma_3 + \gamma_4}{\mu^2 - \gamma_3\gamma_4}\,\mu.$$

(3.7.34)

Representing quantities ϑ_1^* and ϑ_2^* in terms of series of the orthogonal functions $Z(\mu_j\zeta)$[1], we determine the constants A_j and B_j from condition

---

[1] The orthogonality property

$$\int_0^{\zeta_1} Z(\mu_n\zeta)\,Z(\mu_m\zeta)\,d\zeta = 0$$

(1)

of functions $Z(\mu_j\zeta)$ can be established in a similar manner to that used to prove the orthogonality of the functions $\mu_0(\beta_n\rho)$.

With the aid of equation (3.7.38), we find

$$(\mu_n^2 - \mu_m^2)\int_0^{\zeta_1} Z(\mu_n\zeta)\,Z(\mu_m\zeta)\,d\zeta = \left[Z(\mu_n\zeta)\frac{dZ(\mu_m\zeta)}{d\zeta} - Z(\mu_m\zeta)\frac{dZ(\mu_n\zeta)}{d\zeta}\right]_0^{\zeta_1}.$$

In view of relation (3.7.43) the validity of the orthogonality property is clear.

(3.7.15):

$$s\vartheta_1^* = \sum_{j=1}^{\infty} C_j Z(\mu_j \zeta), \qquad s\vartheta_2^* = \sum_{j=1}^{\infty} D_j Z(\mu_j \zeta), \qquad (3.7.35)$$

where the coefficients in expansion (3.7.35) have the values

$$C_j = \frac{s}{p_j} \int_0^{\zeta_1} \vartheta_1^* Z(\mu_j \zeta) d\zeta, \qquad D_j = \frac{s}{p_j} \int_0^{\zeta_1} \vartheta_2^* Z(\mu_j \zeta) d\zeta, \qquad (3.7.36)$$

$$p_j = \int_0^{\zeta_1} Z^2(\mu_j \zeta) d\zeta = \frac{\zeta_1(\mu_j^2 + \gamma_3^2)(\mu_j^2 + \gamma_4^2) + (\gamma_3 + \gamma_4)(\mu_j^2 + \gamma_3 \gamma_4)}{2\mu_j^2(\mu_j^2 + \gamma_4^2)}. \qquad (3.7.37)$$

Integral (3.7.37) can be calculated in the following manner. The functions $Z(\mu_n \zeta)$ satisfy the equation

$$\frac{d^2 Z(\mu_n \zeta)}{d\zeta^2} + \mu_n^2 Z(\mu_n \zeta) = 0. \qquad (3.7.38)$$

Setting $n = j$ in this equation, we find

$$\mu_j^2 \int_0^{\zeta_1} Z^2(\mu_j \zeta) d\zeta = - \left[Z(\mu_j \zeta) \frac{dZ(\mu_j \zeta)}{d\zeta} \right]_0^{\zeta_1} + \int_0^{\zeta_1} \left[\frac{dZ(\mu_j \zeta)}{d\zeta} \right]^2 d\zeta. \qquad (3.7.39)$$

With the aid of expression (3.7.33), we determine

$$\mu_j^2 Z^2(\mu_j \zeta) + \left[\frac{dZ(\mu_j \zeta)}{d\zeta} \right]^2 = \mu_j^2 + \gamma_3^2 \qquad (3.7.40)$$

and

$$\mu_j^2 \int_0^{\zeta_1} Z^2(\mu_j \zeta) d\zeta = (\mu_j^2 + \gamma_3^2)\zeta_1 - \int_0^{\zeta_1} \left[\frac{dZ(\mu_j \zeta)}{d\zeta} \right]^2 d\zeta. \qquad (3.7.41)$$

Adding expressions (3.7.39) and (3.7.41), we find

$$2\mu_j^2 \int_0^{\zeta_1} Z^2(\mu_j \zeta) d\zeta = (\mu_j^2 + \gamma_3^2)\zeta_1 - \left[Z(\mu_j \zeta) \frac{dZ(\mu_j \zeta)}{d\zeta} \right]_0^{\zeta_1}. \qquad (3.7.42)$$

Function $Z(\mu_j \zeta)$ satisfies condition (3.7.16), whence follows the relations

$$Z(\mu_j\zeta)\frac{dZ(\mu_j\zeta)}{d\zeta} = \gamma_3 Z^2(\mu_j\zeta) \qquad \text{when} \qquad \zeta = 0,$$

$$Z(\mu_j\zeta)\frac{dZ(\mu_j\zeta)}{d\zeta} = -\gamma_4 Z^2(\mu_j\zeta) \qquad \text{when} \qquad \zeta = \zeta_1$$

(3.7.43)

or

$$\left[\frac{dZ(\mu_j\zeta)}{d\zeta}\right]^2 = \gamma_3^2 Z^2(\mu_j\zeta) \qquad \text{when} \qquad \zeta = 0,$$

$$\left[\frac{dZ(\mu_j\zeta)}{d\zeta}\right]^2 = \gamma_4^2 Z^2(\mu_j\zeta) \qquad \text{when} \qquad \zeta = \zeta_1.$$

(3.7.44)

Addition of (3.7.43) and (3.7.40) yields

$$Z^2(\mu_j\zeta) = 1 \qquad \text{when} \qquad \zeta = 0,$$

$$Z^2(\mu_j\zeta) = \frac{\mu_j^2 + \gamma_3^2}{\mu_j^2 + \gamma_4^2} \qquad \text{when} \qquad \zeta = \zeta_1.$$

(3.7.45)

On the basis of (3.7.43) and (3.7.45) we find

$$\left[Z(\mu_j\zeta)\frac{dZ(\mu_j\zeta)}{d\zeta}\right]_0^{\zeta_1} = -\frac{(\gamma_3 + \gamma_4)(\mu_j^2 + \gamma_3\gamma_4)}{\mu_j^2 + \gamma_4^2}.$$

(3.7.46)

Finally, by substituting (3.7.46) into (3.7.42), we obtain expression (3.7.37).

Substitution of the values of A_j and B_j found from the boundary conditions into solution (3.7.32) yields the final result

$$T_2^* = \sum_{j=1}^{\infty} \frac{\gamma_1 C_j w_0(\epsilon_j\rho) + \gamma_2 D_j v_0(\epsilon_j\rho)}{s[\gamma_2 v_0(\epsilon_j) + \epsilon_j v_1(\epsilon_j)]} Z(\mu_j\zeta),$$

(3.7.47)

where

$$v_0(\epsilon\rho) = \left[K_1(\epsilon\rho_1) + \frac{\gamma_1}{\epsilon} K_0(\epsilon\rho_1)\right] I_1(\epsilon\rho) + \left[I_1(\epsilon\rho_1) - \frac{\gamma_1}{\epsilon} I_0(\epsilon\rho_1)\right] K_0(\epsilon\rho),$$

$$v_1(\epsilon\rho) = \left[K_1(\epsilon\rho_1) + \frac{\gamma_1}{\epsilon} K_0(\epsilon\rho_1)\right] I_1(\epsilon\rho) - \left[I_1(\epsilon\rho_1) - \frac{\gamma_1}{\epsilon} I_0(\epsilon\rho_1)\right] K_1(\epsilon\rho),$$

$$w_0(\epsilon\rho) = \left[K_1(\epsilon) - \frac{\gamma_2}{\epsilon} K_1(\epsilon)\right] I_0(\epsilon\rho) + \left[I_1(\epsilon) + \frac{\gamma_2}{\epsilon} I_0(\epsilon)\right] K_0(\epsilon\rho),$$

$$I_1(x) = I_0'(x), \qquad K_1(x) = -K_0'(x).$$

For various laws of time dependence of the surface temperatures ϑ_n ($n = 1, 2, 3, 4$), the expansion theorem of the operational calculus can be used to convert the transforms (3.7.27) and (3.7.47) into the corresponding solutions for the temperature field in the cylinder.

As an example we shall consider the case where the surface temperatures ϑ_n ($n = 1, 2, 3, 4$) are constant. Application of formula (3.6.10) for the transition from the transform to the original function yields the temperature field in the cylinder in the form

$$T = T_I - T_{II}, \tag{3.7.48}$$

where function T_I is independent of time and function T_{II} has a damped character and decreases with time. The expressions for these functions are

$$T_I = \sum_{n=1}^{\infty} \frac{\gamma_3 A_n X_1(\beta_n \zeta) + \gamma_4 B_n X_2(\beta_n \zeta)}{(\gamma_3 + \gamma_4)\beta_n \operatorname{ch}\beta_n \zeta_1 + (\gamma_3 \gamma_4 + \beta_n^2)\operatorname{sh}\beta_n \zeta_1}\beta_n u_0(\beta_n \rho) +$$

$$+ \sum_{j=1}^{\infty} \frac{\gamma_1 C_j w_0(\mu_j \rho) + \gamma_2 D_j v_0(\mu_j \rho)}{\gamma_2 v_0(\mu_j) + \mu_j v_1(\mu_j)} Z(\mu_j \zeta), \tag{3.7.49}$$

$$T_{II} = \sum_{n=1}^{\infty} u_0(\beta_n \rho)\, e^{-\beta_n^2 \tau} \sum_{j=1}^{\infty} M_{nj}\left[\gamma_3 A_n Z_1(\mu_j \zeta) + \gamma_4 B_n Z(\mu_j \zeta)\right] e^{-\mu_j^2 \tau} +$$

$$+ \sum_{j=1}^{\infty} Z(\mu_j \zeta)\, e^{-\mu_j^2 \tau} \sum_{n=1}^{\infty} N_{nj}\left[\gamma_1 C_j w_1(\beta_n \rho) + \gamma_2 D_j u_0(\beta_n \rho)\right] e^{-\beta_n^2 \tau}, \tag{3.7.50}$$

where

$$A_n = \vartheta_3 q_n', \quad B_n = \vartheta_4 q_n',$$

$$q_n' = \frac{1}{q_n \beta_n}\left[u_1(\beta_n) - \rho_1 u_1(\beta_n \rho_1)\right],$$

$$C_j = \vartheta_1 p_j', \quad D_j = \vartheta_2 p_j', \quad p_j' = \frac{\mu_j \sin \mu_j \zeta_1 + \gamma_3(1 - \cos \mu_j \zeta_1)}{p_j \mu_j^2},$$

$$w_1(\beta_n \rho) = \left[Y_1(\beta_n) - \frac{\gamma_2}{\beta_n} Y_0(\beta_n)\right] J_0(\beta_n \rho) - \left[J_1(\beta_n) - \frac{\gamma_2}{\beta_n} J_0(\beta_n)\right] Y_0(\beta_n \rho),$$

$$Z_1(\mu_j \zeta) = \cos\left[\mu_j(\zeta_1 - \zeta)\right] + \frac{\gamma_4}{\mu_j} \sin\left[\mu_j(\zeta_1 - \zeta)\right],$$

$$M_{nj} = \frac{2\mu_j^2}{(\beta_n^2 + \mu_j^2)} \times$$

$$\times \frac{1}{\left[(\gamma_3 + \gamma_4)\,\zeta_1 + 2\right]\mu_j \sin\mu_j\zeta_1 - \left[\gamma_3 + \gamma_4 + \zeta_1\,(\gamma_3\gamma_4 - \mu_j^2)\right]\cos\mu_j\zeta_1},$$

$$N_{nj} = \frac{(1 - \gamma_1\rho_1 \ln\rho_1)\,\beta_n^2 q_n'}{(\beta_n^2 + \mu_j^2)\left[\gamma_2(1 - \gamma_1\rho_1 \ln\rho_1) + \gamma_1\rho_1\right]}.$$

The rest of the notation has been explained above.

For a solid cylinder ($\rho_1 = 0$) expressions (3.7.49) and (3.7.50) assume the form

$$T_{\mathrm{I}} = \vartheta_1 - \sum_{n=1}^{\infty} \frac{A_n\beta_n\left[\gamma_3(\vartheta_1 - \vartheta_3)X_1(\beta_n\zeta) + \gamma_4(\vartheta_1 - \vartheta_4)X_2(\beta_n\zeta)\right]}{(\gamma_3 + \gamma_4)\beta_n\,\mathrm{ch}\,\beta_n\zeta_1 + (\gamma_3\gamma_4 + \beta_n^2)\,\mathrm{sh}\,\beta_n\zeta_1} J_0(\beta_n\rho),$$

$$(3.7.51)$$

$$T_{\mathrm{II}} = \sum_{n=1}^{\infty} A_n J_0(\beta_n\rho)\,e^{-\beta_n^2\tau} \sum_{j=1}^{\infty} M_{nj}\,\gamma_3\vartheta_3 Z_1(\mu_j\zeta) +$$

$$+ \gamma_4\vartheta_4 Z(\mu_j\zeta)\big]\,e^{-\mu_j^2\tau} + \sum_{j=1}^{\infty} D_j Z(\mu_j\zeta)\,e^{-\mu_j^2\tau} \sum_{n=1}^{\infty} \frac{A_n\beta_n^2 J_0(\beta_n\rho)}{\beta_n^2 + \mu_j^2}\,e^{-\beta_n^2\tau},$$

$$(3.7.52)$$

where

$$A_n = \frac{2J_1(\beta_n)}{\beta_n\left[J_0^2(\beta_n) + J_1^2(\beta_n)\right]},$$

and β_n are the roots of the equation

$$\beta J_1(\beta)/J_0(\beta) = \gamma_2. \qquad (3.7.53)$$

Other numerical cases of unsteady heat conduction in cylinders have been treated in [32].

Chapter IV

THE PLANE PROBLEM IN THERMOELASTICITY

4.1. Basic equations

In the quasi–static formulation with a plane temperature field $T(x,y,t)$, we will distinguish two typical types of plane problem: (1) that of plane strain, and (2) that of plane stress.

The state of plane strain arises in infinite cylinders whose axis coincides with the z–axis (see Fig. 13).

In the case of plane strain the displacements are

$$u = u(x, y), \quad v = v(x, y), \quad w = 0, \tag{4.1.1}$$

which means that the strains ϵ_z, ϵ_{xz}, ϵ_{yz} and the stresses σ_{xz}, σ_{yz} vanish. Setting $\epsilon_{ij} = \epsilon_z = 0$ in (1.5.13), we obtain

$$\sigma_z = \nu(\sigma_x + \sigma_y) - \alpha_T E\,(T - T_0). \tag{4.1.2}$$

Having the value of σ_z, we can write the relations between the strain ϵ_x, ϵ_y, ϵ_{xy} and the stresses σ_x, σ_y, σ_{xy} in the form

$$\epsilon_x = \frac{1}{E_1}(\sigma_x - \nu_1\sigma_y) + \alpha_{T1}(T - T_0),$$

$$\epsilon_y = \frac{1}{E_1}(\sigma_y - \nu_1\sigma_x) + \alpha_{T1}(T - T_0), \tag{4.1.3}$$

$$\epsilon_{xy} = \frac{1 + \nu_1}{E_1}\,\sigma_{xy},$$

where

$$E_1 = \frac{E}{1 - \nu^2}, \quad \nu_1 = \frac{\nu}{1 - \nu}, \quad \alpha_{T1} = \alpha_T(1 + \nu). \tag{4.1.4}$$

The state of plane stress arises in thin sheets whose middle surface lies in the x, y–plane. Moreover, the faces $z \pm h/2$ must be free of external tractions (see Fig. 13).

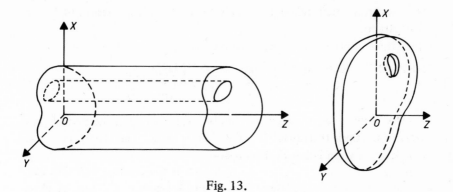

Fig. 13.

In the case of the plane state of stress, the stresses $\sigma_x, \sigma_y, \sigma_{xy}$ are distributed uniformly through the thickness of the plate, and the stresses

$$\sigma_z = \sigma_{xz} = \sigma_{yz} = 0 \qquad (4.1.5)$$

vanish.

The strains $\epsilon_x, \epsilon_y, \epsilon_z, \epsilon_{xy}$ are given by the formulae

$$\epsilon_x = \frac{1}{E}(\sigma_x - \nu\sigma_y) + \alpha_T(T - T_0),$$

$$\epsilon_y = \frac{1}{E}(\sigma_y - \nu\sigma_x) + \alpha_T(T - T_0), \qquad (4.1.6)$$

$$\epsilon_{xy} = \frac{1 + \nu}{E}\,\sigma_{xy};$$

$$\epsilon_z = -\frac{\nu}{E}(\sigma_x + \sigma_y) + \alpha_T(T - T_0). \qquad (4.1.7)$$

In the general formulation of the plane problem of thermoelasticity in cartesian coordinates, we have to determine the eight functions $\sigma_x, \sigma_y, \sigma_{xy}$, $\epsilon_x, \epsilon_y, \epsilon_{xy}, u, v$ which, in the case of zero body forces, satisfy
a) two equilibrium equations

$$\frac{\partial \sigma_x}{\partial x} + \frac{\partial \sigma_{xy}}{\partial y} = 0,$$

$$\frac{\partial \sigma_{xy}}{\partial x} + \frac{\partial \sigma_y}{\partial y} = 0, \qquad (4.1.8)$$

83

b) three stress–strain relations (namely (4.1.6) for plane stress or (4.1.3) for plane strain), and

c) the three displacement–strain relations

$$\epsilon_x = \frac{\partial u}{\partial x}, \quad \epsilon_y = \frac{\partial v}{\partial y}, \quad \epsilon_{xy} = \frac{1}{2}\left(\frac{\partial u}{\partial y} + \frac{\partial v}{\partial x}\right). \qquad (4.1.9)$$

After solving this problem we find ϵ_z from (4.1.7) in the case of plane stress or σ_z from (4.1.2) in the case of plane strain. The conditions on the boundary are given either in the stresses

$$\sigma_x n_x + \sigma_{xy} n_y = f_x\,(x,\,y),$$
$$\sigma_{xy} n_x + \sigma_y n_y = f_y\,(x,\,y), \qquad (4.1.10)$$

or in the displacements

$$u = g_1(x,\,y), \quad v = g_2(x,\,y). \qquad (4.1.11)$$

where f_x and f_y are the components of the surface traction, and n_x, n_y are the components of the unit outward normal to the contour.

If the boundary conditions of the plane problem of thermoelasticity are given in the displacements, it is advantageous to use displacement formulation of the problem.

Setting $u_3 = w = 0$ in (2.2.1), we obtain the following two equations governing the displacements in the two–dimensional thermoelastic problem:

$$\mu\nabla^2 u + (\lambda + \mu)\,\frac{\partial}{\partial x}\left(\frac{\partial u}{\partial x} + \frac{\partial v}{\partial y}\right) - (3\lambda + 2\mu)\alpha_T\,\frac{\partial T}{\partial x} = 0,$$

$$\mu\nabla^2 v + (\lambda + \mu)\,\frac{\partial}{\partial y}\left(\frac{\partial u}{\partial x} + \frac{\partial v}{\partial y}\right) - (3\lambda + 2\mu)\alpha_T\,\frac{\partial T}{\partial y} = 0, \qquad (4.1.12)$$

where

$$\nabla^2 = \frac{\partial^2}{\partial x^2} + \frac{\partial^2}{\partial y^2}$$

In order to set up the corresponding equations for the plane state of stress, we proceed as follows.

Equations (4.1.4) can be rewritten as

$$E = E_1\,\frac{1 + 2\nu_1}{(1 + \nu_1)^2}, \quad \nu = \frac{\nu_1}{1 + \nu_1}, \quad \alpha_T = \alpha_{T1}\,\frac{1 + \nu_1}{1 + 2\nu_1}. \qquad (4.1.13)$$

These values yield

$$\lambda = \frac{E\nu}{(1+\nu)(1-2\nu)} = \frac{E_1\nu_1}{1-\nu_1^2}, \quad \mu = \frac{E_1}{2(1+\nu_1)},$$

$$(3\lambda + 2\mu)\alpha_T = \frac{\alpha_{T_1}E_1}{1-\nu_1}. \tag{4.1.14}$$

Substituting expressions (4.1.13) into equation (4.1.12) and changing E_1, ν_1, α_{T_1} into E, ν, α_T, we obtain the basic equations in the displacements for the plane state of stress.

The particular solution of equations (4.1.12) corresponding to solution (2.2.7) has the form

$$u(T) = \frac{\partial \Phi}{\partial x}, \quad v(T) = \frac{\partial \Phi}{\partial y}, \tag{4.1.15}$$

where in virtue of (2.2.8) the thermoelastic displacement potential Φ for plane strains satisfies the equation

$$\nabla^2 \Phi = \frac{\partial^2 \Phi}{\partial x^2} + \frac{\partial^2 \Phi}{\partial y^2} = \frac{1+\nu}{1-\nu}\alpha_T(T-T_0). \tag{4.1.16}$$

When the values ν and α_T in this equation are taken from (4.1.13), and ν_1, α_{T_1} are changed to ν, α_T, respectively, the corresponding equation for the plane state of stress is found to be

$$\nabla^2 \Phi = (1+\nu)\alpha_T(T-T_0). \tag{4.1.17}$$

The particular solution (4.1.15) of equations (4.1.12) must be supplemented by the complementary solution of the corresponding homogeneous equations. This solution must contain a sufficient number of constants of integration so that we can satisfy the displacement boundary conditions (4.1.11). Such a formulation of the problem is suitable for simply connected and multiply connected bodies.

Without dwelling any further on this problem, we shall proceed to the plane stress problem of thermoelasticity.

Firstly we will consider simply connected bodies.

In the two—dimensional problem, the six compatibility equations reduce to the single relation

$$\frac{\partial^2 \epsilon_x}{\partial y^2} + \frac{\partial^2 \epsilon_y}{\partial x^2} = 2\frac{\partial^2 \epsilon_{xy}}{\partial x \partial y}. \tag{4.1.18}$$

85

Formulae (4.1.6) can be used to replace the strains in (4.1.18) by the stresses. Then, taking account of the equilibrium equations (4.1.8), we find the following compatibility equation in terms of the stresses:

$$\nabla^2(\sigma_x + \sigma_y) + E\alpha_T \nabla^2 T = 0. \tag{4.1.19}$$

With the Airy stress function F defined by

$$\sigma_x = \frac{\partial^2 F}{\partial y^2}, \quad \sigma_y = \frac{\partial^2 F}{\partial x^2}, \quad \sigma_{xy} = -\frac{\partial^2 F}{\partial x \partial y}, \tag{4.1.20}$$

the equilibrium equations (4.1.8) are satisfied identically.

Substitution of expressions (4.1.20) into equation (4.1.19) shows that for the plane state of stress the Airy function is governed by the equation

$$\nabla^4 F + E\alpha_T \nabla^2 T = 0, \tag{4.1.21}$$

where

$$\nabla^4 F = \nabla^2(\nabla^2 F) = \frac{\partial^4 F}{\partial x^4} + 2\frac{\partial^4 F}{\partial x^2 \partial y^2} + \frac{\partial^4 F}{\partial y^4}. \tag{4.1.22}$$

Replacing the E, α_T here by E_1, α_{T1} and substituting these into expression (4.1.4), we obtain the corresponding equation for F in the case of plane strain:

$$\nabla^4 F + \frac{E}{1-\nu}\alpha_T \nabla^2 T = 0. \tag{4.1.23}$$

The general solution of equation (4.1.21) or (4.1.23) has the form

$$F = F^* + F^{(T)}, \tag{4.1.24}$$

where function F^* satisfies the biharmonic equation

$$\nabla^4 F^* = 0, \tag{4.1.25}$$

In the case of plane stress, $F^{(T)}$ is a particular solution of the equation

$$\nabla^2 F^{(T)} + E\alpha_T(T - T_0) = 0, \tag{4.1.26}$$

and in the case of plane strain $F^{(T)}$ is a particular solution of

$$\nabla^2 F^{(T)} + \frac{E}{1-\nu}\alpha_T(T - T_0) = 0. \tag{4.1.27}$$

86

Now we will set up the boundary–value problem for the stress function using the orthogonal curvilinear coordinates s, n for a simply connected body.

Suppose that the boundary conditions (4.1.10) are to be satisfied at each point P on the boundary shown in Fig. 14. Expressing the stresses in terms of the stress function according to (4.1.20) and taking account of the relations

$$n_x = \cos{(n, x)} = \cos{(s, y)} \frac{dx}{dn} = \frac{dy}{ds},$$

$$n_y = \cos{(n, y)} = -\cos{(s, x)} \frac{dy}{dn} = -\frac{dx}{ds},$$

(4.1.28)

boundary conditions (4.1.10) can be written as

$$f_x = \frac{\partial^2 F}{\partial y^2} \frac{dy}{ds} + \frac{\partial^2 F}{\partial x \partial y} \frac{dx}{ds} = \frac{\partial}{\partial s} \left(\frac{\partial F}{\partial y} \right),$$

$$f_y = -\frac{\partial^2 F}{\partial x \partial y} \frac{dy}{ds} - \frac{\partial^2 F}{\partial x^2} \frac{dx}{ds} =$$

$$= -\frac{\partial}{\partial s} \left(\frac{\partial F}{\partial x} \right).$$

(4.1.29)

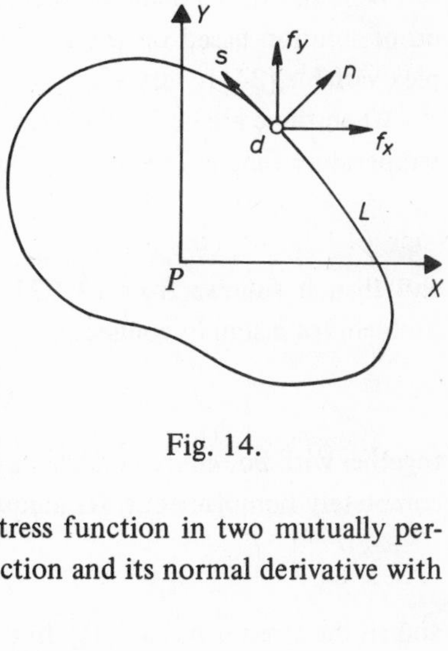

Integration of (4.1.29) yields

$$\frac{\partial F}{\partial x} = -\int_0^s f_y ds + \alpha, \quad \frac{\partial F}{\partial y} = \int_0^s f_x ds + \beta,$$

(4.1.30)

Fig. 14.

where α and β are constants.

Having the partial derivatives of the stress function in two mutually perpendicular directions, we can find the function and its normal derivative with the aid of integration by parts as follows.

$$F = \int_0^s \left[-\frac{dx}{ds} \int_0^s f_y ds + \frac{dy}{ds} \int_0^s f_x ds \right] ds + \alpha x + \beta y + \gamma =$$

$$= -x \int_0^s f_y ds + y \int_0^s f_x ds + \int_0^s (f_y x - f_x y) ds + \alpha x + \beta y + \gamma, (4.1.31)$$

$$\frac{\partial F}{\partial n} = \frac{dx}{dn} \left(-\int_0^s f_y ds + \alpha \right) + \frac{dy}{dn} \left(\int_0^s f_x ds + \beta \right). \quad (4.1.32)$$

87

Since the linear terms in F give no contribution to the stresses, the constants α, β, γ can be set equal to zero.

When there are no surface tractions $(f_x = f_y = 0)$ and the body is simply connected, the boundary conditions for F are

$$F = \frac{\partial F}{\partial n} = 0 \quad \text{on boundary } L. \tag{4.1.33}$$

Thus, the plane stress problem of thermoelasticity leads to the determination of the general solution (4.1.24) for the stress function F, i.e., we must find a general solution F^* of the biharmonic equation (4.1.25) and a particular solution $F^{(T)}$ of the Poisson equation (4.1.26) or (4.1.27) so that F satisfies the boundary conditions (4.1.33).

Once a particular solution $F^{(T)}$ is known, the plane thermoelastic problem can be reduced to a plane problem in theory of isotropic elasticity. The method of solution based on the application of the theory of functions of a complex variable [34] is very effective in this theory.

When there are no heat sources and the steady state has been attained, the temperature field is governed by the equation

$$\nabla^2 T(x, y) = 0, \tag{4.1.34}$$

and then it follows from (4.1.21) or (4.1.23) that the plane thermoelastic problem for a simply connected body is described by the equation

$$\nabla^4 F = 0 \tag{4.1.35}$$

together with boundary conditions (4.1.33). In this case the problem becomes completely homogeneous. Its unique solution is

$$F \equiv 0,$$

and all the stresses $\sigma_x, \sigma_y, \sigma_{xy}$ In the x, y–plane vanish.

In the case of plane strain the only nonzero stress component is σ_z. On the basis of (4.1.2) its value is

$$\sigma_z = -\alpha E(T - T_0).$$

Thus, when a simply connected body is subject to conditions of plane stress or plane strain, a steady temperature field without heat sources does not affect the stress components $\sigma_x, \sigma_y, \sigma_{xy}$. This fact was first pointed out by Muskhelishvili [33].

When formulating the plane stress problem in thermoelasticity for the case of multiply connected bodies, one must add additional equations ensuring that the displacements are single valued (see Section 4.2). In virtue of these constraints, a steady two—dimensional temperature field in a multiply connected body can in general give rise to stresses in the x, y—plane.

To conclude this Section we quote the basic relations for the plane problem in terms of polar coordinates r, θ. The strain—deformation relations (4.1.9) become

$$\epsilon_r = \frac{\partial u_r}{\partial r}, \quad \epsilon_\theta = \frac{u_r}{r} + \frac{1}{r}\frac{\partial u_\theta}{\partial \theta}, \quad \epsilon_{r\theta} = \frac{1}{2}\left(\frac{1}{r}\frac{\partial u_r}{\partial \theta} + \frac{\partial u_\theta}{\partial r} - \frac{u_\theta}{r}\right) ; \quad (4.1.36)$$

In the case of plane stress, the stress—strain relations are

$$\sigma_r = \frac{E}{1-\nu^2}[\epsilon_r + \nu\epsilon_\theta - (1+\nu)\alpha_T(T-T_0)],$$

$$\sigma_\theta = \frac{E}{1-\nu^2}[\epsilon_\theta + \nu\epsilon_r - (1+\nu)\alpha_T(T-T_0)], \quad (4.1.37)$$

$$\sigma_{r\theta} = \frac{E}{1+\nu}\epsilon_{r\theta}.$$

Expressions (4.1.20) for the stresses become

$$\sigma_r = \frac{1}{r}\frac{\partial F}{\partial r} + \frac{1}{r^2}\frac{\partial^2 F}{\partial \theta^2}, \quad \sigma_\theta = \frac{\partial^2 F}{\partial r^2}, \quad \sigma_{r\theta} = -\frac{\partial}{\partial r}\left(\frac{1}{r}\frac{\partial F}{\partial \theta}\right), \quad (4.1.38)$$

and the Laplace operator is

$$\nabla^2 = \frac{\partial^2}{\partial r^2} + \frac{1}{r}\frac{\partial}{\partial r} + \frac{1}{r^2}\frac{\partial^2}{\partial \theta^2} = \frac{1}{r}\frac{\partial}{\partial r}\left(r\frac{\partial}{\partial r}\right) + \frac{1}{r^2}\frac{\partial^2}{\partial \theta^2}. \quad (4.1.39)$$

4.2. Plane state of stress in multiply—connected bodies

Here we will consider the state of plane stress in an N—fold multiply connected body in a two—dimensional temperature field.

Suppose that the body is bounded by a certain number of closed contours and that the external contour L contains all the others (e.g. a plate with N holes as shown in Fig. 15). The governing equation (4.1.21) for this problem contains the stress function F which has continuous derivatives up to the fourth order.

Since the stresses σ_x, σ_y, σ_{xy} are single–valued functions, the first– and higher–order derivatives of F must be single–valued. For a simply– connected body the single–valued- ness of the derivatives also guarantees the single–valuedness of the function itself.

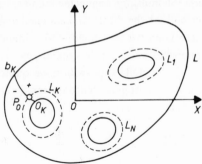

Fig. 15.

In the case of a multiply con- nected body the displacements may be multi–valued functions. The for- mulation of the plane stress problem of thermoelasticity given in Section 4.1 for a simply connected region must therefore be modified for multiply– connected regions; one must add the conditions that the displacements u and v and the rotation ω_z are single valued.

The above conditions could be obtained as a particular case of the cor- responding conditions for single–valuedness in three–dimensional elasticity (see Section 2.3). However, in order to give a clearer explanation of the features of this problem, we shall now deduce these conditions using a system of orthogonal curvilinear coordinates s, n.

Let us begin by deducing the condition for the single–valuedness of the rotation

$$\omega_z = \frac{1}{2}\left(\frac{\partial v}{\partial x} - \frac{\partial u}{\partial y}\right).$$ (4.2.1)

Since the strains are single–valued, it follows from the equation

$$\omega_z = \epsilon_{xy} - \frac{\partial u}{\partial y} = \frac{\partial v}{\partial x} - \epsilon_{xy}$$ (4.2.2)

and the third relation in (4.1.9) that the single–valuedness of the rotation requires the single–valuedness of the derivatives $\partial u/\partial y$ and $\partial v/\partial x$.

The requirement that $\partial u/\partial y$ is single–valued can be expressed in the form

$$\int_{L_K} d\frac{\partial u}{\partial y} = \int_{L_K}\left[\frac{\partial}{\partial x}\left(\frac{\partial u}{\partial y}\right)dx + \frac{\partial}{\partial y}\left(\frac{\partial u}{\partial y}\right)dy\right] = 0,$$ (4.2.3)

$$K = 1, \ldots, N,$$

90

where the integration extends over each of the closed contours L_K ($K = 1, 2,$ $\ldots, N$) each enclosing just one hole as shown in Fig. 15.

Using equation (4.1.9) to introduce the strains into the integrand and expressing these in terms of the stress function by means of (4.1.6) and (4.1.20), we finally have

$$\int_{L_K} d\,\frac{du}{\partial y} = \int_{L_K} \left[\frac{\partial \epsilon_x}{\partial y}\,dx + \left(2\,\frac{\partial \epsilon_{xy}}{\partial y} - \frac{\partial \epsilon_y}{\partial x}\right)dy \right] =$$

$$= -\frac{1}{E}\int_{L_K} \left[\frac{\partial}{\partial x}\,\nabla^2 F dy - \frac{\partial}{\partial y}\,\nabla^2 F dx + \right.$$

$$\left. + (1+\nu)\left(\frac{\partial}{\partial x}\,\frac{\partial^2 F}{\partial x \partial y}\,dx + \frac{\partial}{\partial y}\,\frac{\partial^2 F}{\partial x \partial y}\,dy\right) + E\alpha_T\left(\frac{\partial T}{\partial x}\,dy - \frac{\partial T}{\partial y}\,dx\right) \right] .$$

On account of the identities cf. (4.1.28)

$$\frac{\partial}{\partial s} = \frac{\partial}{\partial x}\,\frac{dx}{ds} + \frac{\partial}{\partial y}\,\frac{dy}{ds},$$

$$\frac{\partial}{\partial n} = \frac{\partial}{\partial x}\,\frac{dx}{dn} + \frac{\partial}{\partial y}\,\frac{dy}{dn} = \frac{\partial}{\partial y}\,\frac{dy}{ds} - \frac{\partial}{\partial x}\,\frac{dx}{ds};$$

(4.2.4)

$$-\frac{1+\nu}{E}\int_{L_K}\left(\frac{\partial}{\partial x}\,\frac{\partial^2 F}{\partial x \partial y}\,dx + \frac{\partial}{\partial y}\,\frac{\partial^2 F}{\partial x \partial y}\,dy\right) = -\frac{1+\nu}{E}\int_{L_K} d\,\frac{\partial^2 F}{\partial x \partial y} = 0,$$

the condition for the single–valuedness of the rotation becomes

$$-\int_{L_K} d\left(\frac{\partial u}{\partial y}\right) = \frac{1}{E}\int_{L_K}\frac{\partial}{\partial n}\,\nabla^2 F ds + \alpha_T\int_{L_K}\frac{\partial T}{\partial n}\,ds = 0, \qquad (4.2.5)$$

$$K = 1, 2, \ldots, N.$$

The condition for the single–valuedness of the displacement u can be written as

$$\int_{L_K} du = \int_{L_K}\left(\frac{\partial u}{\partial x}\,dx + \frac{\partial u}{\partial y}\,dy\right) = 0. \qquad (4.2.6)$$

Integration by parts yields

$$\int_{L_K} du = \left[\frac{\partial u}{\partial x} x\right]_{P_0}^{P_0} + \left[\frac{\partial u}{\partial y} y\right]_{P_0}^{P_0} - \int_{L_K}\left[x\, d\left(\frac{\partial u}{\partial x}\right) + y\, d\left(\frac{\partial u}{\partial y}\right)\right]. \quad (4.2.7)$$

The condition for the single–valuedness of the derivative $\partial u/\partial y$ has already been satisfied. Thus, after introducing the strains, we have

$$\int_{L_K} du = -\int_{L_K} x\left[\left(\frac{\partial^2 u}{\partial x^2}\, dx + \frac{\partial^2 u}{\partial x \partial y}\, dy\right) + y\left(\frac{\partial^2 u}{\partial x \partial y}\, dx + \frac{\partial^2 u}{\partial y^2}\, dy\right)\right] =$$

$$= -\int_{L_K}\left\{\left(x\frac{\partial \epsilon_x}{\partial x} + y\frac{\partial \epsilon_x}{\partial y}\right) dx + \left[x\frac{\partial \epsilon_x}{\partial y} + y\left(2\frac{\partial \epsilon_{xy}}{\partial y} - \frac{\partial \epsilon_y}{\partial x}\right)\right] dy\right\} = 0.$$

Expressing the strains in terms of the stress function and taking account of identities (4.2.4), we find

$$\int_{L_K} du = -\frac{1}{E}\int_{L_K}\left[x\left(\frac{\partial \nabla^2 F}{\partial x}\, dx + \frac{\partial \nabla^2 F}{\partial y}\, dy\right) - y\left(\frac{\partial \nabla^2 F}{\partial x}\, dy - \frac{\partial \nabla^2 F}{\partial y}\, dx\right)\right] -$$

$$-\alpha_T\int_{L_K}\left[x\left(\frac{\partial T}{\partial x}\, dx + \frac{\partial T}{\partial y}\, dy\right) - y\left(\frac{\partial T}{\partial x}\, dy - \frac{\partial T}{\partial x}\, dx\right)\right] +$$

$$+\frac{1+\nu}{E}\int_{L_K}\left\{x\left[\frac{\partial}{\partial x}\left(\frac{\partial^2 F}{\partial x^2}\right) dx + \frac{\partial}{\partial y}\left(\frac{\partial^2 F}{\partial x^2}\right) dy\right] +$$

$$+ y\left[\frac{\partial}{\partial x}\left(\frac{\partial^2 F}{\partial x \partial y}\right) dx + \frac{\partial}{\partial y}\left(\frac{\partial^2 F}{\partial x \partial y}\right) dy\right]\right\} =$$

$$= -\frac{1}{E}\int_{L_K}\left(x\frac{\partial \nabla^2 F}{\partial s} - y\frac{\partial \nabla^2 F}{\partial n}\right) ds - \alpha_T\int_{L_K}\left(x\frac{\partial T}{\partial s} - y\frac{\partial T}{\partial n}\right) ds +$$

$$+\frac{1+\nu}{E}\int_{L_K}\left[x\, d\left(\frac{\partial^2 F}{\partial x^2}\right) + y\, d\left(\frac{\partial^2 F}{\partial x \partial y}\right)\right] = 0.$$

Then, transforming the last integral here with the aid of the first boundary condition (4.1.30) into the form

$$\frac{1+\nu}{E}\int_{L_K}\left[x\, d\left(\frac{\partial^2 F}{\partial x^2}\right) + y\, d\left(\frac{\partial^2 F}{\partial x \partial y}\right)\right] =$$

$$= \frac{1+\nu}{E} \left\{ \left[x \frac{\partial^2 F}{\partial x^2} \right]_{P_0}^{P_0} + \left[y \frac{\partial^2 F}{\partial x \partial y} \right]_{P_0}^{P_0} - \int_{L_K} \left(\frac{\partial^2 F}{\partial x^2} dx + \frac{\partial^2 F}{\partial x \partial y} dy \right) \right\} =$$

$$= -\frac{1+\nu}{E} \int_{L_K} d\left(\frac{\partial F}{\partial x} \right) = \frac{1+\nu}{E} \int_{L_K} f_y^{(K)} ds,$$

we finally obtain the following condition for the single—valuedness of u

$$\int_{L_K} du = -\frac{1}{E} \int_{L_K} \left(x \frac{\partial}{\partial s} - y \frac{\partial}{\partial n} \right) \nabla^2 F ds - \alpha_T \int_{L_K} \left(x \frac{\partial}{\partial s} - y \frac{\partial}{\partial n} \right) T ds +$$

$$+ \frac{1+\nu}{E} \int_{L_K} f_y^{(K)} ds = 0, \qquad K = 1, 2, \ldots, N. \tag{4.2.8}$$

Similar reasoning leads to the third condition for the single—valuedness of v:

$$\int_{L_K} dv = \left[\frac{dv}{dx} x \right]_{P_0}^{P_0} + \left[\frac{\partial v}{\partial y} y \right]_{P_0}^{P_0} - \int_{L_K} \left[x \, d\left(\frac{\partial v}{\partial x} \right) + y \, d\left(\frac{\partial v}{\partial y} \right) \right] =$$

$$= -\frac{1}{E} \int_{L_K} \left(y \frac{\partial}{\partial s} + x \frac{\partial}{\partial n} \right) \nabla^2 F ds - \alpha_T \int_{L_K} \left(y \frac{\partial}{\partial s} + x \frac{\partial}{\partial n} \right) T ds -$$

$$- \frac{1+\nu}{E} \int_{L_K} f_x^{(K)} ds = 0, \qquad K = 1, 2, \ldots, N, \tag{4.2.9}$$

where $f_x^{(K)}$, $f_y^{(K)}$ are the components of the surface tractions on the interior contours L_K ($K = 1, 2, \ldots, N$) (see Fig. 15).

Replacement of the quantities E, ν, α_T in conditions (4.2.5), (4.2.8), and (4.2.9) by the quantities E_1, ν_1, α_{T1} defined in (4.1.4) yields the corresponding conditions for single—valuedness in the case of plane strain.

The conditions for single—valuedness in the plane problem of elasticity were first derived by Michell [64].

The plane problem in thermoelasticity can be formulated as follows:

We have to determine the stress function $F(x, y)$ which in the case of plane—stress is governed by (4.1.21) and in the case of plane—strain is governed by (4.1.23). The boundary conditions (4.1.31) and (4.1.32) are to be satisfied on the external boundary L and each of the internal boundaries L_K

93

$(K = 1, 2, \ldots, N)$ shown in Fig. 15. In addition, the conditions (4.2.5), (4.2.8), and (4.2.9) for the single–valuedness of the solution must be satisfied. These equations are written for the case of plane stress. In the case of plane strain, the quantities E, ν, α_T must be replaced by E_1, ν_1, α_{T1}, respectively.

The boundary conditions contain the constants α, β, γ on the external boundary and the constants α_K, β_K, γ_K $(K = 1, 2, \ldots, N)$ on the internal boundaries. One of these groups of constants can be chosen arbitrarily.

As was shown in Section 4.1, the constants α, β, γ can be set equal to zero. Then the remaining $3N$ constants can be determined so as to satisfy the $3N$ conditions of single–valuedness for the displacements and the rotation.

An example illustrating the formulation of the plane problem of thermoelasticity will be treated in Section 4.4.

The single–valuedness of the displacements and rotation in multiply connected bodies can be interpreted physically. This lack of single–valuedness is connected with *dislocation stresses*, i.e. with those stresses that arise in multiply connected bodies independent of the action of the external forces. These stresses play an important role in connection with a type of deformation called a *dislocation*. Such a deformation can arise, for instance, if the two boundaries of the body obtained by cutting it along $a_K b_K$ (in Fig. 15) are rejoined after either removing or adding a narrow strip of material.

It is evident that the process of reclosing the cut by means of external forces gives rise to new values of the displacements and of the rotation. After the cut has been closed and the external influences removed, there is a residual state of stress in the body, and along the line $a_K b_K$ there will be an abrupt change in the displacements and the rotation.

When the temperature field is absent, it follows from (4.2.1), (4.2.5), and (4.2.7) to (4.2.9) that around contour L_K the changes Δu, Δv in the displacements and $\Delta \omega_z$ in the rotation will be

$$
\Delta u = u^+ - u^- = -y\Delta\omega_z - \frac{1}{E} \int\limits_{L_K} \left(x \frac{\partial}{\partial s} - y \frac{\partial}{\partial n} \right) \nabla^2 F ds,
$$

$$
\nabla v = v^+ - v^- = x\Delta\omega_z - \frac{1}{E} \int\limits_{L_K} \left(y \frac{\partial}{\partial s} + x \frac{\partial}{\partial n} \right) \nabla^2 F ds, \qquad (4.2.10)
$$

$$
\Delta \omega_z = \omega_z^+ - \omega_z^- = \frac{1}{E} \int\limits_{L_K} \frac{\partial}{\partial n} \nabla^2 F ds,
$$

where u^+, v^+, ω_z^+ are the displacements and angle rotation at point P_0 on one boundary and u^-, v^-, ω_z^- are the corresponding values at the opposite point on the other side of the cut as indicated in Fig. 15.

There is an analogy between the plane thermoelastic problem in multiply connected bodies when the temperature field is steady and the plane problem in the theory of isotropic elasticity when dislocations are present. This analogy was first pointed out by Muskhelishvili [33] in 1916. In fact, when the surface tractions vanish $(f_x = f_y = 0)$ and dislocations are present, the solution of problems in the isotropic theory of elasticity reduces to finding a stress function satisfying the differential equation

$$\nabla^4 F = 0, \tag{4.2.11}$$

and the boundary conditions

$$F = \frac{\partial F}{\partial n} = 0 \quad (\alpha = \beta = \gamma = 0) \quad \text{on contour } L, \tag{4.2.12}$$

$$\left.\begin{array}{l} F = \alpha_K x + \beta_K y + \gamma_K \\[2mm] \dfrac{\partial F}{\partial n} = \alpha_K \dfrac{dx}{dn} + \beta_K \dfrac{dy}{dn} \end{array}\right\} \quad \text{on contour } L_K, \quad K = 1, 2, \ldots, N \tag{4.2.13}$$

and the conditions

$$-\frac{1}{E} \int_{L_K} \left(x \frac{\partial}{\partial s} - y \frac{\partial}{\partial n} \right) \nabla^2 F ds = \Delta u + y \Delta \omega_z,$$

$$-\frac{1}{E} \int_{L_K} \left(y \frac{\partial}{\partial s} + x \frac{\partial}{\partial n} \right) \nabla^2 F ds = \Delta v - x \Delta \omega_z, \tag{4.2.14}$$

$$\frac{1}{E} \int_{L_K} \frac{\partial}{\partial n} \nabla^2 F ds = \Delta \omega_z,$$

resulting from expressions (4.2.10).

In the case of plane strain, quantity E in (4.2.14) must be replaced by $E_1 = E/(1 - \nu^2)$.

The formulation of the plane problem of thermoelasticity with a steady temperature field without heat sources, i.e. satisfying equation (4.1.34), leads to the solution of the same differential equation (4.2.11) and the same boundary conditions (4.2.12), (4.2.13) but with the following conditions for the single–valuedness of the displacements u, v and the rotation ω_z

$$\frac{1}{E} \int_{L_K} \left(x \frac{\partial}{\partial s} - y \frac{\partial}{\partial n} \right) \nabla^2 F ds = -\alpha_T \int_{L_K} \left(x \frac{\partial}{\partial s} - y \frac{\partial}{\partial n} \right) T ds,$$

$$\frac{1}{E} \int_{L_K} \left(y \frac{\partial}{\partial s} + x \frac{\partial}{\partial n} \right) \nabla^2 F ds = -\alpha_T \int_{L_K} \left(y \frac{\partial}{\partial s} + x \frac{\partial}{\partial n} \right) T ds, \quad (4.2.15)$$

$$\frac{1}{E} \int_{L_K} \frac{\partial}{\partial n} \nabla^2 F ds = -\alpha_T \int_{L_K} \frac{\partial T}{\partial n} ds.$$

Here again it should be noted that in the case of plane strain the quantities E and α_T in (4.2.15) must be replaced by $E_1 = E/(1 - \nu^2)$ and $\alpha_{T1} = \alpha_T(1 + \nu)$.

Comparison of conditions (4.2.14) and (4.2.15) yields the equations

$$\alpha_T \int_{L_K} \left(x \frac{\partial}{\partial s} - y \frac{\partial}{\partial n} \right) T ds = \Delta u + y \Delta \omega_z,$$

$$\alpha_T \int_{L_K} \left(y \frac{\partial}{\partial s} + x \frac{\partial}{\partial n} \right) T ds = \Delta v - x \Delta \omega_z, \quad (4.2.16)$$

$$\alpha_T \int_{L_K} \frac{\partial T}{\partial n} ds = -\Delta \omega_z, \quad K = 1, 2, \ldots, N,$$

determining the magnitudes of the dislocations Δu, Δv, $\Delta \omega_z$ which must be introduced when solving the plane problem in the theory of isotropic elasticity for a multiply connected body in order to obtain the same distribution of stresses as in the corresponding plane problem of thermoelasticity with a steady temperature field.

Plane thermoelastic problems for multiply connected regions can be solved effectively by using a method based on the theory of functions of a complex variable. This method has been developed in detail by Muskhelishvili [34]. The application of the theory of functions of a complex variable to the study of plane problems in thermoelasticity is also treated by Lebedev [21].

4.3. Thermal stresses in a disk and a cylinder with a plane axisymmetric temperature field

We shall consider first the problem of the plane axisymmetric state of stress in a thin annular disk with external radius r_2 and internal radius r_1. Such a state of stress in the disk is caused by the plane axisymmetric temperature field $T(r, t)$.

The temperature field $T(r, t)$ is assumed to be known beforehand or to be furnished by the heat—conduction equation. Making use of the first of equations (4.1.12) and substituting the values $\dfrac{E}{2(1 + \nu)}$, $\dfrac{\nu}{1 + \nu}$, $\alpha_T \dfrac{1 + \nu}{1 + 2\nu}$ given in (4.1.13) and (4.1.14) for μ, ν and α_T, we obtain the following governing equation for the present problem

$$\frac{d}{dr}\left(\frac{1}{r}\frac{dru_r}{dr}\right) = \alpha_T(1 + \nu)\frac{dT}{dr}, \tag{4.3.1}$$

where u_r is the radial displacement of the disk.

The general solution of (4.3.1) is

$$u_r = C_1 r + \frac{C_2}{r} + \frac{(1 + \nu)\alpha_T}{r}\int_{r_1}^{r}(T - T_0)r\,dr, \tag{4.3.2}$$

where C_1 and C_2 are constants of integration.

Once u has been found, formulae (4.1.36) and (4.1.37) yield the stresses

$$\sigma_r = C_1\frac{E}{1 - \nu} - C_2\frac{E}{(1 + \nu)r^2} - \frac{\alpha_T E}{r^2}\int_{r_1}^{r}(T - T_0)r\,dr,$$

$$\tag{4.3.3}$$

$$\sigma_\theta = C_1\frac{E}{1 - \nu} + C_2\frac{E}{(1 + \nu)r^2} - \alpha_T E(T - T_0) + \frac{\alpha_T E}{r^2}\int_{r_1}^{r}(T - T_0)r\,dr.$$

When there are no loads on the edges, the constants of integration are determined by the boundary conditions

$$\sigma_r = 0 \quad \text{when} \quad r = r_1 \quad \text{and} \quad r = r_2. \tag{4.3.4}$$

The solution satisfying these conditions is

$$\sigma_r = \frac{\alpha_T E}{r^2}\left[\frac{r - r_1^2}{r_2^2 - r_1^2}\int_{r_1}^{r_2}(T - T_0)r\,dr - \int_{r_1}^{r}(T - T_0)r\,dr\right],$$

$$\sigma_\theta = \frac{\alpha_T E}{r^2}\left[\frac{r^2 + r_1^2}{r_2^2 - r_1^2}\int_{r_1}^{r_2}(T - T_0)r\,dr + \int_{r_1}^{r}(T - T_0)r\,dr - (T - T_0)r^2\right], \tag{4.3.5}$$

$$u_r = \frac{\alpha_T}{r} \left\{ (1 + \nu) \int_{r_1}^{r} (T - T_0)r dr + \frac{(1 - \nu)r^2 + (1 + \nu)r_1^2}{r_2^2 - r_1^2} \int_{r_1}^{r_2} (T - T_0)r dr \right\}.$$

By setting $r_1 = 0$ in (4.3.5) we obtain the solutions for a solid disk. The indeterminate expressions arising in these solutions can be evaluated by l'Hospital's rule. Thus we have

$$\lim_{r \to 0} \frac{1}{r^2} \int_{0}^{r} (T - T_0)r dr = \frac{1}{2}(T - T_0)_{r=0},$$

$$\lim_{r \to 0} \frac{1}{r} \int_{0}^{r} (T - T_0)r dr = 0;$$

(4.3.6)

since the temperature in the centre is assumed finite.

By replacing E, ν, α_T in solution (4.3.5) by $E_1 = \dfrac{E}{1 - \nu^2}$, $\nu_1 = \dfrac{\nu}{1 - \nu}$, $\alpha_{T_1} = \alpha_T(1 + \nu)$, we obtain expressions for the thermal stresses σ_r and σ_θ and the radial displacement u_r in an infinite solid cylinder in the case of plane axisymmetric strains due to a plane temperature field $T(r, t)$.

In a solid cylinder, the thermal stress σ_z calculated by means of (4.1.2) is

$$\sigma_z = \frac{2\alpha_T E \nu}{(1 - \nu)(r_2^2 - r_1^2)} \int_{r_1}^{r_2} (T - T_0)r dr - \frac{\alpha_T E}{1 - \nu}(T - T_0). \qquad (4.3.7)$$

This stress arises when the transverse faces are held fixed ($w = 0$). When these faces are stress free, St.–Venant's principle yields the axial stress

$$\sigma_z' = E\epsilon_z + \sigma_z, \qquad (4.3.8)$$

where ϵ_z is the constant longitudinal displacement of the cylinder and σ_z, the stress in the cylinder when $w = 0$, is determined by (4.3.7).

The strain ϵ_z is chosen so that the stress resultant on the transverse faces of the cylinder vanishes. This yields the value

$$\epsilon_z = \frac{2\alpha_T}{r_2^2 - r_1^2} \int_{r_1}^{r_2} (T - T_0)r dr. \qquad (4.3.9)$$

Substituting values (4.3.7) and (4.3.9) into (4.3.8), we obtain

98

$$\sigma_z' = \frac{\alpha_T E}{1-\nu} \left[\frac{2}{r_2^2 - r_1^2} \int_{r_1}^{r_2} (T-T_0) r dr - (T-T_0) \right] = \sigma_r + \sigma_\theta. \quad (4.3.10)$$

Apart from any motion of the cylinder as a solid body, equation (4.3.9) yields the axial displacement

$$u_z = \frac{2\alpha_T z}{r_2^2 - r_1^2} \int_{r_1}^{r_2} (T-T_0) r dr. \quad (4.3.11)$$

for a cylinder whose transverse faces are stress free.

There is an extensive literature devoted to thermal stresses in disks and cylinders. The early works in this field are those of Lorenz [63] and Dinnik [11]. An account of contemporary research on stresses in disks and cylinders is given in [54].

4.4. Thermal stresses in disks and cylinders when the plane steady temperature field is not axially symmetric

Let the plane, asymmetric temperature field in the annular disk be $T(r, \theta)$. This will give rise to an asymmetric state of stress. It will be assumed that the disk is stress free on the inner contour $(r = r_1)$ and on the outer contour $(r = r_2)$. We will use the stress formulation in Section 4.2 to attack this problem.

The temperature, which satisfies the Laplace equation

$$\nabla^2 T(r, \theta) = \frac{1}{r} \frac{\partial}{\partial r} \left(r \frac{\partial T}{\partial r} \right) + \frac{1}{r^2} \frac{\partial^2 T}{\partial \theta^2} = 0, \quad (4.4.1)$$

will be expanded in the Fourier series

$$T(r, \theta) - T_0 = \sum_{k=0}^{\infty} T^{(k)}(r) \cos k\theta + \sum_{k=1}^{\infty} T_1^{(k)}(r) \sin k\theta, \quad (4.4.2)$$

where the coefficients $T^{(k)}$ and $T_1^{(k)}$ are solutions of the equations

$$\frac{1}{r} \frac{d}{dr} \left(r \frac{dT^{(k)}}{dr} \right) - \frac{k^2}{r^2} T^{(k)} = 0 \quad (k = 0, 1, \ldots),$$

$$\frac{1}{r} \frac{d}{dr} \left(r \frac{dT_1^{(k)}}{dr} \right) - \frac{k^2}{r^2} T_1^{(k)} = 0 \quad (k = 1, 2, \ldots). \quad (4.4.3)$$

99

In view of expression (4.4.1) for the temperature field $T(r, \theta)$, we will choose the solution for the stress function $F(r, \theta)$ in the form

$$F(r, \theta) = \sum_{k=0}^{\infty} F^{(k)}(r) \cos k\theta + \sum_{k=1}^{\infty} F_1^{(k)}(r) \sin k\theta. \qquad (4.4.4)$$

On the basis of the results in Section 4.2, where for the present case we have $x = r \cos \theta$, $y = r \sin \theta$, $ds = rd\theta$, and $dn = dr$, the stress function $F(r,\theta)$ must satisfy the following three conditions:

1) the differential equation

$$\nabla^4 F + \alpha_T E \nabla^2 T = 0; \qquad (4.4.5)$$

2) the boundary conditions

$$F = \frac{\partial F}{\partial r} = 0 \qquad \text{when} \qquad r = r_2, \qquad (4.4.6)$$

$$\left. \begin{aligned} F &= \alpha_1 r \cos \theta + \beta_1 r \sin \theta + \gamma_1 \\[2mm] \frac{\partial F}{\partial r} &= \alpha_1 \cos \theta + \beta_1 \sin \theta \end{aligned} \right\} \quad \text{when} \quad r = r_1; \qquad (4.4.7)$$

3) The conditions for single—valuedness of the displacements and the rotation

$$\left. \begin{aligned} \int_0^{2\pi} &\left(r \sin \theta \, \frac{\partial \nabla^2 F}{\partial r} - \cos \theta \, \frac{\partial \nabla^2 F}{\partial \theta} \right) r d\theta = \\[2mm] &= -E\alpha_T \int_0^{2\pi} \left(r \sin \theta \, \frac{\partial T}{\partial r} - \cos \theta \, \frac{\partial T}{\partial \theta} \right) r d\theta \\[4mm] \int_0^{2\pi} &\left(r \cos \theta \, \frac{\partial \nabla^2 F}{\partial r} + \sin \theta \, \frac{\partial \nabla^2 F}{\partial \theta} \right) r d\theta = \\[2mm] &= -E\alpha_T \int_0^{2\pi} \left(r \cos \theta \, \frac{\partial T}{\partial r} + \sin \theta \, \frac{\partial T}{\partial \theta} \right) r d\theta \end{aligned} \right\} \quad \text{when} \quad r = r_1; \qquad (4.4.8)$$

$$\int_0^{2\pi} \frac{\partial \nabla^2 F}{\partial r} r d\theta = -E\alpha_T \int_0^{2\pi} \frac{\partial T}{\partial r} r d\theta \qquad \text{when} \quad r = r_1. \qquad (4.4.9)$$

Substituting expressions (4.4.2), (4.4.3), and (4.4.4) into equations (4.4.5) to (4.4.8), we obtain the following three conditions:

1) the differential equation for $F^{(k)}(r)$

$$\frac{d^4 F^{(k)}}{dr^4} + \frac{2}{r}\frac{d^3 F^{(k)}}{dr^3} - \frac{1+2k^2}{r^2}\frac{d^2 F^{(k)}}{dr^2} + \frac{1+2k^2}{r^3}\frac{dF^{(k)}}{dr} +$$

$$\frac{k^2(k^2-4)}{r^4} F^{(k)} = 0 \qquad (k=0, 1, \ldots); \qquad (4.4.10)$$

2) the boundary conditions for $F^{(k)}$

$$F^{(k)}(r_2) = \frac{dF^{(k)}}{dr}(r_2) = 0 \qquad (k = 0, 1, \ldots), \qquad (4.4.11)$$

$$F^{(0)}(r_1) = \gamma_1, \quad F^{(1)}(r_1) = \alpha_1 r_1, \quad F^{(k)}(r_1) = 0 \quad (k \geqslant 2),$$

$$\frac{dF^{(0)}}{dr}(r_1) = 0, \quad \frac{dF^{(1)}}{dr}(r_1) = \alpha_1, \quad \frac{dF^{(k)}}{dr}(r_1) = 0 \quad (k \geqslant 2); \qquad (4.4.12)$$

3) the conditions for single—valuedness of $F^{(k)}$ on $r = r_1$

$$\left(\frac{1}{r} - \frac{d}{dr}\right)\left[-\frac{F^{(1)}}{r^2} + \frac{1}{r}\frac{d}{dr}\left(r\frac{dF^{(1)}}{dr}\right)\right] = -\alpha_T E \left(\frac{1}{r} - \frac{d}{dr}\right) T^{(1)}(r), \qquad (4.4.13)$$

$$\frac{d}{dr}\left[\frac{1}{r}\frac{d}{dr}\left(r\frac{dF^{(0)}}{dr}\right)\right] = -\alpha_T E \frac{dT^{(0)}}{dr}. \qquad (4.4.14)$$

The same method leads to corresponding conditions for $F_1^{(k)}(r)$ $(k = 1, 2, \ldots)$.

In deducing conditions (4.4.13) and (4.4.14) for single—valuedness, use has been made of the orthogonality of the trigonometric functions.

It should be noticed that only the functions $F^{(0)}$, $F^{(1)}$, and hence the $F_1^{(1)}$, appear in conditions (4.4.13) and (4.4.14). The functions $F^{(k)}$ and $F_1^{(k)}$ $(k \geqslant 2)$ satisfy the conditions for single—valuedness automatically.

In connection with the zero boundary conditions (4.4.12) for the functions $F^{(k)}$ $(k \geqslant 2)$ and $F_1^{(k)}$ $(k \geqslant 2)$, we conclude that

$$F^{(k)} \equiv F_1^{(k)} = 0 \qquad (k \geqslant 2). \qquad (4.4.15)$$

Hence it follows that the only part of the steady temperature field which produces thermal stresses is

$$T(r, \theta) - T_0 = T^{(0)}(r) + T^{(1)}(r)\cos\theta + T_1^{(1)}(r)\sin\theta; \qquad (4.4.16)$$

The corresponding stress function is

$$F(r, \theta) = F^{(0)}(r) + F^{(1)}(r) \cos \theta + F^{(1)}(r) \sin \theta. \qquad (4.4.17)$$

The absence of thermal stresses corresponding to temperature fields of the form $T^{(k)}(r) \cos k\theta$ ($k \geq 2$) can easily be explained by means of the analogy between the plane thermoelastic problem and the plane problem in the theory of isotropic elasticity when dislocations are present.

Consider a thermally insulated disk that has a central hole. In view of equation (4.2.16) and the formulae $x = r \cos \theta$, $y = r \sin \theta$, it is evident that there are no dislocations equivalent to temperature terms containing harmonic functions with $k = 2, 3, \ldots$. Thus, there are no corresponding thermal stresses $\sigma_r, \sigma_\theta, \sigma_{r\theta}$.

We shall now calculate the thermal stresses $\sigma_r^{(0)}$, $\sigma_\theta^{(0)}$ and $\sigma_r^{(1)}$, $\sigma_\theta^{(1)}$, $\sigma_{r\theta}^{(1)}$ due to the temperature fields $T^{(0)}(r)$ and $T^{(1)}(r) \cos \theta$, respectively.

The solutions for the functions $T^{(0)}(r)$ and $T^{(1)}(r)$ satisfying the differential equations (4.4.3) are

$$T^{(0)}(r) = \Theta_0 \ln \frac{r}{r_1} + \Theta_0', \qquad (4.4.18)$$

$$T^{(1)}(r) = \frac{\Theta_1}{r} + \Theta_1' r, \qquad (4.4.19)$$

where Θ_0, Θ_0', Θ_1, Θ_1' are constants to be determined from the boundary conditions for the corresponding heat–conduction problems.

It is to be noted that the temperature fields Θ_0' and $\Theta_1' r \cos \theta = \Theta_1' x$ do not give rise to thermal stresses.

The thermal stresses $\sigma_r^{(0)}$, $\sigma_\theta^{(0)}$ associated with the temperature field (4.4.18) could be determined by directly replacing $T - T_0$ in formula (4.3.5) by expression (4.4.18) for $T^{(0)}(r)$. In order to illustrate the method, we will determine the thermal stresses $\sigma_r^{(0)}$, $\sigma_\theta^{(0)}$ by making use of the stress formulation of the plane problem in thermoelasticity.

The solution of equation (4.4.10) for $k = 0$ is

$$F^{(0)} = C_1 + C_2 \left(\frac{r}{r_1} \right) + C_3 \left(\frac{r}{r_1} \right)^2 + C_4 \left(\frac{r}{r_1} \right)^2 \ln \frac{r}{r_1}. \qquad (4.4.20)$$

There are five equations for the determination of the five constants C_1, C_2, C_3, C_4, and γ_1, namely, the two boundary conditions (4.4.11), two of the boundary conditions (4.4.12), and one condition for single–valuedness (4.4.14). The constants C_1 and γ_1 have no effect on the values of the stresses. The values of the other constants are

$$C_2 = -\frac{\alpha_T E\Theta_0 r_2^2 r_1^2}{2(r_2^2 - r_1^2)} \ln\frac{r_2}{r_1},$$

$$C_3 = \frac{\alpha_T E\Theta_0 r_1^2}{8(r_2^2 - r_1^2)} \left[\left(1 + 2\ln\frac{r_2}{r_1}\right) r_2^2 - r_1^2 \right], \qquad (4.4.21)$$

$$C_4 = -\frac{\alpha_T E r_1^2 \Theta_0}{4}.$$

Substitution of these expressions into formulae (4.1.38) yields

$$\sigma_r^{(0)} = \frac{\alpha_T E\Theta_0}{2} \left[\left(\frac{r_2}{r}\right)^2 \frac{r^2 - r_1^2}{r_2^2 - r_1^2} \ln\frac{r_2}{r_1} - \ln\frac{r}{r_1} \right],$$

$$\sigma_\theta^{(0)} = \frac{\alpha_T E\Theta_0}{2} \left[\left(\frac{r_2}{r}\right)^2 \frac{r^2 + r_1^2}{r_2^2 - r_1^2} \ln\frac{r_2}{r_1} - \ln\frac{r}{r_1} - 1 \right]. \qquad (4.4.22)$$

The thermal stresses $\sigma_r^{(1)}$, $\sigma_\theta^{(1)}$, $\sigma_{r\theta}^{(1)}$ are found in the same way.

When $k = 1$, the solution of (4.4.10) is

$$F^{(1)} = C_1 \frac{r}{r_1} + C_2 \frac{r_1}{r} + C_3 \left(\frac{r}{r_1}\right)^3 + C_4 \frac{r}{r_1} \ln\frac{r}{r_1}. \qquad (4.4.23)$$

For the determination of the constants of integration in the stress function $F^{(1)}$, one has a system of five equations for the five constants C_1, C_2, C_3, C_4, and α_1. These are the two boundary conditions (4.4.11), two of the boundary conditions (4.4.12), and the single–valuedness condition (4.4.13):

$$C_1 \frac{r_2}{r_1} + C_2 \frac{r_1}{r_2} + C_3 \left(\frac{r_2}{r_1}\right)^3 + C_4 \frac{r_2}{r_1} \ln\frac{r_2}{r_1} = 0,$$

$$C_1 \frac{1}{r_1} - C_2 \frac{r_1}{r_2^2} + C_3 \frac{3r_2^2}{r_1^3} + C_4 \left(\frac{1}{r_1} \ln\frac{r_2}{r_1} + \frac{1}{r_1}\right) = 0,$$

$$C_1 + C_2 + C_3 = \alpha_1 r_1, \qquad (4.4.24)$$

$$C_1 \frac{1}{r_1} - C_2 \frac{1}{r_1} + C_3 \frac{3}{r_1} + C_4 \frac{1}{r_1} = \alpha_1;$$

$$C_4 = -\frac{\alpha_T E \Theta_1 r_1}{2}. \tag{4.4.25}$$

The constants C_1 and α_1 have no effect on the stress distribution. In addition to the value of C_4 given by (4.4.25), we have the values

$$C_2 = -\frac{\alpha_T E \Theta_1 r_1 r_2^2}{4(r_1^2 + r_2^2)}, \qquad C_3 = \frac{\alpha_T E \Theta_1 r_1^3}{4(r_1^2 + r_2^2)} \tag{4.4.26}$$

given by (4.4.24).

Expressing the thermal stresses $\sigma_r^{(1)}$, $\sigma_\theta^{(1)}$, $\sigma_{r\theta}^{(1)}$ in terms of formulae (4.1.38) with the stress function $F^{(1)} \cos \theta$, where $F^{(1)}$ is given by (4.4.23), and substituting the values (4.4.25) and (4.4.26) for the constants of integration, we finally obtain the expressions

$$\sigma_r^{(1)} = \frac{\alpha_T E r \Theta_1}{2(r_1^2 + r_2^2)} \left(1 - \frac{r_1^2}{r^2}\right) \left(1 - \frac{r_2^2}{r^2}\right) \cos \theta,$$

$$\sigma_\theta^{(1)} = \frac{\alpha_T E r \Theta_1}{2(r_1^2 + r_2^2)} \left(3 - \frac{r_1^2 + r_2^2}{r^2} + \frac{r_1^2 r_2^2}{r^4}\right) \cos \theta, \tag{4.4.27}$$

$$\sigma_{r\theta}^{(1)} = \frac{\alpha_T E r \Theta_1}{2(r_1^2 + r_2^2)} \left(1 - \frac{r_1^2}{r^2}\right) \left(1 - \frac{r_2^2}{r^2}\right) \sin \theta.$$

By replacing E and α_T in (4.4.27) by $E_1 = E/(1 - \nu^2)$ and $\alpha_{T1} = \alpha_T(1 - \nu)$, respectively, we obtain the formulae for the thermal stresses $\sigma_r^{(1)}$, $\sigma_\theta^{(1)}$, $\sigma_{r\theta}^{(1)}$ in an infinite solid cylinder in a state of plane strain under the action of the plane, steady temperature field $T^{(1)}(r) \cos \theta$.

The complete thermal stresses in a thin circular disk with a central hole and in an infinite hollow cylinder due to the steady temperature field $T^{(0)}(r) + T^{(1)}(r) \cos \theta$, can be determined in the form

$$\sigma_r = \sigma_r^{(0)} + \sigma_r^{(1)},$$

$$\sigma_\theta = \sigma_\theta^{(0)} + \sigma_\theta^{(1)}, \tag{4.4.28}$$

$$\sigma_{r\theta} = \sigma_{r\theta}^{(1)}.$$

In the case of plane strain, we have in addition the axial thermal stress given by (4.1.2).

The problem treated in the present Section has been studied by several authors. The first solution of this problem using the associated problem of the dislocation of a cylinder and applying the theory of functions of a complex variable is due to Muskhelishvili [33, 34]. Later, Gatewood [5] also applied the method of functions of a complex variable to the present problem.

Melan and Parkus solved a similar problem without the use of complex variables. Their method makes use of a combination of a thermoelastic displacement potential and a stress function [31].

The method explained in this Section is taken from [54].

4.5. Thermal stresses in circular plates

We next consider the quasi—static, axisymmetric compression and bending of a solid circular plate due to the steady axisymmetric temperature field

$$T(r, z) = T^{(0)}(r) + zT^{(1)}(r), \qquad (4.5.1)$$

where z is measured from the middle surface of the plate (see Fig. 11). Further, the influence of the compression on the bending will be disregarded.

It will be assumed that there is a steady convective heat exchange on the outer contour $r = r_2$ and on the surface $z = \pm h/2$ and that the temperature of the surrounding fluid contiguous with the faces $z = h/2$ are different. Under these conditions of heat exchange the temperature field varies in the radial and axial directions. This gives rise to dilatation and thermal bending of the plate.

The appropriate heat conduction problem was solved in Section 3.4. If it is assumed that the axial temperature change is linear, the solution for the steady axisymmetric temperature field is given by expression (3.4.5). Setting the constants C_2 and C'_2 in this expression equal to zero (since there is no central hole), we obtain the temperature field (4.5.1), in which the functions $T^{(0)}(r)$ and $T^{(1)}(r)$ are given by

$$T^{(0)}(r) = \vartheta + C_1 I_0 (\delta\rho), \qquad (4.5.2)$$

$$T^{(1)}(r) = \mu [1 + C'_1 I_0 (\delta_1\rho)], \qquad (4.5.3)$$

where

$$\vartheta = \frac{\vartheta_3 + \vartheta_4}{2}, \quad \mu = \frac{\gamma(\vartheta_3 - \vartheta_4)}{(2 + \gamma)h},$$

$$\delta^2 = \frac{2\gamma r_2^2}{h^2}, \quad \delta_1^2 = \frac{6(2 + \gamma)r_2^2}{h^2}, \quad \gamma = \frac{\alpha h}{\lambda_T}.$$

105

Here ϑ_3 and ϑ_4 are the temperatures of the medium contiguous with the surfaces $z = h/2$ and $- h/2$, respectively, α is the coefficient of diffusivity on the surfaces $z = \pm h/2$, λ_T is the coefficient of thermal conductivity of the plate material, and $\rho = r/r_2$ is the dimensionless radial distance.

The constants C_1 and C_1' have the values determined by the first equations in (3.3.6) and (3.4.6). Moreover, since there is no central hole, one must set $\gamma_1 = 0$.

We next determine the thermal stresses for the dilatation and bending due to the temperature field (4.5.1).

Making use of the theory of thin circular plates [15], we determine the basic equations for the present problem.

Let the radial and axial displacements of the middle surface of the plate be denoted by u_r and u_z.

The radial and azimuthal strains ϵ_r and ϵ_θ in the middle surface are given by

$$\epsilon_r = \frac{du_r}{dr}, \quad \epsilon_\theta = \frac{u_r}{r}. \tag{4.5.4}$$

As a result of the strains the middle surface will warp. It will be assumed that normal sections remain plane. Then the parameters characterizing the above warping can be found from the fact that the element PP_1 before the deformation assumes the position normal to the deformed middle surface, which has rotated through the small angle ϑ_r in the plane rOz, as shown in Fig. 16. The small angle ϑ_r is connected with the deflection u_z through the relation

$$\vartheta_r = -\frac{du_z}{dr}. \tag{4.5.5}$$

In view of the hypotheses concerning the nature of the deformation of the plate, we can formulate the following relations between the displacements $u_r^{(z)}$, $u_z^{(z)}$ at point P_1 distance z from the middle surface and the displacements u_r, u_z at the corresponding point P on the middle surface:

$$u_r^{(z)} = u_r + z\vartheta_r,$$
$$u_z^{(z)} = u_z. \tag{4.5.6}$$

Substituting $u_r^{(z)}$, $u_z^{(z)}$ for u_r, u_z in formulae (4.5.4), we obtain the corresponding values $\epsilon_r^{(z)}$, $\epsilon_\theta^{(z)}$ at point P_1, namely

$$\epsilon_r^{(z)} = \epsilon_r + z\kappa_r,$$
$$\epsilon_\theta^{(z)} = \epsilon_\theta + z\kappa_\theta, \tag{4.5.7}$$

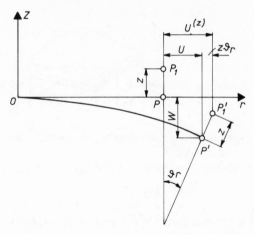

Fig. 16.

where

$$\kappa_r = \frac{d\vartheta_r}{dr} = -\frac{d^2 u_z}{dr^2}, \quad \kappa_\theta = \frac{\vartheta_r}{r} = -\frac{1}{r}\frac{du_z}{dr}. \tag{4.5.8}$$

The quantities κ_r and κ_θ are the curvatures of the middle surface in the radial and azimuthal directions.

The element of the plate bounded by the two radial planes and two cylindrical surfaces, as shown in Fig. 17, is subjected to the normal stresses σ_r, σ_θ, and the shear stress σ_{rz}.

We now replace the stresses by the following statically equivalent forces and moments

$$N_r = \int_{-h/2}^{h/2} \sigma_r dz, \quad N_\theta = \int_{-h/2}^{h/2} \sigma_\theta dz, \quad Q = \int_{-h/2}^{h/2} \sigma_{rz} dz,$$

$$M_r = \int_{-h/2}^{h/2} \sigma_r z dz, \quad M_\theta = \int_{-h/2}^{h/2} \sigma_\theta z dz, \tag{4.5.9}$$

Here N_r, Q, and M_r are the normal force, the shear force and the bending moment, respectively, acting on the cylindrical surface. On the other hand, the normal force N_θ and the bending moment M_θ act on the radial section.

The internal forces and moments are calculated per unit length of the corresponding coordinate line (the circumference or polar radius).

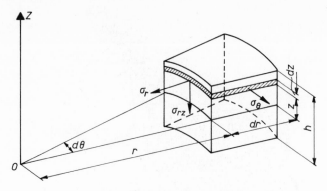

Fig. 17.

By means of the internal forces and moments the problem of the equilibrium of a spatial element of the plate has been reduced to the problem of the equilibrium of the corresponding element of the middle surface. By considering the equilibrium of an element of the middle surface (see Fig. 18), we arrive at the following equilibrium equations,

$$\frac{dN_r r}{dr} - N_\theta = 0, \tag{4.5.10}$$

$$\frac{dQr}{dr} = 0, \tag{4.5.11}$$

$$\frac{dM_r r}{dr} - M_\theta - Qr = 0. \tag{4.5.12}$$

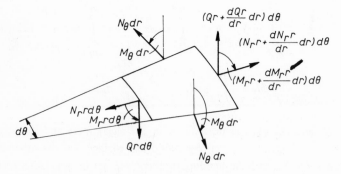

Fig. 18.

The strains (4.5.7) comprise the elastic strains due to the known stresses and the *purely thermal strains*.

If the temperature of the plate increases by $T - T_0$, the thermal expansion gives rise to a strain $\alpha_T(T - T_0)$ in all directions, where α_T is the coefficient of linear expansion.

Thus we obtain

$$\epsilon_r^{(z)} = \frac{\sigma_r - \nu\sigma_\theta}{E} + \alpha_T(T - T_0),$$

$$\epsilon_\theta^{(z)} = \frac{\sigma_\theta - \nu\sigma_r}{E} + \alpha_T(T - T_0),$$

(4.5.13)

where E is Young's modulus and ν is Poisson's ratio.

We now multiply both sides of equations (4.5.13) first by dz and then by zdz and integrate from $z = -h/2$ to $z = h/2$. Introducing the stress resultants (4.5.9) and making use of expression (4.5.7), we find

$$\epsilon_r = \frac{N_r - \nu N_\theta}{Eh} + \epsilon_T, \quad \epsilon_\theta = \frac{N_\theta - \nu N_r}{Eh} + \epsilon_T,$$

(4.5.14)

$$\kappa_r = \frac{12(M_r - \nu M_\theta)}{Eh^3} + \kappa_T, \quad \kappa_\theta = \frac{12(M_\theta - \nu M_r)}{Eh^3} + \kappa_T,$$

(4.5.15)

where

$$\epsilon_T = \frac{1}{h} \int_{-h/2}^{h/2} \alpha_T(T - T_0)dz, \quad \kappa_T = \frac{12}{h^3} \int_{-h/2}^{h/2} \alpha_T(T - T_0)zdz.$$

(4.5.16)

The quantities ϵ_T and κ_T can be regarded as generalized pure thermal strains.

When the temperature varies linearly in the axial direction and the coefficient of linear expansion α_T is constant, the quantities ϵ_T and κ_T become

$$\epsilon_T = \alpha_T(T_* - T_0),$$

(4.5.17)

$$\kappa_T = \frac{\alpha_T}{h} \Delta T,$$

(4.5.18)

where

$$T_* = \frac{1}{2}[(T)_{z = \frac{h}{2}} + (T)_{z = -\frac{h}{2}}],$$

(4.5.19)

$$\Delta T = (T)_{z = \frac{h}{2}} - (T)_{z = -\frac{h}{2}}.$$

(4.5.20)

In this case ϵ_T is the pure thermal strain of the middle surface of the plate, and κ_T is the curvature of the middle surface due to the thermal expansion.

Substituting expression (4.5.1) for the temperature field into equations (4.5.19) and (4.5.20), we obtain the quantities T_* and ΔT. Then, according to formulae (4.5.17) and (4.5.18) the pure thermal strains are

$$\epsilon_T = \alpha_T [\vartheta - T_0 + C_1 I_0(\delta\rho)], \tag{4.5.21}$$

$$\kappa_T = \alpha_T \mu [1 + C_1' I_0(\delta_1\rho)]. \tag{4.5.22}$$

Solution of expressions (4.5.14) and (4.5.15) for the forces and moments yields the following expressions

$$N_r = D_N [\epsilon_r + \nu\epsilon_\theta - (1 + \nu)\epsilon_T],$$
$$N_\theta = D_N [\epsilon_\theta + \nu\epsilon_r - (1 + \nu)\epsilon_T], \tag{4.5.23}$$

$$M_r = D_M [\kappa_r + \nu\kappa_\theta - (1 + \nu)\kappa_T]$$
$$M_\theta = D_M [\kappa_\theta + \nu\kappa_r - (1 + \nu)\kappa_T], \tag{4.5.24}$$

where $D_N = Eh/(1 - \nu^2)$ is the tensile rigidity and $D_M = Eh^3/12(1 - \nu^2)$ the flexural rigidity of the plate.

The shear force Q appearing in the equilibrium equations (4.5.11) and (4.5.12) must vanish because there are no external shear forces.

The formulae for the calculation of the stresses are determined from (4.5.13) to be

$$\sigma_r = \frac{E}{1 - \nu^2} [\epsilon_r^{(z)} + \nu\epsilon_\theta^{(z)} - (1 + \nu)\alpha_T (T - T_0)],$$

$$\sigma_\theta = \frac{E}{1 - \nu^2} [\epsilon_\theta^{(z)} + \nu\epsilon_r^{(z)} - (1 + \nu)\alpha_T (T - T_0)]. \tag{4.5.25}$$

Replacing the strains $\epsilon_r^{(z)}$ and $\epsilon_\theta^{(z)}$ by the expressions (4.5.7) and using (4.5.14–15) to express ϵ_r, ϵ_θ and κ_r, κ_θ in terms of the stress resultants, we obtain

$$\sigma_r = \frac{N_r}{h} + \frac{12M_r z}{h^3} + \frac{E\epsilon_T}{1 - \nu} + \frac{E\kappa_T z}{1 - \nu} - \frac{E\alpha_T(T - T_0)}{1 - \nu},$$

$$\sigma_\theta = \frac{N_\theta}{h} + \frac{12M_\theta z}{h^3} + \frac{E\epsilon_T}{1 - \nu} + \frac{E\kappa_T z}{1 - \nu} - \frac{E\alpha_T(T - T_0)}{1 - \nu}. \tag{4.5.26}$$

110

When the temperature difference $T - T_0$ is linear through the thickness, the temperature terms in formulae (4.5.26) vanish. In this case the total thermal stresses are found from the formulae

$$\sigma_r = \sigma_r^I + \sigma_r^{II},$$
$$\sigma_\theta = \sigma_\theta^I + \sigma_\theta^{II}, \qquad (4.5.27)$$

where

$$\sigma_r^I = \frac{N_r}{h}, \quad \sigma_\theta^I = \frac{N_\theta}{h} \qquad (4.5.28)$$

are the dilatational thermal stresses

$$\sigma_r^{II} = \frac{12M_r z}{h^3}, \quad \sigma_\theta^{II} = \frac{12M_\theta z}{h^3} \qquad (4.5.29)$$

are the flexural thermal stress.

We will assume that there are no radial forces or bending moments on the contour $r = r_2$. The boundary conditions are then

$$N_r = 0, \quad M_r = 0 \quad \text{when} \quad r = r_2. \qquad (4.5.30)$$

When the interaction between the expansion and bending of the plate is ignored, the present problem reduces to two independent problems. The first is the axisymmetric two–dimensional problem of the state of stress in a plate due to the thermal strains (4.5.19). The second is the axisymmetric flexure problem for a circular plate due to the pure thermal strains (4.5.20). Between these two problems there is a complete analogy in the basic equations and the boundary conditions.

The quantities N_r, N_θ, u, Eh, ϵ_T in the first problem correspond to the quantities M_r, M_θ, ϑ_r, $Eh^3/12$, κ_T in the second.

To the quantities $\vartheta - T_0$, C_1, δ in expression (4.5.21) for ϵ_T correspond the quantities μ, $\mu C_1'$, δ_1 in expression (4.5.22) for κ_T.

The solution of the first problem has been treated in Section 4.3. Setting $r_1 = 0$ and $T = C_1 I_0\ (\delta\rho)$ in (4.3.5) and taking account of the relation

$$\int x I_0(x) dx = x I_1(x) + C,$$

we obtain the required dilatational thermal stresses:

$$\sigma_r^I = \frac{N_r}{h} = \frac{\alpha_T E C_1}{\delta} \left[I_1(\delta) - \frac{r_2}{r} I_1(\delta\rho) \right],$$

$$\sigma_\theta^I = \frac{N_\theta}{h} = \frac{\alpha_T E C_1}{\delta} \left[I_1(\delta) + \frac{r_2}{r} I_1(\delta\rho) - \delta I_0(\delta\rho) \right].$$

$(4.5.31)$

Replacing N_r, N_θ, Eh, C_1, δ in the formulae by M_r, M_θ, $Eh^3/12$, $\mu C_1'$, δ_1, we obtain the following expressions for the bending moments

$$M_r = \frac{\alpha_T E h^3 \mu C_1'}{12\delta_1} \left[I_1(\delta_1) - \frac{r_2}{r} I_1(\sigma_1\rho) \right],$$

$$M_\theta = \frac{\alpha_T E h^3 \mu C_1'}{12\delta_1} \left[I_1(\delta_1) + \frac{r_2}{r} I_1(\delta_1\rho) - \delta_1 I_0(\delta_1\rho) \right].$$

$(4.5.32)$

The flexural thermal stresses corresponding to these bending moments can be calculated with formulae (4.5.29).

More complicated thermoelastic problems for the bending of plates (such as thermal bending of a circular plate of variable thickness with a temperature field that is not axisymmetric, thermal stresses in a circular plate when Young's modulus is not constant, etc.) are treated in [15].

Chapter V

THERMOELASTIC BEHAVIOUR OF SHELLS OF REVOLUTION

5.1. Preliminaries. Basic Formulae. Theory of Surfaces

In this chapter we shall consider a shell of revolution with a thin wall of uniform thickness. The external forces and the temperature field will be symmetric with respect to the axis of the shell.

The middle surface of such a shell is also a surface of revolution whose lines of principal curvature are the meridians θ = const. and the parallel circles s = const., where θ is the angle between the given meridian and the initial meridian $\theta = 0$, and s is the length along the meridian measured from a fixed transverse section (see Fig. 19).

The first principle radius of curvature R_1 of the middle surface is the radius of curvature of the meridian. The second principle radius of curvature R_2 is equal to length of the normal between the point P and the axis. The radius r of the parallel circle is related to the radius of curvature R_2 through the relation

$$r = R_2 \sin \varphi, \tag{5.1.1}$$

where φ is the angle between the normal to the middle surface and the axis of rotation (see Fig. 19).

The temperature field is assumed to be two dimensional, and in the general case it is time dependent, i.e. $T \equiv T(s, z, t)$, where s is the meridian coordinate, and z is the coordinate measured along the outward normal from the middle surface. The thermoelastic behaviour of the shell will be treated in the quasi–static case. The time t is then a parameter.

The problem of the deformation of the shell can be reduced to that of the middle surface by making the hypothesis that plane normal sections remain plane and normal to the middle surface.

The position of an arbitrary point P on the middle surface is described by the coordinates s and θ (Fig. 19).

At point P we define the right–handed triad of unit vectors e_s, e_θ, e_z. The unit vector e_s is tangential to the meridian and points in the direction of

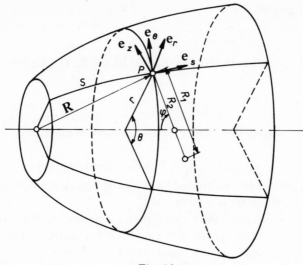

Fig. 19.

increasing s. The unit vector e_θ is tangential to the parallel circle and points in the direction of increasing θ. The unit vector e_z is the outward normal to the middle surface.

The vectors e_s, e_θ, and e_z satisfy the relations

$$e_s = e_\theta \times e_z, \tag{5.1.2}$$

$$e_\theta = e_z \times e_s, \tag{5.1.3}$$

$$e_z = e_s \times e_\theta, \tag{5.1.4}$$

where the cross indicates a vector product.

Since the first derivative of the position vector with respect to arc length is the unit tangent to the curve, we have

$$e_s = \frac{\partial R}{\partial s}, \quad e_\theta = \frac{1}{r}\frac{\partial R}{\partial \theta}. \tag{5.1.5}$$

In the following we shall need formulae for the derivatives of the unit vectors with respect to arc length along the lines of principal curvature.

In differential geometry it is well known that the first derivative of a unit vector with respect to arc length is a vector whose magnitude is equal to the radius of curvature. Moreover, this vector is directed along the principal normal to this curve and points to the concave side.

We will assume that the meridian is concave toward the axis of the shell. Then, since the principal normal of a plane curve lies in this plane, we have

$$\frac{\partial e_s}{\partial s} = -\frac{1}{R_1} e_z, \qquad \frac{\partial e_\theta}{\partial \theta} = -e_r, \tag{5.1.6}$$

where e_r is the unit vector along the radius of the parallel circle (Fig. 19).

Vector e_r can be resolved into components along the directions of e_s and e_z, namely

$$e_r = \cos \varphi e_s + \sin \varphi e_z.$$

Substitution of this expression for e_r into (5.1.6) yields

$$\frac{\partial e_\theta}{\partial \theta} = -\cos \varphi e_s - \sin \varphi e_z. \tag{5.1.7}$$

When the vertex of the triad moves along the meridian, vector e_θ does not change its direction. Hence, we have

$$\frac{\partial e_\theta}{\partial s} = 0. \tag{5.1.8}$$

Differentiation of the vector product (5.1.4) with respect to s yields

$$\frac{\partial e_z}{\partial s} = \frac{\partial e_s}{\partial s} \times e_\theta + e_s \times \frac{\partial e_\theta}{\partial s}.$$

Making use of the first formula in (5.1.6) and formula (5.1.8), and remembering that a permutation of the factors in a vector product changes the sign, we can write the above equation as

$$\frac{\partial e_z}{\partial s} = \frac{1}{R_1} e_\theta \times e_z = \frac{1}{R_1} e_s. \tag{5.1.9}$$

After using (5.1.7), the derivative with respect to θ of the vector product (5.1.2) becomes

$$\frac{\partial e_s}{\partial \theta} = \frac{\partial e_\theta}{\partial \theta} \times e_z + e_\theta \times \frac{\partial e_z}{\partial \theta} = -\cos \varphi e_s \times e_z -$$

$$- \sin \varphi e_z \times e_z + e_\theta \times \frac{\partial e_z}{\partial \theta}.$$

115

Since the vectors e_θ and $\partial e_z/\partial \theta$ are parallel and the vector product of parallel vectors vanishes, the last relation reduces to

$$\frac{\partial e_s}{\partial \theta} = \cos \varphi e_\theta. \qquad (5.1.10)$$

In a similar fashion we obtain

$$\frac{\partial e_z}{\partial \theta} = \sin \varphi e_\theta. \qquad (5.1.11)$$

The complete table of derivatives of the unit vectors is

$$\frac{\partial e_s}{\partial s} = -\frac{1}{R_1} e_z, \qquad \frac{\partial e_s}{\partial \theta} = \cos \varphi e_\theta,$$

$$\frac{\partial e_\theta}{\partial s} = 0, \qquad \frac{\partial e_\theta}{\partial \theta} = -\cos \varphi e_s - \sin \varphi e_z, \qquad (5.1.12)$$

$$\frac{\partial e_z}{\partial s} = \frac{1}{R_1} e_s, \qquad \frac{\partial e_z}{\partial \theta} = \sin \varphi e_\theta.$$

Now we will determine those differential relations between the radii of curvature R_1 and R_2 which will be required in the following.

It is clear from Fig. 20 that $dr/ds = \cos \varphi$. Substitution of $ds = R_1 d\varphi$ and $r = R_2 \sin \varphi$ into this relation yields

$$\frac{dR_2 \sin \varphi}{d\varphi} = R_1 \cos \varphi, \qquad (5.1.13)$$

which is the well—known Codazzi—Gauss relation for a surface of revolution.

The theory of strain and the deduction of the equilibrium equations for shells of revolution on the basis of differential geometry will be treated in Sections 5.2 and 5.3.

The relations between the forces, moments and strains, taking the temperature terms into account, will be derived in Section 5.4.

The governing equation for the thermoelastic equilibrium of shells of revolution in conical, spherical, and toroidal coordinates will be derived in Section 5.5.

With the aid of a statical—geometrical analogy and the complex form of the shell equations, the problem can be reduced to the solution of a single

116

second–order complex differential equation for the complex function $\tilde{N}_s = N_s + k_0\kappa_\theta$, where N_s is the meridian force, κ_θ is the change in curvature in the parallel circle, and k_0 is a complex constant.

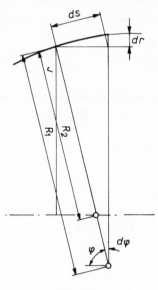

Fig. 20.

The boundary conditions are explained in Section 5.6.

Solutions of the governing equations will be determined only in the case of conical and spherical shells of revolution (see Sections 5.7 and 5.8). We shall not consider the thermoelastic problem for a cylindrical shell, which has been treated in detail in [31, 42] etc.

Special solutions for all forces, moments, and displacements necessary for the calculation of the thermal stresses have been obtained for conical and spherical shells. Moreover, a particular effort has been made to derive exact solutions in terms of special functions (Bessel and hypergeometric).

5.2. Kinematics of shells

When the temperature field and the external tractions are symmetric with respect to the axis of rotation, the middle surface of the deformed shell will also be a surface of revolution, i.e. all points will move in meridian planes.

In this case, the strains in the middle surface are described by the following four quantities: the normal strains ϵ_s and ϵ_θ in the directions of the meridian and the parallel circles, respectively, and the changes κ_s, κ_θ in the curvatures in the meridian and longitudinal directions.

We next establish the relations between the strains and the displacements of the middle surface.

The components of the displacement vector in the directions of the unit vectors $\mathbf{e}_s$ and $\mathbf{e}_z$ at a generic point will be denoted by u_s and u_z. Let the position vector of this point before the deformation be $\mathbf{R}$. Then, after the deformation the corresponding position vector is

117

$$\mathbf{R}' = \mathbf{R} + u_s \mathbf{e}_s + u_z \mathbf{e}_z. \tag{5.2.1}$$

By analogy with (5.1.5), the unit vectors tangential to the meridian and parallel circle in the deformed middle surface are given by the expression

$$\mathbf{e}'_s = \frac{\partial \mathbf{R}'}{\partial s'}, \qquad \mathbf{e}'_\theta = \frac{1}{r'} \frac{\partial \mathbf{R}'}{\partial \theta}, \tag{5.2.2}$$

where ds' and $r'd\theta$ are the elements of arc of the meridian and parallel circle after the deformation. These elements can be represented in the form

$$ds' = ds(1 + \epsilon_s), \qquad r'd\theta = r\,d\theta(1 + \epsilon_\theta), \tag{5.2.3}$$

where ϵ_s and ϵ_θ are the above—mentioned normal strains.

Substitution of (5.2.1) into (5.2.2) and use of (5.2.3) yields

$$(1 + \epsilon_s)\,\mathbf{e}'_s = \frac{\partial \mathbf{R}'}{\partial s} = \frac{\partial \mathbf{R}}{\partial s} + u_s \frac{\partial \mathbf{e}_s}{\partial s} + u_z \frac{\partial \mathbf{e}_z}{\partial s} + \frac{\partial u_s}{\partial s} \mathbf{e}_s + \frac{\partial u_z}{\partial s} \mathbf{e}_z,$$

$$(1 + \epsilon_\theta)\,\mathbf{e}'_\theta = \frac{1}{r} \frac{\partial \mathbf{R}'}{\partial \theta} = \frac{1}{r}\left(\frac{\partial \mathbf{R}}{\partial \theta} + u_s \frac{\partial \mathbf{e}_s}{\partial \theta} + u_z \frac{\partial \mathbf{e}_z}{\partial \theta} \right). \tag{5.2.4}$$

In the second equation in (5.2.4) use has been made of the fact that

$$\frac{\partial u_s}{\partial \theta} = \frac{\partial u_z}{\partial \theta} = 0,$$

when the deformation is axisymmetric.

Replacing the derivatives of the unit vectors in (5.2.4) by expressions (5.1.12) and taking account of formulae (5.1.5), we obtain

$$\frac{\partial \mathbf{R}'}{\partial s} = \left(1 + \frac{\partial u_s}{\partial s} + \frac{u_z}{R_1} \right) \mathbf{e}_s + \left(-\frac{u_s}{R_1} + \frac{\partial u_z}{\partial s} \right) \mathbf{e}_z,$$

$$\frac{1}{r} \frac{\partial \mathbf{R}'}{\partial \theta} = \left(1 + \frac{u_s}{r} \cos\varphi + \frac{u_z}{r} \sin\varphi \right) \mathbf{e}_\theta. \tag{5.2.5}$$

It is clear from equation (5.2.4) that the quantity $(1 + \epsilon_s)$ is the magnitude of the vector $\partial \mathbf{R}'/\partial s$ and the quantity $(1 + \epsilon_\theta)$ is the magnitude of the vector $r^{-1} \partial \mathbf{R}'/\partial \theta$. Since the square of the vector $\partial \mathbf{R}'/\partial s$ is equal to sum of the squares of its projections on $\mathbf{e}_s$ and $\mathbf{e}_z$, we have

118

$$(1 + \epsilon_s)^2 = \left(1 + \frac{\partial u_s}{\partial s} + \frac{u_z}{R_1}\right)^2 + \left(-\frac{u_s}{R_1} + \frac{\partial u_z}{\partial s}\right)^2.$$

Omitting the second—order terms, we find

$$\epsilon_s = \frac{\partial u_s}{\partial s} + \frac{u_z}{R_1}, \tag{5.2.6}$$

$$e'_s = \frac{1}{1 + \epsilon_s} \frac{\partial \mathbf{R}'}{\partial s} = \mathbf{e}_s + \left(-\frac{u_s}{R_1} + \frac{\partial u_z}{\partial s}\right) \mathbf{e}_z. \tag{5.2.7}$$

Comparison of the second equations in (5.2.4) and (5.2.5) yields

$$\epsilon_\theta = \frac{1}{r}(u_s \cos\varphi + u_z \sin\varphi), \tag{5.2.8}$$

$$e'_\theta = \frac{1}{r(1 + \epsilon_\theta)} \frac{\partial \mathbf{R}'}{\partial \theta} = \mathbf{e}_\theta. \tag{5.2.9}$$

The line elements having the direct $\mathbf{e}_z$ before the deformation assume the direction of the unit vector $\mathbf{e}'_z$ after the deformation. This vector is given by the vector product $\mathbf{e}'_s \times \mathbf{e}'_\theta$. Making use of (5.2.7), (5.2.9) and (5.1.2), (5.1.4) and recalling that interchanging the factors in a vector product changes the sign, we find

$$\mathbf{e}'_z = \mathbf{e}'_s \times \mathbf{e}'_\theta = \mathbf{e}_s \times \mathbf{e}_\theta + \left(-\frac{u_s}{R_1} + \frac{\partial u_z}{\partial z}\right) \mathbf{e}_z \times \mathbf{e}_\theta = \mathbf{e}_z + \vartheta \mathbf{e}_s, \tag{5.2.10}$$

where

$$\vartheta = \frac{u_s}{R_1} - \frac{\partial u_z}{\partial s}. \tag{5.2.11}$$

Quantity ϑ is the projection of the unit vector $\mathbf{e}'_z$ normal to the deformed middle surface onto $\mathbf{e}_s$ and is equal to the magnitude of the angle of rotation about the axis $\mathbf{e}_\theta$ of the normal to the middle surface.

The position of an arbitrary point P_1 in the shell is defined by the coordinates s, θ, z, where the coordinate z is the distance PP_1 from the middle surface in the direction of $\mathbf{e}_z$. The surface $z = $ const. is also a surface of revolution equidistant from the middle surface, i.e. a so—called parallel surface. The radii of curvature of the parallel surface are $R_1 + z$ and $R_2 + z$.

119

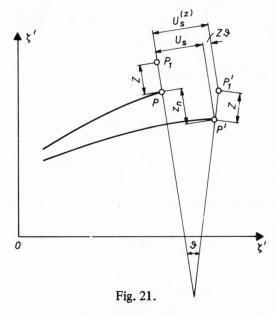

Fig. 21.

Having found the angle of rotation (5.2.11) of the normal to the middle surface during the deformation, on the basis of the theory of thin shells we can find the relations between the displacements $u_s^{(z)}$, $u_z^{(z)}$ at point P_1' at distance z from the middle surface and the displacements at the corresponding point on the middle surface (see Fig. 21):

$$u_s^{(z)} = u_s + z\vartheta,$$
$$u_z^{(z)} = u_z.$$

(5.2.12)

Replacing u_s, u_z, R_n $(n = 1, 2)$ in (5.2.6) and (5.2.8) by $u_s^{(z)}$, $u_z^{(z)}$, $R_n(1 + z/R_n)$ $(n = 1, 2)$, we obtain the following expressions for the normal strains $\epsilon_s^{(z)}$ and $\epsilon_\theta^{(z)}$ at point P_1 at distance z from the corresponding point P on the middle surface

$$\epsilon_s^{(z)} = \frac{1}{1 + \dfrac{z}{R_1}}(\epsilon_s + z\kappa_s),$$

$$\epsilon_\theta^{(z)} = \frac{1}{1 + \dfrac{z}{R_2}}(\epsilon_\theta + z\kappa_\theta),$$

(5.2.13)

120

where

$$\kappa_s = \frac{\partial \vartheta}{\partial s} = \frac{\partial}{\partial s}\left(\frac{u_s}{R_1}\right) - \frac{\partial^2 u_z}{\partial s^2}, \qquad (5.2.14)$$

$$\kappa_\theta = \frac{1}{r}\vartheta \cos \varphi = \frac{1}{r}\left(\frac{u_s}{R_1} - \frac{\partial u_z}{\partial s}\right)\cos \varphi. \qquad (5.2.15)$$

The basic assumptions in the theory of shells give rise to an error h/R compared with unity [37]. Thus, when calculating the strains, there is no sense in considering the terms of order z/R compared with unity.

When terms of the above—mentioned order are discarded, formulae (5.2.13) reduce to

$$\epsilon_s^{(z)} = \epsilon_s + z\kappa_s,$$
$$\epsilon_\theta^{(z)} = \epsilon_\theta + z\kappa_\theta. \qquad (5.2.16)$$

To the order of occuracy of the theory of shells, the quantities κ_s and κ_θ are the changes in the curvatures of the middle surface in the directions of the meridian and the parallel circle.

Positive values of the changes in curvature correspond to positive values of ϵ_s and ϵ_θ on the surface $z = h/2$.

In the case of axisymmetric deformation of a shell of revolution there are two compatibility conditions for the strains which are a particular case of the general compatibility equations in the theory of shells [6]:

$$\frac{d}{ds}(r\kappa_\theta) - \cos \varphi \kappa_s - \frac{1}{R_1}\left[\frac{d\epsilon_\theta r}{ds} - \cos \varphi \epsilon_s\right] = 0,$$

$$(R_1 \kappa_s + R_2 \kappa_\theta)\sin \varphi + R_1 \frac{d}{ds}\left[\frac{d\epsilon_\theta r}{ds} - \cos \varphi \epsilon_s\right] = 0. \qquad (5.2.17)$$

Equation (5.2.17) are satisfied identically by the strains (5.2.6), (5.2.8) with the expressions (5.2.14), (5.2.15).

5.3. Equilibrium equations for shells

The element of shell shown in Fig. 22 is bounded by the two meridian sections $\theta = $ const., $\theta + d\theta = $ const. and two conical surfaces $s = $ const., $s + ds = $ = const. normal to the middle surface. These surfaces are subjected to the normal stresses σ_s and σ_θ and, in the direction of e_z, the shear stress σ_{sz}.

In the theory of shells these stresses are replaced by the stress resultants

$$N_s= \int_{-h/2}^{h/2} \sigma_s dz, \quad N_\theta = \int_{-h/2}^{h/2} \sigma_\theta dz, \quad Q= \int_{-h/2}^{h/2} \sigma_{sz} dz,$$

$$M_s = \int_{-h/2}^{h/2} \sigma_s z dz, \quad M_\theta = \int_{-h/2}^{h/2} \sigma_\theta z dz, \qquad (5.3.1)$$

where N_s, Q, M_s are respectively the normal force, the shear force, and the bending moment in the section s = const., and N_θ, M_θ are respectively the normal force and bending moment in the section θ = const.

These stress resultants are referred to unit length of the corresponding coordinate line in the middle surface (parallel circle or meridian).

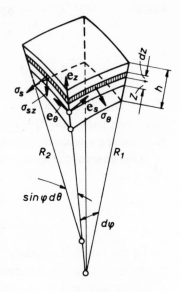

Fig. 22.

The positive directions of the stress resultants are shown in Fig. 23.

The equilibrium conditions for an element of the shell reduce to equations for the corresponding element of the middle surface. This element is bounded by the parallels s = const., $s + ds$ = const. and the meridians θ = const., $\theta + d\theta$ = const.

The face s = const. of the element is subjected to the force

$$- (N_s e_s + Q e_z) r d\theta,$$

and the face $s + ds$ = const. to the force

$$(N_s e_s + Q e_z) r d\theta + \left(\frac{\partial N_s r e_s}{\partial s} + \frac{\partial Q r e_z}{\partial s} \right) ds d\theta.$$

The resultant of these two forces is

$$\left(\frac{\partial N_s r e_s}{\partial s} + \frac{\partial Q r e_z}{\partial s} \right) ds d\theta. \qquad (5.3.2)$$

In the same way, the resultant of the forces on the faces θ = const. and

122

$\theta + d\theta = $ const. is found to be '

$$\frac{\partial N_\theta e_\theta}{\partial \theta} ds d\theta. \tag{5.3.3}$$

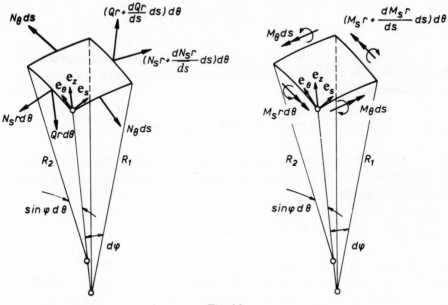

Fig. 23.

The resultant of the bounding moments on the faces $s = $ const. and $s + ds = $ = const. is

$$\frac{\partial M_s r e_\theta}{\partial s} ds d\theta, \tag{5.3.4}$$

and the resultant of the bending moments on the forces $\theta = $ const. and $\theta + d\theta = $ const. is

$$-\frac{\partial M_\theta e_s}{\partial \theta} ds d\theta. \tag{5.3.5}$$

Moreover, to the same order of accuracy as with the bending moments, the shear force on the element is

$$-Qr e_\theta ds d\theta. \tag{5.3.6}$$

The condition that both the resultant force and the resultant moment acting on the elements should vanish, leads to the following two vector equations

$$\frac{\partial N_s r e_s}{\partial s} + \frac{\partial Q r e_z}{\partial s} + \frac{\partial N_\theta e_\theta}{\partial \theta} = 0,$$

$$\frac{\partial M_s r e_\theta}{\partial s} - \frac{\partial M_\theta e_s}{\partial \theta} - Q r e_\theta = 0.$$

(5.3.7)

The derivatives of the scalar multiples of the unit vectors can be evaluated using formulae (5.1.12) for the derivatives of the unit vectors. It should also be noted that

$$\frac{dN_\theta}{d\theta} = 0 \quad \text{and} \quad \frac{dM_\theta}{d\theta} = 0.$$

Since the coefficients of e_s, e_θ, e_z must each vanish, the three vector equations (5.3.7) yield the following three *scalar equilibrium equations for a shell of revolution*

$$\frac{dN_s r}{ds} - N_\theta \cos\varphi + \frac{Qr}{R_1} = 0,$$

$$\frac{dQr}{ds} - N_\theta \sin\varphi - \frac{N_s r}{R_1} = 0,$$

(5.3.8)

$$\frac{dM_s r}{ds} - M_\theta \cos\varphi - Qr = 0.$$

5.4. Relations between forces, moments, and strains

The strains in the shell comprise (1) the elastic strains due to the stresses and (2) the strains due to temperature change, i.e. the so—called *pure thermal strains.*

The pure thermal strain at a given point in the shell due to a temperature change $T - T_0$ at this point, where T_0 is the temperature of the shell in the stress—free state, is characterized by the thermal expansion $\alpha_T (T - T_0)$, where α_T is the coefficient of linear expansion.

If the temperature defendence of α_T is to be considered, $\alpha_T (T - T_0)$ can be regarded as a given function of the coordinates with the time as parameter. Moreover, α_T will be understood to mean the mean value of α_T in the temperative range T_0 to T.

With the assumption that normal elements remain normal, the elastic stress–strain relations expressing the shear strain $\epsilon_{sz}^{(z)}$ and the normal strain $\epsilon_z^{(z)}$ in terms of the stresses reduce to

$$\epsilon_{sz}^{(z)} = 0, \qquad \epsilon_z^{(z)} = \alpha_T\,(T - T_0).$$

The shear stress σ_{sz} and the corresponding shear force Q are purely static quantities and can be determined from the equations of equilibrium.

In accordance with the usual shell theory it will be assumed that the normal stress σ_z on the planes z = const. is negligibly small in comparison with the other stresses.

Thus, using Hooke's law for a plane state of stress and taking the thermal expansion into account, we arrive at the following relations between the strains $\epsilon_s^{(z)}$, $\epsilon_\theta^{(z)}$ at distance z from the middle surface and the corresponding stresses:

$$\epsilon_s^{(z)} = \frac{\sigma_s - \nu\sigma_\theta}{E} + \alpha_T\,(T - T_0),$$

$$\epsilon_\theta^{(z)} = \frac{\sigma_\theta - \nu\sigma_s}{E} + \alpha_T\,(T - T_0), \qquad (5.4.1)$$

where E is Young's modulus and ν is Poisson's ratio.

We multiply both sides of equations (5.4.1) first by dz and later by $z\,dz$ and in both cases we integrate from $z = -h/2$ to $z = h/2$. Moreover, it will be assumed that the elastic modulus E is independent of z.

Expressing firstly the strains $\epsilon_s^{(z)}$, $\epsilon_\theta^{(z)}$ in terms of the strains in the middle surface by means of (5.2.16) and secondly the stresses in terms of the stress resultants according to formulae (5.3.1), we obtain

$$\epsilon_s = \frac{N_s - \nu N_\theta}{Eh} + \epsilon_T, \quad \epsilon_\theta = \frac{N_\theta - \nu N_s}{Eh} + \epsilon_T, \qquad (5.4.2)$$

$$\kappa_s = \frac{12(M_s - \nu M_\theta)}{Eh^3} + \kappa_T, \quad \kappa_\theta = \frac{12(M_\theta - \nu M_s)}{Eh^3} + \kappa_T, \qquad (5.4.3)$$

where

$$\epsilon_T = \frac{1}{h} \int_{-h/2}^{h/2} \alpha_T\,(T - T_0)\,dz, \quad \kappa_T = \frac{12}{h^3} \int_{-h/2}^{h/2} \alpha_T\,(T - T_0)\,z\,dz. \quad (5.4.4)$$

125

The quantities ϵ_T and κ_T are generalized purely thermal strains. In the case of a linear temperature variation $\alpha_T \, (T - T_0)$ through the thickness of the shell, ϵ_T is the purely thermal normal strain in the middle surface and κ_T is the change of curvature due to the thermal expansion.

By inverting relations (5.4.2) and (5.4.3) we obtain the following expressions for the stress resultants in terms of the strains in the middle surface

$$N_s = D_N \left[\epsilon_s + \nu\epsilon_\theta - (1 + \nu)\,\epsilon_T \right],$$
$$N_\theta = D_N \left[\nu\epsilon_s + \epsilon_\theta - (1 + \nu)\,\epsilon_T \right]; \tag{5.4.5}$$

$$M_s = D_M \left[\kappa_s + \nu\kappa_\theta - (1 + \nu)\kappa_T \right],$$
$$M_\theta = D_M \left[\nu\kappa_s + \kappa_\theta - (1 + \nu)\kappa_T \right], \tag{5.4.6}$$

where $D_N = Eh/(1 - \nu^2)$ is the tensile rigidity and $D_M = Eh^3/12(1 - \nu^2)$ is the flexural rigidity of the shell.

Formulae (5.2.16) and (5.4.1) to (5.4.3) yield the following expressions for the stresses in the shell.

$$\sigma_s = \frac{N_s}{h} + \frac{12M_s z}{h^3} + \frac{E}{1 - \nu}[\epsilon_T + z\kappa_T - \alpha_T \, (T - T_0)],$$
$$\sigma_\theta = \frac{N_\theta}{h} + \frac{12M_\theta z}{h^3} + \frac{E}{1 - \nu}[\epsilon_T + z\kappa_T - \alpha_T \, (T - T_0)]. \tag{5.4.7}$$

5.5. Governing equation

Elimination of N_θ from the two equations of equilibrium yields

$$\frac{d}{ds}(N_s r \sin\varphi) - \frac{d}{ds}(Qr \cos\varphi) = 0.$$

The integral of this equation is

$$Q = N_s \, \mathrm{tg}\,\varphi + \frac{C}{r \cos\varphi}, \tag{5.5.1}$$

where C is the constant of integration.

Substitution of expression (5.5.1) for Q into the first and third equations of equilibrium (5.3.8) yields

126

$$\frac{d}{ds}\left(N_s \frac{r}{\cos\varphi}\right) - N_\theta + \frac{C}{R_1\cos^2\varphi} = 0,$$

$$\frac{dM_s r}{ds} - M_\theta \cos\varphi - N_s r \, \mathrm{tg}\,\varphi - \frac{C}{\cos\varphi} = 0. \tag{5.5.2}$$

The mechanical meaning of the constant C becomes evident when we consider the resultant P of the forces along the axis of the shell, namely

$$P = 2\pi r \,(N_s \sin\varphi - Q\cos\varphi). \tag{5.5.3}$$

In view of (5.5.1) we obtain

$$C = -\frac{P}{2\pi}. \tag{5.5.4}$$

Thus, C is equal to $(-1/2\pi)$ times the axial force acting on the shell.

The compatibility equations (5.2.17) for the strains can be reduced to a form similar to (5.5.2).

On the basis of (5.2.14), (5.2.15) we have

$$(R_1 \kappa_s + R_2 \kappa_\theta)\sin\varphi = R_1 \frac{d\vartheta \sin\varphi}{ds} = R_1 \frac{d}{ds}(\kappa_\theta r \, \mathrm{tg}\,\varphi).$$

Substituting this expression into (5.2.17) and integrating, we obtain

$$\kappa_\theta r \, \mathrm{tg}\,\varphi + \frac{d\epsilon_\theta r}{ds} - \cos\varphi\epsilon_s + C' = 0. \tag{5.5.5}$$

The constant C' in (5.5.5) vanishes. This becomes evident after expressing the strains in terms of the displacements by means of (5.2.6), (5.2.8), and (5.2.15).

Taking account of (5.5.5) with $C' = 0$, we can represent the compatibility equations (5.2.17) in the form

$$\frac{d}{ds}\left(\kappa_\theta \frac{r}{\cos\varphi}\right) - \kappa_s = 0,$$

$$\frac{d\epsilon_\theta r}{ds} - \epsilon_s \cos\varphi + \kappa_\theta r \, \mathrm{tg}\,\varphi = 0. \tag{5.5.6}$$

Comparison of equations (5.5.2) and (5.5.6) reveals the well–known *static–geometric analogy* [6], namely, the quantities N_s, N_θ, M_s, and M_θ in (5.5.2)

127

correspond to the quantities κ_θ, κ_s, $-\epsilon_\theta$, $-\epsilon_s$ in equations (5.5.6).

On comparing (5.4.2) and (5.4.6) it is seen that the foregoing analogy can be extended; the quantities ν, $-1/Eh$, ϵ_T in (5.4.2) correspond with the quantities $-\nu$, D_M, $(1+\nu)\kappa_T D_M$ in (5.4.6).

We will choose N_s and κ_θ as the basic unknowns, for which governing equations are to be found. By expressing ϵ_s and ϵ_θ in (5.5.6) in terms of the stress resultants with the aid of (5.4.2) and then eliminating N_θ with the aid of the first of equations (5.5.2), we obtain the *first governing equation*

$$\frac{R_1 r}{\cos\varphi}\frac{d^2 N_s}{ds^2} + \left[\frac{R_1}{r}\frac{d}{ds}\left(\frac{r^2}{\cos\varphi}\right) + R_1\frac{d}{ds}\left(\frac{r}{\cos\varphi}\right)\right]\frac{dN_s}{ds} +$$

$$+\left\{\frac{R_1}{r}\frac{d}{ds}\left[r\frac{d}{ds}\left(\frac{r}{\cos\varphi}\right)\right] - \frac{R_1\cos\varphi}{r} + \nu\,\mathrm{tg}\,\varphi\right\} N_s +$$

$$+ EhR_1\kappa_\theta\,\mathrm{tg}\,\varphi + \frac{Eh}{r}\left[R_1\frac{d}{ds}(\epsilon_T r) - \epsilon_T R_1\cos\varphi\right] +$$

$$+\frac{C}{r}\left[R_1\frac{d}{ds}\left(\frac{r}{R_1\cos^2\varphi}\right) + \frac{\nu}{\cos\varphi}\right] = 0. \qquad (5.5.7)$$

When $R_1 = \text{const.}$ and use is made of relation (5.1.13), equation (5.5.7) reduces to

$$\frac{r}{\cos\varphi}\frac{d^2 N_s}{ds^2} + \left(3 + \frac{2r\,\mathrm{tg}\,\varphi}{R_1\cos\varphi}\right)\frac{dN_s}{ds} + \left[2\frac{\mathrm{tg}\,\varphi}{R_1} + \frac{r(1 + 2\,\mathrm{tg}^2\varphi)}{R_1^2\cos\varphi}\right]N_s +$$

$$+\frac{\nu\,\mathrm{tg}\,\varphi}{R_1}N_s + Eh\,\mathrm{tg}\,\varphi\kappa_\theta + Eh\frac{d\epsilon_T}{ds} + \frac{C}{R_1\cos\varphi}\left(\frac{1+\nu}{r} + \frac{2\,\mathrm{tg}\,\varphi}{R_1\cos\varphi}\right) = 0. \quad (5.5.8)$$

With the aid of the static–geometric analogy one founds the *second governing equation*:

$$\frac{r}{\cos\varphi}\frac{d^2\kappa_\theta}{ds^2} + \left(3 + \frac{2r\,\mathrm{tg}\,\varphi}{R_1\cos\varphi}\right)\frac{d\kappa_\theta}{ds} + \left[2\frac{\mathrm{tg}\,\varphi}{R_1} + \frac{r(1 + 2\,\mathrm{tg}^2\varphi)}{R_1^2\cos\varphi}\right]\kappa_\theta -$$

$$-\frac{\nu\,\mathrm{tg}\,\varphi}{R_1}\kappa_\theta\frac{\mathrm{tg}\,\varphi}{D_M}N_s - (1+\nu)\frac{d\kappa_T}{ds} - \frac{C}{rD_M\cos\varphi} = 0. \qquad (5.5.9)$$

The introduction of the complex stress function

$$\tilde{N}_s = N_s + k_0\kappa_\theta,$$

$$k_0 = \frac{Eh^3}{c_0^2 R_1}(\nu \pm i\mu), \quad \mu = \sqrt{\frac{c_0^2 R_1^2}{h^2} - \nu^2}, \quad c_0^2 = 12(1 - \nu^2), \quad (5.5.10)$$

reduces the two governing equations (5.5.8), (5.5.9) to the single second–order complex differential equation

$$\frac{d^2 \tilde{N}_s}{ds^2} + \frac{\cos\varphi}{r}\left(3 + \frac{2r\,\mathrm{tg}\,\varphi}{R_1 \cos\varphi}\right)\frac{d\tilde{N}_s}{ds} + \frac{\cos\varphi}{r}\left[(2 \mp i\mu)\frac{\mathrm{tg}\,\varphi}{R_1} + \right.$$

$$\left. + \frac{r(1 + 2\,\mathrm{tg}^2\varphi)}{R_1^2 \cos\varphi}\right]\tilde{N}_s + \frac{\cos\varphi}{r}\frac{d}{ds}[Eh\epsilon_T - (1 + \nu)k_0\kappa_T] + $$

$$+ C\frac{1}{r}\left[\frac{1}{R_1}\left(\frac{1 + \nu}{r} + \frac{2\,\mathrm{tg}\,\varphi}{R_1 \cos\varphi}\right) - \frac{k_0}{rD_M}\right] = 0. \qquad (5.5.11)$$

5.6. Form of solutions. Boundary conditions

The general solution of equation (5.5.11) is

$$\tilde{N}_s = \tilde{C}_1 \tilde{N}_s^{(1)} + \tilde{C}_2 \tilde{N}_s^{(2)} + \tilde{N}_s^{(\epsilon_T)} + \tilde{N}_s^{(\kappa_T)} + \tilde{N}_s^{(C)}. \qquad (5.6.1)$$

The corresponding solutions for N_s and κ_θ are

$$N_s = \sum_{n=1}^{4} C_n N_s^{(n)} + N_s^{(\epsilon_T)} + N_s^{(\kappa_T)} + N_s^{(C)},$$

$$\qquad (5.6.2)$$

$$\kappa_\theta = \sum_{n=1}^{4} C_n \kappa_\theta^{(n)} + \kappa_\theta^{(\epsilon_T)} + \kappa_\theta^{(\kappa_T)} + \kappa_\theta^{(C)},$$

where $C_n N_s^{(n)}$ and $C_n \kappa_\theta^{(n)}$ $(n = 1, 2, 3, 4)$ are the homogeneous solutions of and C_n are arbitrary constants of integration. Since this solution does not contain terms due to the action of the axial force and non–uniform heating, it corresponds to a self–equilibrating system of bending moments M_s and radial forces $N_r = N_s \cos\varphi + Q \sin\varphi$ on the boundary. Such a state of stress is usually called a *boundary effect*.

Appropriate choice of the constants C_n in four linearly independent solutions for the boundary effect enable one to satisfy an arbitrary combination of self–equilibrating loads M_s and N_r on the surfaces bounding the shell.

129

The quantities $N_s^{(\epsilon \mathrm{T})}$, $N_s^{(\kappa \mathrm{T})}$, $N_s^{(C)}$ and $\kappa_\theta^{(\epsilon \mathrm{T})}$, $\kappa_\theta^{(\kappa \mathrm{T})}$, $\kappa_\theta^{(C)}$ in solutions (5.6.2) are particular solutions of equation (5.5.11) corresponding respectively to the terms ϵ_T, κ_T, and C in the last two summands of (5.5.11). These particular solutions thus describe the states of stress in the shell associated with the generalized pure thermal strains ϵ_T and κ_T due to non–uniform heating and the axial force $P = -2\pi C$.

Once N_s and κ_θ are known, equations (5.5.2) and (5.5.6) yield N_θ and κ_s. The elastic relations (5.4.2) and (5.4.6) then provide ϵ_s, ϵ_θ and M_s, M_θ. The shear force Q is determined by formulae (5.5.1).

The displacement u_z can be determined by the differential equation

$$\frac{du_z}{ds} + \frac{\mathrm{tg}\,\varphi}{R_1} u_z + \frac{r}{\cos \varphi}\left(\kappa_\theta - \frac{\epsilon_\theta}{R_1}\right) = 0 \qquad (5.6.3)$$

obtaining by eliminating u_s from equations (5.2.8) and (5.2.15). These equations also furnish the following expression for u_s:

$$u_s = \frac{1}{\cos \varphi}(r\epsilon_\theta - u_z \sin \varphi). \qquad (5.6.4)$$

Since the determination of the displacements requires the integrating of the first–order differential equation (5.6.3) the form of their general solutions will differ from those of the solutions (5.6.2) for the stress resultants and the strains in virtue of the presence of an auxiliary particular solution, i.e. we write

$$u_z = \sum_{n=1}^{4} C_n u_z^{(n)} + u_z^{(\epsilon \mathrm{T})} + u_z^{(\kappa \mathrm{T})} + u_z^{(C)} + C_5 u_z^{(5)},$$

$$\qquad (5.6.5)$$

$$u_s = \sum_{n=1}^{4} C_n u_s^{(n)} + u_s^{(\epsilon \mathrm{T})} + u_s^{(\kappa \mathrm{T})} + u_s^{(C)} + C_5 u_s^{(5)}.$$

where $C_5 u_s^{(5)}$ is the solution of the homogeneous form of equation (5.6.3) $u_s^{(5)} = -u_z^{(5)} \,\mathrm{tg}\,\varphi$.

By considering the two homogeneous forms of equations (5.2.8) and (5.2.15), it is easy to verify that

$$C_5 u_s^{(5)} = C_5 \sin \varphi, \quad C_5 u_z^{(5)} = -C_5 \cos \varphi. \qquad (5.6.6)$$

These expressions indicate a simple mechanical interpretation of the constant

C_5; it represents a rigid–body motion of the shell along the symmetry axis.

Since the solutions for the stress resultants and the strains contain the five constants of integration C and C_n ($n = 1, 2, 3, 4$) and the solution for the displacements contains a sixth constant C_5, it is possible to satisfy arbitrary conditions on the boundaries of a shell.

The boundary conditions are those of either loaded or clamped edges. They can be formulated by setting up a table for various concrete problems.

The boundary conditions can be subdivided into static and kinematic conditions. The static conditions describe the loads on an edge and the kinematic ones describe the clamping or the displacements.

In general the following three static and four kinematic conditions are encountered.

Static conditions	Kinematic conditions
1. Meridian bending moment M_s.	1. Angle of rotation $$\vartheta = \frac{u_s}{R_1} - \frac{du_z}{ds} = \frac{r}{\cos \varphi} \kappa_\theta.$$
2. Radial force $$N_r = N_s \cos \varphi + Q \sin \varphi.$$	2. Radial displacement $$\xi = u_s \cos \varphi + u_z \sin \varphi = r\epsilon_\theta.$$
3. Axial force $$P = 2\pi r N_\zeta =$$ $$= 2\pi r (N_s \sin \varphi - Q \cos \varphi).$$	3. Relative axial shift of the shell edges $$\Delta\zeta = \zeta_2 - \zeta_1 = (u_s \sin \varphi -$$ $$-u_z \cos \varphi)_2 - (u_s \sin \varphi - u_z \cos \varphi)_1.$$
	4. Axial displacement of one of the edges $$\zeta = u_s \sin \varphi - u_z \cos \varphi.$$

On each edge the first two of the above static or kinematic conditions can be prescribed independently.

When the axial force P can be determined from equilibrium equations for the shell, the third static condition is prescribed. When the clamping of the shell does not permit the determination of the axial force P from equilibrium considerations, i.e. when the shell is statically indeterminate with respect to this force, the third kinematic condition is prescribed.

The fourth kinematic condition fixes the position from where the axial displacements of the shell are measured. This need only be prescribed on one of the edges.

In this way six boundary conditions can be prescribed in order that the six constants of integration in the particular solution can be determined.

When the shell is statically determinate in the direction of the axial force P, the constants of integration can be determined in the foliowing sequence:

1. The force P is determined and then formula (5.5.4) yields the constant C.

2. On the basis of the first two static or kinematic conditions (two of each edge of the shell) one can set up a system of four equations for the determination of the constants of integration C_n ($n = 1, 2, 3, 4$) appearing in the particular solution of the boundary effect.

3. For an edge with known axial displacement (the fourth kinematic condition), an equation that determines constant C_5 can be written down.

5.7. Thermal stresses in conical shells

For a conical shell $R_1 = \infty$, and $\varphi = (\pi/2) - \alpha = $ const., where α is the angle between the axis and the generators of the cone. The governing equation (5.5.11) then assumes the form

$$\frac{d^2 \tilde{N}_s}{ds^2} + \frac{3 \sin \alpha}{r} \frac{d\tilde{N}_s}{ds} - i \frac{c_0 \cos \alpha}{hr} \tilde{N}_s +$$

$$+ \frac{\sin \alpha}{r} \frac{d}{ds} [Eh\epsilon_T - (1 + \nu) k_0 \kappa_T] - i \frac{c_0}{hr^2} C = 0, \qquad (5.7.1)$$

where $c_0 = \sqrt{12(1 - \nu^2)}$, $k_0 = i(Eh^2/c_0)$.

Introduction of the new variable

$$y = i \frac{c_0 \operatorname{ctg} \alpha}{h} s, \qquad (5.7.2)$$

reduces (5.7.1) to

$$y^2 \frac{d^2 \tilde{N}_s}{dy^2} + 3y \frac{d\tilde{N}_s}{dy} - y\tilde{N}_s + \tilde{f} = 0, \qquad (5.7.3)$$

where

132

$$\tilde{f} = y\frac{d}{dy}[Eh e_T - (1+\nu)k_0\kappa_T] - i\frac{c_0}{h\sin^2\alpha}C.$$

We now construct the solution for the boundary effect.
With the new dependent and independent variables

$$\tilde{N} = y\tilde{N}_s, \quad \eta = 2i\sqrt{y} \tag{5.7.4}$$

the homogeneous form of (5.7.3) becomes the Bessel equation

$$\eta^2\frac{d^2\tilde{N}}{d\eta^2} + \eta\frac{d\tilde{N}}{d\eta} + (\eta^2 - 4)\tilde{N} = 0 \tag{5.7.5}$$

Equation (5.7.5) has the general solution

$$\tilde{N} = \tilde{A}_1 J_2(\eta) + \tilde{A}_2 Y_2(\eta), \tag{5.7.6}$$

where $J_2(\eta)$ and $Y_2(\eta)$ are the second order Bessel functions of first and second kind, and $\tilde{A}_1$, $\tilde{A}_2$ are constants of integration, which are generally complex.

In view of formulae (5.7.4), the general solution $\tilde{N}_s^*$ of the homogeneous form of (5.7.3) is

$$\tilde{N}_s^* = \tilde{A}_1\frac{1}{y}J_2(2i\sqrt{y}) + \tilde{A}_2\frac{1}{y}Y_2(2i\sqrt{y}). \tag{5.7.7}$$

Returning to the variable s and introducing

$$x = 2\sqrt{\frac{c_0\,\text{ctg}\,\alpha}{h}}\,s, \tag{5.7.8}$$

we can represent the general solution for $\tilde{N}_s^*$ in the form

$$\tilde{N}_s^* = -4i\tilde{A}_1\frac{1}{x^2}J_2(ix\sqrt{i}) - 4i\tilde{A}_2\frac{1}{x^2}Y_2(ix\sqrt{i}). \tag{5.7.9}$$

The function $J_2(ix\sqrt{i})$ and $Y_2(ix\sqrt{i})$ can be expressed in terms of the Bessel function $I_2(x\sqrt{i})$ and $K_2(x\sqrt{i})$ with purely imaginary argument as follows:

$$J_2(ix\sqrt{i}) = -I_2(x\sqrt{i}),$$

$$Y_2(ix\sqrt{i}) = -iI_2(x\sqrt{i}) + \frac{2}{\pi}K_2(x\sqrt{i}). \tag{5.7.10}$$

133

On the basis of these formulae it is found that

$$\tilde{N}_s^* = \tilde{C}_1 \frac{1}{x^2} I_2(x\sqrt{i}) + \tilde{C}_2 \frac{1}{x^2} K_2(x\sqrt{i}), \qquad (5.7.11)$$

where

$$\tilde{C}_1 = 4i(\tilde{A}_1 + i\tilde{A}_2), \quad \tilde{C}_2 = -\frac{8i}{\pi} \tilde{A}_2.$$

The second order Bessel functions can be expressed in terms of Bessel functions of zeroth order by means of the relations

$$I_2(x\sqrt{i}) = I_0(x\sqrt{i}) + \frac{2i}{x} \frac{dI_0(x\sqrt{i})}{dx},$$

$$K_2(x\sqrt{i}) = K_0(x\sqrt{i}) + \frac{2i}{x} \frac{dK_0(x\sqrt{i})}{dx}. \qquad (5.7.12)$$

Solution (5.7.11) can then be written as

$$\tilde{N}_s^* = \tilde{C}_1 \frac{1}{x^2} \left[I_0(x\sqrt{i}) + \frac{2i}{x} \frac{dI_0(x\sqrt{i})}{dx} \right] +$$

$$+ \tilde{C}_2 \frac{1}{x^2} \left[K_0(x\sqrt{i}) + \frac{2i}{x} \frac{dK_0(x\sqrt{i})}{dx} \right]. \qquad (5.7.13)$$

The functions $I_0(x\sqrt{i})$ and $K_0(x\sqrt{i})$ can with the aid of the Kelvin functions be decomposed into real and imaginary parts:

$$I_0(x\sqrt{i}) = \operatorname{ber} x + i \operatorname{bei} x,$$

$$K_0(x\sqrt{i}) = \operatorname{ker} x + i \operatorname{kei} x. \qquad (5.7.14)$$

Then, replacing the complex constants of integration $\tilde{C}_1$ and $\tilde{C}_2$ by the expressions[1]

$$\tilde{C}_1 = 4(C_1 + iC_2),$$

$$\tilde{C}_2 = \frac{8i}{\pi} (C_3 + iC_4),$$

_____

[1] These expressions have been chosen so as to yield the well-known solutions for the stress resultants and displacements quoted in [12, 25, 48].

one can write out the following four particular solutions of the homogeneous equation for the force N_s and the strain

$$N_s^{(1)} = \frac{Eh^2}{c_0} \kappa_\theta^{(2)} = \frac{4}{x^2} \left(\psi_1 + \frac{2}{x} \psi_2' \right),$$

$$N_s^{(2)} = -\frac{Eh^2}{c_0} \kappa_\theta^{(1)} = \frac{4}{x^2} \left(\psi_2 - \frac{2}{x} \psi_1' \right),$$

$$N_s^{(3)} = \frac{Eh^2}{c_0} x_\theta^{(4)} = \frac{4}{x^2} \left(\psi_3 + \frac{2}{x} \psi_4' \right), \qquad (5.7.15)$$

$$N_s^{(4)} = -\frac{Eh^2}{c_0} x_\theta^{(3)} = \frac{4}{x^2} \left(\psi_4 - \frac{2}{x} \psi_3' \right),$$

where

$$\psi_1 = \text{ber } x, \qquad \psi_2 = -\text{bei } x,$$

$$\psi_3 = -\frac{2}{\pi} \text{kei } x, \quad \psi_4 = -\frac{2}{\pi} \text{ker } x,$$

$$\psi_n' = \frac{d\psi_n}{dx} \quad (n = 1, 2, 3, 4). \qquad (5.7.16)$$

All the other forces, moments, and displacements can be determined in terms of the known solution for N_s and κ_θ.

As described in Section 5.6, the first equation in (5.5.2) yields

$$N_\theta = N_s + s \frac{dN_s}{ds}. \qquad (5.7.17)$$

After expressing the strain κ_s in terms of κ_θ by means of the first formula in (5.5.6), we obtain

$$M_s = D_M \left[(1 + \nu)\kappa_\theta + s \frac{d\kappa_\theta}{ds} - (1 + \nu)\kappa_T \right],$$

$$\qquad (5.7.18)$$

$$M_\theta = D_M \left[(1 + \nu)\kappa_\theta + \nu s \frac{d\kappa_\theta}{ds} - (1 + \nu)\kappa_T \right],$$

where

135

$$D_M = \frac{Eh^3}{12(1-\nu^2)}.$$

The displacement u_z can be determined from the differential equation (5.6.3); discarding the constant of integration, which is included in the general solution (5.6.5), we find

$$u_z = -\int \kappa_\vartheta s ds. \qquad (5.7.19)$$

The following particular solutions for the forces $N_\vartheta^{(n)}$, the moments $M_s^{(n)}$, $M_\vartheta^{(n)}$, and the displacements $u_z^{(n)}$ ($n = 1, 2, 3, 4$) are obtained

$$N_\vartheta^{(1)} = \frac{2}{x}\psi_1' - N_s^{(1)},$$

$$N_\vartheta^{(2)} = \frac{2}{x}\psi_2' - N_s^{(2)},$$

$$N_\vartheta^{(3)} = \frac{2}{x}\psi_3' - N_s^{(3)}, \qquad (5.7.20)$$

$$N_\vartheta^{(4)} = \frac{2}{x}\psi_4' - N_s^{(4)};$$

$$M_s^{(1)} = -\frac{h}{c_0}(\nu N_s^{(2)} + N_\vartheta^{(2)}),$$

$$M_s^{(2)} = \frac{h}{c_0}(\nu N_s^{(1)} + N_\vartheta^{(1)}),$$

$$M_s^{(3)} = -\frac{h}{c_0}(\nu N_s^{(4)} + N_\vartheta^{(4)}), \qquad (5.7.21)$$

$$M_s^{(4)} = \frac{h}{c_0}(\nu N_s^{(3)} + N_\vartheta^{(3)});$$

$$M_\vartheta^{(1)} = -\frac{h}{c_0}(N_s^{(2)} + \nu N_\vartheta^{(2)}),$$

$$M_\theta^{(2)} = \frac{h}{c_0} (N_s^{(1)} + \nu N_\theta^{(1)}),$$

$$M_\theta^{(3)} = -\frac{h}{c_0} (N_s^{(4)} + \nu N_\theta^{(4)}), \tag{5.7.22}$$

$$M_\theta^{(4)} = \frac{h}{c_0} (N_s^{(3)} + \nu N_\theta^{(3)});$$

$$u_z^{(1)} = \frac{\text{tg}^2 \alpha}{E c_0} \left(\frac{x}{2} \psi_1' - \psi_1 \right),$$

$$u_z^{(2)} = \frac{\text{tg}^2 \alpha}{E c_0} \left(\frac{x}{2} \psi_2' - \psi_2 \right),$$

$$u_z^{(3)} = \frac{\text{tg}^2 \alpha}{E c_0} \left(\frac{x}{2} \psi_3' - \psi_3 \right), \tag{5.7.23}$$

$$u_z^{(4)} = \frac{\text{tg}^2 \alpha}{E c_0} \left(\frac{x}{2} \psi_4' - \psi_4 \right),$$

where

$$c_0 = \sqrt{12(1-\nu^2)}.$$

The remaining displacements can be determined in the following way.

The displacement u_s is found from relation (5.6.4), where the strain ϵ_θ is expressed in terms of the forces by means of the second formula in (5.4.2). Thus it is found that

$$u_s = s \left[\frac{N_\theta - \nu N_s}{Eh} + \epsilon_T \right] - \text{ctg}\, \alpha u_z. \tag{5.7.24}$$

The radial displacement ξ and the axial displacement ζ, which are related to u_s and u_z through the formulae

$$\xi = u_s \sin \alpha + u_z \cos \alpha,$$

$$\zeta = u_s \cos \alpha - u_z \sin \alpha, \tag{5.7.25}$$

have the following particular solutions

$$\xi = s \sin \alpha \left[\frac{N_\theta - \nu N_s}{Eh} + \epsilon_T \right],$$

$$\zeta = \operatorname{ctg} \alpha \xi - \frac{u_z}{\sin \alpha}.$$

(5.7.26)

Formulae (5.2.15), (5.4.3) yield the angle of rotation

$$\vartheta = s \left[\frac{12(M_\theta - \nu M_s)}{Eh^3} + \kappa_T \right].$$

(5.7.27)

In order to construct particular solutions of the nonhomogeneous equation (5.7.3), it suffices to consider the particular solutions of this equation corresponding to the nonhomogeneous terms

$$\tilde{f} = As^\lambda,$$

(5.7.28)

$$\tilde{f} = A_0.$$

(5.7.29)

In the case of (5.7.28), the particular integral can be determined by the power series

$$\tilde{N}_{s*}^{(p)} = - \frac{As^\lambda}{\lambda(\lambda + 2)} F(y) \quad (p = \epsilon_T, \kappa_T),$$

(5.7.30)

where

$$F(y) = 1 + \lambda!(\lambda + 2)! \sum_{n=1}^{\infty} \frac{y^n}{(\lambda + n)! \, (\lambda + 2 + n)!}.$$

In the case of (5.7.29), the particular integral is represented in the form

$$\tilde{N}_{s*}^{(C)} = -A_0 \Phi(y),$$

(5.7.31)

where

$$\Phi(y) = I_2(x\sqrt{i}) \frac{\ln y}{y} -$$

$$- \sum_{n=1}^{\infty} \frac{1}{n!(n+2)!} \left(\frac{1}{1} + \ldots + \frac{1}{n} + \frac{1}{3} + \ldots + \frac{1}{n+2} \right) y^n,$$

138

and $I_2(x\sqrt{i}) = \sum_{n=0}^{\infty} \dfrac{1}{n!(n+2)!} \left(\dfrac{x\sqrt{i}}{2}\right)^{2n+2}$ is the second—order Bessel function

of the imaginary argument $y = i(x/2)^2$.

By forming linear combinations of the particular integrals (5.7.30), (5.7.31) with the corresponding homogeneous solutions, one obtains particular solutions of the nonhomogeneous equation in the form of the polynomials

$$\widetilde{N}_s^{(p)} = -Ai\left(i\frac{c_0\,\mathrm{ctg}\,\alpha}{h}\right)^{-\lambda}(\lambda-1)!\,(\lambda+1)!\,\widetilde{N}_s^{(1)} + \widetilde{N}_{s*}^{(p)} =$$

$$= \frac{A}{2}\left(i\frac{c_0\,\mathrm{ctg}\,\alpha}{h}\right)^{-\lambda}(\lambda-1)!\,(\lambda+1)!\left(1 + 2\sum_{n=1}^{\lambda-1}\frac{1}{n!\,(n+2)!}\,y^n\right). \quad (5.7.32)$$

$$(p = \epsilon_T, \kappa_T),$$

$$\widetilde{N}_s^{(C)} = A_0\left[\pi\widetilde{N}_s^{(2)} + i\left(2\gamma_E - \frac{3}{2}\right)\widetilde{N}_s^{(1)}\right] + N_{s*}^{(C)} = A_0\left(1 - \frac{1}{y}\right)\frac{1}{y}. \quad (5.7.33)$$

where

$$\widetilde{N}_s^{(1)} = \frac{4}{x^2}\,I_2(x\sqrt{i}),$$

$$\widetilde{N}_s^{(2)} = \frac{8i}{\pi x^2}\,K_2(x\sqrt{i}),$$

and $\gamma_E = 0{,}5772157$ is Euler's constant.

In the case of the non—uniform heating corresponding to the purely thermal strains

$$\epsilon_T = \epsilon_j s^j \ (\epsilon_j = \mathrm{const}, \ j = 1, 2, 3, 4, 5), \ \kappa_T = 0,$$

the constant A in (5.7.29) is

$$A = Ehj\epsilon_j, \quad (5.7.34)$$

and the particular integrals of the nonhomogeneous equation can be written as: when $j = 1$

$$N_s^{(\epsilon_T)} = N_\theta^{(\epsilon_T)} = 0,$$

$$M_s^{(\epsilon_T)} = M_\theta^{(\epsilon_T)} = -\frac{(1+\nu)Eh^3\epsilon_1\,\mathrm{tg}\,\alpha}{c_0^2}, \qquad (5.7.35)$$

$$u_z^{(\epsilon_T)} = \frac{\epsilon_1 h^2\,\mathrm{tg}^3\,\alpha}{32c_0^2}x^4\,;$$

when $j = 2$

$$N_s^{(\epsilon_T)} = N_\theta^{(\epsilon_T)} = -\frac{6\epsilon_2 Eh^3\,\mathrm{tg}^2\,\alpha}{c_0^2},$$

$$M_s^{(\epsilon_T)} = -\frac{(2+\nu)\epsilon_2 Eh^4\,\mathrm{th}^2\,\alpha}{2c_0^3}x^2\,,$$

$$M_\theta^{(\epsilon_T)} = -\frac{(1+2\nu)\epsilon_2 Eh^4\,\mathrm{tg}^2\,\alpha}{2c_0^3}x^2\,,$$

$$u_z^{(\epsilon_T)} = \frac{1}{96}\frac{\epsilon_2 h^3\,\mathrm{tg}^4\,\alpha}{c_0^3}x^6\,;$$

when $j = 3$

$$N_s^{(\epsilon_T)} = \frac{1}{2}N_\theta^{(\epsilon_T)} = -\frac{6\epsilon_3 Eh^4\,\mathrm{tg}^3\,\alpha}{c_0^3}x^2\,,$$

$$M_s^{(\epsilon_T)} = \frac{72(1+\nu)\epsilon_3 Eh^5\,\mathrm{tg}^3\,\alpha}{c_0^4}\left[1 - \frac{3+\nu}{384(1+\nu)}x^4\right]\,,$$

$$M_\theta^{(\epsilon_T)} = \frac{72(1+\nu)\epsilon_3 Eh^5\,\mathrm{tg}^3\,\alpha}{c_0^4}\left[1 - \frac{1+3\nu}{384(1+\nu)}x^4\right]\,,$$

$$u_z^{(\epsilon_T)} = -\frac{9\epsilon_3 h^4\,\mathrm{tg}^5\,\alpha}{4c_0^4}x^4\left(1 - \frac{1}{768}x^4\right)\,;$$

when $j = 4$

$$N_s^{(\epsilon_T)} = \frac{1440\epsilon_4 Eh^5\,\mathrm{tg}^4\,\alpha}{c_0^4}\left(1 - \frac{1}{384}x^4\right)\,,$$

$$N_\theta^{(\epsilon_T)} = \frac{1440\epsilon_4 Eh^5\,\mathrm{tg}^4\,\alpha}{c_0^4}\left(1 - \frac{1}{128}x^4\right)\,,$$

140

$$M_s^{(\epsilon_T)} = \frac{120(2+\nu)\epsilon_4 Eh^6 \operatorname{tg}^4\alpha}{c_0^5}x^2 \left[1 - \frac{4+\nu}{1920(2+\nu)}x^4\right] , \quad (5.7.38)$$

$$M_\theta^{(\epsilon_T)} = \frac{120(1+2\nu)\epsilon_4 Eh^6 \operatorname{tg}^4\alpha}{c_0^5}x^2 \left[1 - \frac{1+4\nu}{1920(1+2\nu)}x^4\right] ,$$

$$u_z^{(\epsilon_T)} = -\frac{5\epsilon_4 h^5 \operatorname{tg}^6\alpha}{2c_0^5}x^6 \left(1 - \frac{1}{3200}x^4\right) ;$$

when $j = 5$

$$N_s^{(\epsilon_T)} = \frac{3600\epsilon_5 Eh^6 \operatorname{tg}^5\alpha}{c_0^5}x^2 \left(1 - \frac{1}{1920}x^4\right) ,$$

$$N_\theta^{(\epsilon_T)} = \frac{7200\epsilon_5 Eh^6 \operatorname{tg}^5\alpha}{c_0^5}x^2 \left(1 - \frac{1}{960}x^4\right) ,$$

$$M_s^{(\epsilon_T)} = -\frac{43200(1+\nu)\epsilon_5 Eh^7 \operatorname{tg}^5\alpha}{c_0^6} \left[1 - \frac{3+\nu}{384(1+\nu)}x^4 + \right.$$

$$\left. + \frac{5+\nu}{2211840(1+\nu)}x^8\right] , \quad (5.7.39)$$

$$M_\theta^{(\epsilon_T)} = -\frac{43200(1+\nu)\epsilon_5 Eh^7 \operatorname{tg}^5\alpha}{c_0^6} \left[1 - \frac{1+3\nu}{384(1+\nu)}x^4 + \right.$$

$$\left. + \frac{1+5\nu}{2211840(1+\nu)}x^8\right] ,$$

$$u_z^{(\epsilon_T)} = \frac{1350\epsilon_5 h^6 \operatorname{tg}^7\alpha}{c_0^6}x^4 \left[1 - \frac{1}{768}x^4 + \frac{1}{6635520}x^8\right] .$$

In the case of non—uniform heating corresponding to the purely thermal strains

$$\epsilon_T = 0, \quad \kappa_T = \frac{\mu_j}{h}s^j \quad (\mu_j = \text{const}, \ j = 0, 1, 2, 3, 4, 5),$$

the constant A in (5.7.28) has the value

$$A = -i\frac{(1+\nu)Ehj\mu_j}{c_0}, \tag{5.7.40}$$

and the particular integrals of the nonhomogeneous equation are
when $j = 0$

$$N_s^{(\kappa T)} = N_\theta^{(\kappa T)} = 0,$$

$$M_s^{(\kappa T)} = M_\theta^{(\kappa T)} = -\frac{(1+\nu)\mu_0 Eh^2}{c_0^2}, \tag{5.7.41}$$

$$u_z^{(\kappa T)} = 0;$$

when $j = 1$

$$N_s^{(\kappa T)} = N_\theta^{(\kappa T)} = -\frac{(1+\nu)\mu_1 Eh^2 \ \text{tg}\,\alpha}{c_0^2},$$

$$M_s^{(\kappa T)} = M_\theta^{(\kappa T)} = -\frac{(1+\nu)\mu_1 Eh^3 \ \text{tg}\,\alpha}{4c_0^3} x^2, \tag{5.7.42}$$

$$u_z^{(\kappa T)} = 0;$$

when $j = 2$

$$N_s^{(\kappa T)} = \frac{1}{2} N_\theta^{(\kappa T)} = -\frac{(1+\nu)\mu_2 Eh^3 \ \text{tg}^2\alpha}{2c_0^3} x^2,$$

$$M_s^{(\kappa T)} = M_\theta^{(\kappa T)} = \frac{6(1+\nu)^2\mu_2 Eh^4 \ \text{tg}^2\alpha}{c_0^4}\left[1 - \frac{1}{96(1+\nu)} x^4\right], \tag{5.7.43}$$

$$u_z^{(\kappa T)} = -\frac{3(1+\nu)\mu_2 h^3 \ \text{tg}^4\alpha}{16c_0^4} x^4;$$

when $j = 3$

$$N_s^{(\kappa T)} = \frac{72(1+\nu)\mu_3 Eh^4 \ \text{tg}^3\alpha}{c_0^4}\left(1 - \frac{1}{384} x^4\right),$$

$$N_\theta^{(\kappa T)} = \frac{72(1+\nu)\mu_3 Eh^4 \ \text{tg}^3\alpha}{c_0^4}\left(1 - \frac{1}{128} x^4\right),$$

142

$$M_s^{(\kappa T)} = \frac{6(1+\nu)(2+\nu)\mu_3 Eh^5 \text{ tg}^3\alpha}{c_0^5} x^2 \left[1 - \frac{1}{384(2+\nu)}x^4\right], (5.7.44)$$

$$M_\theta^{(\kappa T)} = \frac{6(1+\nu)(1+2\nu)\mu_3 Eh^5 \text{ tg}^3\alpha}{c_0^5} x^2 \left[1 - \frac{1}{384(1+2\nu)}x^4\right],$$

$$u_z^{(\kappa T)} = -\frac{(1+\nu)\mu_3 h^4 \text{ tg}^5\alpha}{8c_0^5}x^6;$$

when $j = 4$

$$N_s^{(\kappa T)} = \frac{120(1+\nu)\mu_4 Eh^5 \text{ tg}^4\alpha}{c_0^5} x^2 \left(1 - \frac{1}{1920}x^4\right),$$

$$N_\theta^{(\kappa T)} = \frac{240(1+\nu)\mu_4 Eh^5 \text{ tg}^4\alpha}{c_0^5} x^2 \left(1 - \frac{1}{960}x^4\right),$$

$$M_s^{(\kappa T)} = -\frac{1440(1+\nu)^2\mu_4 Eh^6 \text{ tg}^4\alpha}{c_0^6} \left[1 - \frac{3+\nu}{384(1+\nu)}x^4 + \right.$$

$$\left. + \frac{1}{368640(1+\nu)}x^8\right], \qquad (5.7.45)$$

$$M_\theta^{(\kappa T)} = -\frac{1440(1+\nu)^2\mu_4 Eh^6 \text{ tg}^4\alpha}{c_0^6} \left[1 - \frac{1+3\nu}{384(1+\nu)}x^4 + \right.$$

$$\left. + \frac{1}{368640(1+\nu)}x^8\right],$$

$$u_z^{(\kappa T)} = \frac{45(1+\nu)\mu_4 h^5 \text{ tg}^6\alpha}{c_0^6} x^4 \left(1 - \frac{1}{768}x^4\right);$$

when $j = 5$

$$N_s^{(\kappa T)} = -\frac{43200(1+\nu)\mu_5 Eh^6 \text{ tg}^5\alpha}{c_0^6} \left(1 - \frac{1}{384}x^4 + \frac{1}{2211840}x^8\right),$$

$$N_\theta^{(\kappa T)} = -\frac{43200(1+\nu)\mu_5 Eh^6 \text{ tg}^5\alpha}{c_0^6} \left(1 - \frac{1}{128}x^4 + \frac{1}{442368}x^8\right),$$

$$M_s^{(\kappa_T)} = -\frac{3600(1+\nu)(2+\nu)\,\mu_s Eh^7\,\text{tg}^5\alpha}{c_0^7}x^2\left[1-\frac{1+4\nu}{1920(2+\nu)}\,x^4+\right.$$

$$\left.+\frac{1}{3686400(1+2\nu)}\,x^8\right]\ ,$$

$$M_\theta^{(\kappa_T)} = -\frac{3600(1+\nu)(1+2\nu)\mu_s Eh^7\,\text{tg}^5\alpha}{c_0^7}x^2\left[1-\frac{1+4\nu}{1920(1+2\nu)}\,x^4+\right.$$

$$\left.+\frac{1}{3686400(1+2\nu)}\,x^8\right]\ ,$$

$$u_z^{(\kappa_T)} = \frac{75(1+\nu)\mu_s h^6\,\text{tg}^7\alpha}{c_0^7}x^6\left(1-\frac{1}{3200}\,x^4\right)\ . \tag{5.7.46}$$

When the shell is loaded by axial boundary forces, the constant A_0 in (5.7.29) is

$$A_0 = -\frac{ic_0}{h}\,C, \tag{5.7.47}$$

and the integral of the nonhomogeneous equation can be written in the form

$$N_s^{(C)} = -\frac{4c_0}{hx^2}\,C,$$

$$N_\theta^{(C)} = 0,$$

$$M_s^{(C)} = -M_\theta^{(C)} = \frac{4c_0^2}{3(1+\nu)x^4}\,C, \tag{5.7.48}$$

$$u_z^{(C)} = \frac{2\,\text{tg}^2\alpha\ln x}{Eh}\,C.$$

5.8. Thermal stresses in spherical shells

In the case of a spherical shell

$$R_1 = R_2 = r_0, \quad r = r_0\sin\varphi, \quad ds = r_0\,d\varphi.$$

The governing equations (5.5.11) for the spherical shell, with the upper sign before i, assume the form

$$\frac{d^2\tilde{N}_s}{d\varphi^2} + (3\,\text{ctg}\,\varphi + 2\,\text{tg}\,\varphi)\frac{d\tilde{N}_s}{d\varphi} + (2\,\text{tg}^2\varphi + 3 - i\mu)\tilde{N}_s +$$

$$+ \text{ctg}\,\varphi\,\frac{d}{d\varphi}[Eh\epsilon_T - (1 + \nu)k_0\kappa_T] +$$

$$+ C\left[\frac{2}{r_0\cos^2\varphi} + \frac{(1 + \nu)D_M - r_0 k_0}{D_M r_0\sin^2\varphi}\right] = 0, \tag{5.8.1}$$

where

$$k_0 = \frac{D_M}{r_0}(\nu + i\mu), \quad \mu = \sqrt{\frac{c_0^2 r_0^2}{h^2} - \nu^2} \approx \frac{c_0 r_0}{h},$$

$$D_M = \frac{Eh^3}{c_0^2}, \quad c_0^2 = 12(1 - \nu^2). \tag{5.8.2}$$

Introduction of the new variable

$$x = \cos\varphi \tag{5.8.3}$$

transforms (5.8.1) into

$$(1 - x^2)\frac{d^2\tilde{N}_s}{dx^2} - 2\frac{1 + x^2}{x}\frac{d\tilde{N}_s}{dx} + \left(\frac{2}{x^2} + 1 - i\mu\right)\tilde{N}_s -$$

$$-x\frac{d}{dx}[Eh\epsilon_T - (1 + \nu)k_0\kappa_T] + \frac{2C}{r_0 x^2} + \frac{[(1 + \nu)D_M - r_0 k_0]C}{D_M r_0(1 - x^2)} = 0. \tag{5.8.4}$$

With the substitution

$$\tilde{N}_s = x\tilde{N}, \quad \xi = \frac{1 - x}{2}, \tag{5.8.5}$$

equation (5.8.4) is changed into

$$\frac{d^2\tilde{N}}{d\xi^2} + \frac{c - (a + b + 1)\xi}{\xi(1 - \xi)}\frac{d\tilde{N}}{d\xi} - \frac{ab}{\xi(1 - \xi)}\tilde{N} +$$

$$+ F(\xi) + \frac{A}{\xi(1 - \xi)(1 - 2\xi)^3} + \frac{B}{\xi^2(1 - \xi)^2(1 - 2\xi)} = 0, \tag{5.8.6}$$

145

where

$$a, b = \frac{3}{2} \pm \delta, \quad \delta = \frac{1}{2}\sqrt{5 - 4i\mu}, \quad c = 2, \tag{5.8.7}$$

$$F(\xi) = \frac{1}{2\xi(1 - \xi)} \frac{d}{d\xi} [Eh\epsilon_T - (1 + \nu)k_0\kappa_T],$$

$$A = \frac{2C}{r_0}, \quad B = \frac{[(1 + \nu)D_M - r_0 k_0]C}{4D_M r_0}. \tag{5.8.8}$$

The homogeneous form of (5.8.6), namely

$$\xi(1 - \xi) \frac{d^2\tilde{N}}{d\xi^2} + [c - (a + b + 1)\xi] \frac{d\tilde{N}}{d\xi} - ab\tilde{N} = 0, \tag{5.8.9}$$

is the Gauss hypergeometric differential equation. The solutions $\tilde{N}^{(1)}$ and $\tilde{N}^{(2)}$ are defined in terms of hypergeometric functions. Making use of a theorem concerning hypergeometric functions[1], we find the following particular solutions of this equation:

$$\tilde{N}^{(1)} = F(a, b; c; \xi), \tag{5.8.10}$$

$$\tilde{N}^{(2)} = F(a, b; a + b + 1 - c; 1 - \xi), \tag{5.8.11}$$

where $F(a, b; c; x)$ is the hypergeometric function. The solution of (5.8.9) that is regular in the vicinity of $\xi = 0$ has been chosen as $\tilde{N}^{(1)}$ and the solution that is regular in the vicinity of $\xi = 1$ has been chosen as $\tilde{N}^{(2)}$.

Eliminating the singularities in the solutions (5.8.10) and (5.8.11) by means of the well–known formula [15]:

$$F(a, b; c; x) = (1 - x)^{c-a-b} F(c - a, c - b; c; x) \tag{5.8.12}$$

and taking account of the substitution (5.8.5) and the values of the parameters (5.8.7), we find the following general solution of the homogeneous form of (5.8.1)

$$\tilde{N}_s^* = \tilde{C}_1 \tilde{N}_s^{(1)} + \tilde{C}_2 \tilde{N}_s^{(2)}. \tag{5.8.13}$$

---

1) The basic properties of hypergeometric functions used in deriving the solutions for a spherical shell are explained in [15] (cf. pp. 280–294).

where

$$\tilde{N}_s^{(1)} = \frac{1 - 2\xi}{1 - \xi} F\left(\frac{1}{2} + \delta, \frac{1}{2} - \delta; 2; \xi\right), \qquad (5.8.14)$$

$$\tilde{N}_s^{(2)} = \frac{1 - 2\xi}{\xi} F\left(\frac{1}{2} + \delta, \frac{1}{2} - \delta; 2; 1 - \xi\right). \qquad (5.8.15)$$

The solutions (5.8.14) and (5.8.15) have singularities at the points $\xi = 1$ and $\xi = 0$, respectively. For the calculation of the stresses in a closed spherical shell with vertex at either the point $\xi = 0$ or $\xi = 1$, one must use either solution (5.8.14) or (5.8.15).

Having the two linearly independent solutions (5.8.10) and (5.8.11), one can use the method of variation of parameters to find the solution of the nonhomogeneous equation (5.8.6) with the nonhomogeneous term $F(\xi)$. This method yields the solution

$$\tilde{N}^{(\epsilon_T, \kappa_T)} = \tilde{N}^{(1)} \int \frac{\tilde{N}^{(2)} F(\xi)}{\Delta(\tilde{N}^{(1)}, \tilde{N}^{(2)})} d\xi - \tilde{N}^{(2)} \int \frac{\tilde{N}^{(1)} F(\xi)}{\Delta(\tilde{N}^{(1)}, \tilde{N}^{(2)})} d\xi, \quad (5.8.16)$$

where $\Delta(\tilde{N}^{(1)}, \tilde{N}^{(2)})$ is the Wronski determinant of the solutions $\tilde{N}^{(1)}$ and $\tilde{N}^{(2)}$.

$$\Delta(\tilde{N}^{(1)}, \tilde{N}^{(2)}) = \Delta_0 \exp \int_\xi^{\xi_0} \frac{c - (a + b + 1)\xi}{\xi(1 - \xi)} d\xi =$$

$$= \Delta_0 \left(\frac{\xi_0}{\xi}\right)^c \left(\frac{1 - \xi}{1 - \xi_0}\right)^{c - a - b - 1}, \qquad (5.8.17)$$

and Δ_0 is a constant equal to $\Delta(\tilde{N}^{(1)}, \tilde{N}^{(2)})$ for $\xi = \xi_0$.

Substituting (5.8.17) into solution (5.8.16) and recalling the substitution (5.8.5), the relation (5.8.12), and values (5.8.7) of the parameters, we find the following solution of the nonhomogeneous equation (5.8.1)

$$\tilde{N}_s^{(\epsilon_T, \kappa_T)} = \frac{1 - 2\xi}{\Delta_0 \xi_0^2 (1 - \xi_0)^2} \left[\frac{F\left(\frac{1}{2} + \delta, \frac{1}{2} - \delta; 2; \xi\right)}{1 - \xi} \times \right.$$

$$\times \int F\left(\frac{1}{2} + \delta, \frac{1}{2} - \delta; 2; 1 - \xi\right) F(\xi) \xi (1 - \xi)^2 d\xi -$$

$$-\frac{F\left(\frac{1}{2}+\delta,\frac{1}{2}-\delta;2;1-\xi\right)}{\xi}\int F\left(\frac{1}{2}+\delta,\frac{1}{2}-\delta;2;\xi\right)\times$$

$$\times F(\xi)\,\xi^2(1-\xi)d\xi\Bigg].\qquad(5.8.18)$$

When $F(\xi)$ in solution (5.8.18) is replaced by

$$\frac{A}{\xi(1-\xi)(1-2\xi)^3}+\frac{B}{\xi^2(1-\xi)^2(1-2\xi)},$$

we obtain the particular solution $\tilde{N}_s^{(C)}$ corresponding to the axial force $P=-2\pi C$ (see Section 5.6).

The particular integral $\tilde{N}_s^{(C)}$ can be found without quadrature as follows:
With the new independent variable x_1 and dependent variable $\tilde{N}_1$ defined by

$$x_1=\cos^2\varphi,\quad \tilde{N}_s=\frac{x_1}{1-x_1}\tilde{N}_1,\qquad(5.8.19)$$

equation (5.8.1) for the special case $\epsilon_T=\kappa_T=0$ assumes the form

$$x_1^2(1-x_1)\frac{d^2\tilde{N}_1}{dx_1^2}+x_1[c_1-(a_1+b_1+1)x_1]\frac{d\tilde{N}_1}{dx_1}-a_1b_1x_1\tilde{N}_1+$$

$$+A_0+A_1x_1^{-1}=0,\qquad(5.8.20)$$

where

$$a_1,b_1=\frac{1}{4}\pm\delta_1,\quad \delta_1=\frac{1}{4}\sqrt{5-4i\mu};\quad c_1=\frac{3}{2},\qquad(5.8.21)$$

$$A_0=\frac{C}{4}\left(\frac{-1+\nu}{r_0}-\frac{k_0}{D_M}\right),\quad A_{-1}=\frac{C}{2r_0}.\qquad(5.8.22)$$

The particular integral of equation (5.8.20) can be found using well–known results in the theory of hypergeometric equations[1].

---

1) See A.D. Kovalenko, On a generalization of the Lommel function [in Ukranian]. DAN Ukranian RSR, No. 4, 1964.

The particular integral of the equation

$$\left[z \frac{d}{dz} \left(z \frac{d}{dz} + \beta_1 - 1 \right) - z \left(z \frac{d}{dz} + \alpha_1 \right) \left(z \frac{d}{dz} + \alpha_2 \right) \right] W + Az^\lambda =$$

$$= z^2 (1 - z) \frac{d^2 W}{dz^2} + z[\beta_1 - (\alpha_1 + \alpha_2 + 1)z] \frac{dW}{dz} - \alpha_1 \alpha_2 z W + Az^\lambda = 0, \quad (5.8.23)$$

when $\lambda = -m$ $(m = 0, 1, ...)$ is given by

$$W = - \frac{A[\alpha_1 - m]_m [\alpha_2 - m]_m}{[-m]_m [\beta_1 - m]_m (\beta_1 - m - 1)} \times$$

$$\times \,_3\Phi_2 (\alpha_1, \alpha_2, 1 + m; 1 + m, \beta_1; z), \quad (5.8.24)$$

$$[\alpha]_m = \alpha(\alpha + 1) \ldots (\alpha + m - 1), \quad [\alpha]_0 = 1.$$

The function

$$_3\Phi_2 (\alpha_1, \alpha_2, \alpha_3; 1 + m, \beta_2; z)$$

is defined by the expression

$$_3\Phi_2 (\alpha_1, \alpha_2, \alpha_3; 1 + m, \beta_2; z) = \,_3F_2 (\alpha_1, \alpha_2, \alpha_3; 1 + m, \beta_2; z) \ln z -$$

$$- \sum_{n=1}^{m} \frac{(n-1)! \, [-m]_n [1 - \beta_2]_n}{[1 - \alpha_1]_n [1 - \alpha_2]_n [1 - \alpha_3]_n} z^{-n} + \sum_{n=1}^{m} \frac{[\alpha_1]_n [\alpha_2]_n [\alpha_3]_n}{n! \, [1 + m]_n [\beta_2]_n} z^n \times$$

$$\times \sum_{s=1}^{n} \left(\frac{1}{\alpha_1 + s - 1} + \frac{1}{\alpha_2 + s - 1} + \frac{1}{\alpha_3 + s - 1} - \frac{1}{m + s} - \frac{1}{\beta_2 + s - 1} - \frac{1}{s} \right),$$

$$(5.8.25)$$

where

$$_3F_2 (\alpha_1, \alpha_2, \alpha_3; \beta_1, \beta_2; z) = \sum_{n=0}^{\infty} \frac{[\alpha_1]_n [\alpha_2]_n [\alpha_3]_n}{n! \, [\beta_1]_n [\beta_2]_n} z^n. \quad (5.8.26)$$

The functions (5.8.25) and (5.8.26) are particular solutions of the third-order hypergeometric equation

$$\left[z\frac{d}{dz}\left(z\frac{d}{dz}+\beta_1-1\right)\left(z\frac{d}{dz}+\beta_2-1\right) - \right.$$

$$\left. - z\left(z\frac{d}{dz}+\alpha_1\right)\left(z\frac{d}{dz}+\alpha_2\right)\left(z\frac{d}{dz}+\alpha_3\right)\right] W = 0, \quad (5.8.27)$$

in which the parameter $\beta_1 = 1 + m$ $(m = 0, 1, ...)$.

In view of the solution (5.8.24) and the values of the parameters (5.8.21), the particular integral of equation (5.8.20) is found to be

$$\widetilde{N}_1^{(C)} = -2A_0\,{}_3\Phi_2\left(\frac{1}{4}+\delta_1,\ \frac{1}{4}-\delta_1,\ 1;\ 1,\ \frac{3}{2};x_1\right) -$$

$$-4\left(\frac{3}{4}+\delta_1\right)\left(\frac{3}{4}-\delta_1\right) A_{-1}\,{}_3\Phi_2\left(\frac{1}{4}+\delta_1,\frac{1}{4}-\delta_1,2;\ 2,\ \frac{3}{2};x_1\right). \quad (5.8.28)$$

Finally, in virtue of the relation

$${}_3\Phi_2\left(\frac{1}{4}+\delta_1,\ \frac{1}{4}-\delta_1,\ 2;\ 2,\ \frac{3}{2};x_1\right) =$$

$$= {}_3\Phi_2\left(\frac{1}{4}+\delta_1,\frac{1}{4}-\delta_1,1;1,\frac{3}{2};x_1\right) + \frac{1}{2\left(\frac{3}{4}+\delta_1\right)\left(\frac{3}{4}-\delta_1\right)}\ \frac{1}{x_1} \quad (5.8.29)$$

and the substitution (5.8.19), the particular integral of the nonhomogeneous equation (5.8.1) corresponding to an axial load $P = -2\pi C$ is

$$\widetilde{N}_s^{(C)} = -\frac{x_1}{1-x_1}\left\{ \left[2A_0 + 4\left(\frac{3}{4}+\delta_1\right)\left(\frac{3}{4}-\delta_1\right) A_{-1}\right] \times\right.$$

$$\times {}_3\Phi_2\left(\frac{1}{4}+\delta_1,\frac{1}{4}-\delta_1,1;1,\frac{3}{2};x_1\right) + \frac{2A_{-1}}{x_1}\Bigg\}.$$

On the basis of the identity $2A_0 + 4\left(\frac{3}{4}+\delta_1\right)\left(\frac{3}{4}-\delta_1\right) A_{-1} = 0$, this integral reduces to

$$\widetilde{N}_s^{(C)} = -\frac{2A_{-1}}{1-x_1}. \quad (5.8.30)$$

Having found the solution (5.6.1) for $\tilde{N}_s$, we will now determine the solution for the function

$$\tilde{N}_\theta = N_\theta + k_0 \kappa_s, \qquad (5.8.31)$$

where the constant k_0 is defined in (5.8.2). An equation for N_θ is found by multiplying the first equation in (5.5.6) by k_0 and adding the result to the first equation in (5.5.2). In the case of a spherical shell this yields

$$\tilde{N}_\theta = \frac{d}{d\varphi}(\tilde{N}_s \text{ tg } \varphi) + \frac{C}{r_0 \cos^2 \varphi}. \qquad (5.8.32)$$

Substitution of (5.8.13) into (5.8.32), and use of the known transformation and differentiation formulae for hypergeometric functions (see [15]) yields the following general solution $\tilde{N}_\theta$ of the homogeneous equation

$$\tilde{N}_\theta^* = \tilde{N}_s^* + \left(\frac{9}{4} - \delta^2\right) \left[\tilde{C}_1 \frac{\xi}{1-\xi} F\left(\frac{1}{2} + \delta, \frac{1}{2} - \delta; 3; \xi\right) - \right.$$
$$\left. - \tilde{C}_2 \frac{1-\xi}{\xi} F\left(\frac{1}{2} + \delta, \frac{1}{2} - \delta; 3; 1 - \xi\right) \right]. \qquad (5.8.33)$$

Resolution of solutions (5.6.1) and (5.8.32) into real and imaginary parts leads to the solutions for the forces N_s, N_θ and the strains κ_s, κ_θ. Formulae (5.4.6) then furnish the bending moments.

Formulae for the displacements are derived as follows. Setting $R_1 = R_2 = r_0$ in relations (5.2.6) and (5.2.8) and eliminating the displacement u_z in them, we obtain

$$u_s = \sin \varphi \left[r_0 \int \frac{1}{\sin \varphi}(\epsilon_s - \epsilon_\theta) d\varphi + C_s \right]. \qquad (5.8.34)$$

With the aid of relations (5.4.2) and equations (5.5.2) one finds

$$\epsilon_s - \epsilon_\theta = \frac{(1 + \nu)(N_s - N_\theta)}{Eh} = \frac{1 + \nu}{Eh} \left[N_s - \frac{d(N_s \text{ tg } \varphi)}{d\varphi} - \frac{C}{r_0 \cos^2 \varphi} \right] =$$
$$= \frac{1 + \nu}{Eh} \left[-\sin \varphi \frac{d}{d\varphi} \left(\frac{N_s}{\cos \varphi}\right) - \frac{C}{r_0 \cos^2 \varphi} \right]. \qquad (5.8.35)$$

Substitution of expression (5.8.35) into (5.8.34) yields

151

$$u_s = \sin \varphi \left\{ -\frac{(1+\nu)r_0}{Eh} \left[\frac{N_s}{\cos \varphi} + \frac{C}{r_0} \left(\frac{1}{\cos \varphi} + \ln \text{tg} \frac{\varphi}{2} \right) \right] + C_5 \right\}. \qquad (5.8.36)$$

With the known values of u_s, relation (5.2.6) yields

$$u_z = r_0 \epsilon_s - \frac{du_s}{d\varphi} = \frac{r_0}{Eh} (N_s + N_\theta) + r_0 \epsilon_T +$$

$$+ \frac{1+\nu}{Eh} C \left(1 + \cos \varphi \ln \text{tg} \frac{\varphi}{2} \right) - C_5 \cos \varphi. \qquad (5.8.37)$$

It is to be noted that C_5 is the rigid—body displacement of the shell in the axial direction.

For the determination of the homogeneous solutions for the stress resultants and displacements in terms of real functions, we set

$$\tilde{C}_1 = C_1 \div iC_2, \quad \tilde{C}_2 = C_3 + iC_4, \qquad (5.8.38)$$

$$F \left(\frac{1}{2} + \delta, \frac{1}{2} - \delta; c; \xi \right) = \varphi_c(\xi) + i\psi_c(\xi) \qquad (5.8.39)$$

$$(c = 2, 3),$$

where C_n (n = 1, 2, 3, 4) are real constants and $\varphi_c(\xi)$, $\psi_c(\xi)$ (c = 2, 3) are real—valued functions defined by the power series

$$\varphi_c(\xi) = 1 + \sum_{n=1}^{\infty} a_{nc} \xi^n, \qquad (5.8.40)$$

$$\psi_c(\xi) = \sum_{n=1}^{\infty} b_{nc} \xi^n. \qquad (5.8.41)$$

The coefficients a_{nc}, b_{nc} are calculated by means of the recurrence relations

$$a_{nc} = \frac{n(n-1)-1}{n(n+c-1)} a_{(n-1)c} - \frac{\mu}{n(n+c-1)} b_{(n-1)c},$$

$$b_{nc} = \frac{n(n-1)-1}{n(n+c-1)} b_{(n-1)c} + \frac{\mu}{n(n+c-1)} a_{(n-1)c} \qquad (5.8.42)$$

$$(c = 2, 3; \; n = 1, 2, ...; \; a_{oc} = 1; \; b_{oc} = 0).$$

Resolving solutions (5.8.13), (5.8.33) into real and imaginary parts and making use of expressions (5.8.38, 39), we find the particular solutions $N_s^{(n)}$, $N_\theta^{(n)}$, $\kappa_s^{(n)}$, $\kappa_\theta^{(n)}$ ($n = 1, 2, 3, 4$) appearing in the following general solutions of the homogeneous equations

$$N_s^* = \sum_{n=1}^4 C_n N_s^{(n)}, \quad N_\theta^* = \sum_{n=1}^4 C_n N_\theta^{(n)},$$

$$\kappa_s^* = \sum_{n=1}^4 C_n \kappa_s^{(n)}, \quad \kappa_\theta^* = \sum_{n=1}^4 C_n \kappa_\theta^{(n)}.$$

(5.8.43)

After some calculation we obtain

$$N_s^{(1)} = \frac{1 - 2\xi}{1 - \xi} \left[\varphi_2(\xi) - \frac{\nu}{\mu} \psi_2(\xi) \right],$$

$$N_s^{(2)} = -\frac{1 - 2\xi}{1 - \xi} \left[\psi_2(\xi) + \frac{\nu}{\mu} \varphi_2(\xi) \right],$$

$$N_s^{(3)} = \frac{1 - 2\xi}{\xi} \left[\varphi_2(1 - \xi) - \frac{\nu}{\mu} \psi_2(1 - \xi) \right],$$

$$N_s^{(4)} = -\frac{1 - 2\xi}{\xi} \left[\psi_2(1 - \xi) + \frac{\nu}{\mu} \varphi_2(1 - \xi) \right];$$

(5.8.44)

$$N_\theta^{(1)} = N_s^{(1)} + \frac{\xi}{1 - \xi} \left[(1 - \nu) \varphi_3(\xi) - \left(\mu + \frac{\nu}{\mu} \right) \psi_3(\xi) \right],$$

$$N_\theta^{(2)} = N_s^{(2)} - \frac{\xi}{1 - \xi} \left[(1 - \nu) \psi_3(\xi) + \left(\mu + \frac{\nu}{\mu} \right) \varphi_3(\xi) \right],$$

$$N_\theta^{(3)} = N_s^{(3)} - \frac{1 - \xi}{\xi} \left[(1 - \nu) \varphi_3(1 - \xi) - \left(\mu + \frac{\nu}{\mu} \right) \psi_3(1 - \xi) \right],$$

$$N_\theta^{(4)} = N_s^{(4)} + \frac{1 - \xi}{\xi} \left[(1 - \nu) \psi_3(1 - \xi) + \left(\mu + \frac{\nu}{\mu} \right) \varphi_3(1 - \xi) \right];$$

(5.8.45)

$$\kappa_s^{(1)} = \kappa_\theta^{(1)} + \frac{\xi}{1-\xi} \left[\psi_3(\xi) + \mu\varphi_3(\xi) \right] \frac{r_0}{\mu D_M},$$

$$\kappa_s^{(2)} = \kappa_\theta^{(2)} + \frac{\xi}{1-\xi} \left[\varphi_3(\xi) - \mu\psi_3(\xi) \right] \frac{r_0}{\mu D_M},$$

$$\kappa_s^{(3)} = \kappa_\theta^{(3)} - \frac{1-\xi}{\xi} \left[\psi_3(1-\xi) + \mu\varphi_3(1-\xi) \right] \frac{r_0}{\mu D_M}, \tag{5.8.46}$$

$$\kappa_s^{(4)} = \kappa_\theta^{(4)} - \frac{1-\xi}{\xi} \left[\varphi_3(1-\xi) - \mu\psi_3(1-\xi) \right] \frac{r_0}{\mu D_M};$$

$$\kappa_\theta^{(1)} = \frac{1-2\xi}{1-\xi} \psi_2(\xi) \frac{r_0}{\mu D_M},$$

$$\kappa_\theta^{(2)} = \frac{1-2\xi}{1-\xi} \varphi_2(\xi) \frac{r_0}{\mu D_M},$$

$$\kappa_\theta^{(3)} = \frac{1-2\xi}{\xi} \psi_2(1-\xi) \frac{r_0}{\mu D_M}, \tag{5.8.47}$$

$$\kappa_\theta^{(4)} = \frac{1-2\xi}{\xi} \varphi_2(1-\xi) \frac{r_0}{\mu D_M},$$

Substitution of solutions (5.8.43) in the special forms of (5.4.6), (5.8.36), and (5.8.37) for the case $\epsilon_T = 0$, $\kappa_T = 0$, $C = 0$, $C_5 = 0$ yields

$$M_s^* = \sum_{n=1}^{4} C_n M_s^{(n)}, \quad M_\theta^* = \sum_{n=1}^{4} C_n M_\theta^{(n)},$$

$$u_s^* = \sum_{n=1}^{4} C_n u_s^{(n)}, \quad u_z^* = \sum_{n=1}^{4} C_n u_z^{(n)}, \tag{5.8.48}$$

where

$$M_s^{(1)} = \left\{ (1+\nu) \frac{1-2\xi}{1-\xi} \varphi_2(\xi) + \frac{\xi}{1-\xi} \left[\psi_3(\xi) + \mu\varphi_3(\xi) \right] \right\} \frac{r_0}{\mu},$$

$$M_s^{(2)} = \left\{ (1+\nu) \frac{1-2\xi}{1-\xi} \varphi_2(\xi) + \frac{\xi}{1-\xi} \left[\varphi_3(\xi) - \mu\psi_3(\xi) \right] \right\} \frac{r_0}{\mu},$$

154

$$M_s^{(3)} = \left\{ (1+\nu)\frac{1-2\xi}{\xi}\,\psi_2(1-\xi) - \frac{1-\xi}{\xi}\,[\psi_3(1-\xi) + \mu\varphi_3(1-\xi)] \right\}\frac{r_0}{\mu},$$

$$M_s^{(4)} = \left\{ (1+\nu)\frac{1-2\xi}{\xi}\,\varphi_2(1-\xi) - \frac{1-\xi}{\xi}\,[\varphi_3(1-\xi) - \mu\psi_3(1-\xi)] \right\}\frac{r_0}{\mu}; \quad (5.8.49)$$

$$M_\theta^{(1)} = M_s^{(1)} - \frac{\xi}{1-\xi}\,[\psi_3(\xi) + \mu\varphi_3(\xi)]\,\frac{(1-\nu)r_0}{\mu},$$

$$M_\theta^{(2)} = M_s^{(2)} - \frac{\xi}{1-\xi}\,[\varphi_3(\xi) - \mu\psi_3(\xi)]\,\frac{(1-\nu)r_0}{\mu},$$

$$\qquad\qquad\qquad (5.8.50)$$

$$M_\theta^{(3)} = M_s^{(3)} + \frac{1-\xi}{\xi}\,[\psi_3(1-\xi) + \mu\varphi_3(1-\xi)]\,\frac{(1-\nu)r_0}{\mu},$$

$$M_\theta^{(4)} = M_s^{(4)} + \frac{1-\xi}{\xi}\,[\varphi_3(1-\xi) - \mu\psi_3(1-\xi)]\,\frac{(1-\nu)r_0}{\mu};$$

$$u_s^{(n)} = -(1+\nu)\,\mathrm{tg}\,\varphi N_s^{(n)}\frac{r_0}{Eh} = -(1+\nu)\frac{\sqrt{1-(1-2\xi)^2}}{1-2\xi}\,N_s^{(n)}\frac{r_0}{Eh} \qquad (5.8.51)$$

$$(n = 1, 2, 3, 4),$$

$$u_z^{(n)} = (N_s^{(n)} + N_\theta^{(n)})\frac{r_0}{Eh} \qquad (n = 1, 2, 3, 4). \qquad (5.8.52)$$

Similar resolution of solutions (5.8.18) and (5.8.30) leads in virtue of (5.4.6), (5.8.36), and (5.8.37) to the determination of the particular non-homogeneous solutions

$$N_s^{(\epsilon_T, \kappa_T)}, \dots, u_z^{(\epsilon_T, \kappa_T)},$$

$$N_s^{(C)}, \dots, u_z^{(C)},$$

which must be added to the general solution of the homogeneous equations (5.8.43), (5.8.48) in order to obtain the general solutions for the forces N_s, N_θ, the strains κ_s, κ_θ and the bending moments M_s, M_θ, and the displacements u_s, u_z:

$$N_s = N_s^* + N_s^{(\epsilon_T, \kappa_T)} + N_s^{(C)},$$

$$\dots\dots\dots\dots\dots\dots\dots\dots\dots \qquad (5.8.53)$$

$$u_z = u_z^* + u_z^{(\epsilon_T, \kappa_T)} + u_z^{(C)} - C_5 \cos\varphi.$$

When determining the particular solutions associated with the purely thermal strains ϵ_T, κ_T, we will limit consideration to the case when the temperature field $T - T_0$ varies only through the thickness of the shell. In this case $\epsilon_T = $ const., $\kappa_T = $ const., and the corresponding nonhomogeneous term in (5.8.1) vanishes. Then, $\tilde{N}_s^{(\epsilon_T, \kappa_T)} = 0$, and on the basis of formula (5.8.32) it follows that $C = 0$, $\tilde{N}_\theta^{(\epsilon_T, \kappa_T)} = 0$. In virtue of these results, it is found from (5.4.6), (5.8.36), and (5.8.37) that

$$N_s^{(\epsilon_T, \kappa_T)} = N_\theta^{(\epsilon_T, \kappa_T)} = 0,$$

$$\kappa_s^{(\epsilon_T, \kappa_T)} = \kappa_\theta^{(\epsilon_T, \kappa_T)} = 0,$$

$$M_s^{(\epsilon_T, \kappa_T)} = M_\theta^{(\epsilon_T, \kappa_T)} = -(1 + \nu)D_M \kappa_T, \qquad (5.8.54)$$

$$u_s^{(\epsilon_T, \kappa_T)} = 0,$$

$$u_z^{(\epsilon_T, \kappa_T)} = r_0 \epsilon_T.$$

Resolving (5.8.30), (5.8.32) into real and imaginary parts and using (5.5.10), (5.8.31), we obtain

$$N_s^{(C)} = -N_\theta^{(C)} = -\frac{C}{r_0 \sin^2 \varphi}, \qquad (5.8.55)$$

$$\kappa_s^{(C)} = \kappa_\theta^{(C)} = 0. \qquad (5.8.56)$$

Formulae (5.4.6), (5.8.36), and (5.8.37) then yield

$$M_s^{(C)} = M_\theta^{(C)} = 0, \qquad (5.8.57)$$

$$u_s^{(C)} = \left(\text{ctg}\, \varphi - \sin \varphi \ln \text{tg}\, \frac{\varphi}{2} \right) \frac{(1 + \nu)\,C}{Eh} + C_5 \sin \varphi,$$
$$\qquad (5.8.58)$$
$$u_z^{(C)} = \left(1 + \cos \varphi \ln \text{tg}\, \frac{\varphi}{2} \right) \frac{(1 + \nu)\,C}{Eh} - C_5 \cos \varphi.$$

Once N_s is known, formulae (5.4.2), (5.5.1) yield the corresponding particular solutions for ϵ_s, ϵ_θ, and Q. With the particular solutions for the forces N_s, N_θ, the bending moments M_s, M_θ, the strains ϵ_s, ϵ_θ, κ_s, κ_θ, and the displacements u_s, u_z, the boundary conditions discussed in Section 5.6 lead to the determination of the constants of integration C_n ($n = 1, ..., 5$) entering in solutions (5.8.43), (5.8.48), and (5.8.53). The above procedure is an effective solution of the thermoelastic problem for a spherical shell in an axisymmetric temperature field.

156

Chapter VI

AXISYMMETRIC PROBLEM OF THERMOELASTICITY

6.1. Basic equations

In this chapter we shall consider thermal stresses in bodies of revolution due to a temperature field that is symmetric with respect to the axis of revolution. An axisymmetric temperature field in a body of revolution gives rise to an axisymmetric state of stress.

When the body is cylindrical or spherical this state of stress is best studied with the aid of cylindrical or spherical coordinates (see Figs. 5 and 7).

When the z-axis coincides with the axis of revolution, it follows from the symmetry of the strains with respect to the z-axis that none of the components of the stress tensor depend on the angle θ.

In the quasi-static formulation, we study such problems with the aid of the Papkovich-Neuber general solution

$$\mathbf{u} = \mathbf{u}^{(T)} + \mathbf{u}^* = \operatorname{grad} \Phi + 4(1 - \nu)\mathbf{B} - \operatorname{grad}(\mathbf{B} \cdot \mathbf{r} + B_0), \qquad (6.1.1)$$

in which the scalar function Φ, the harmonic vector $\mathbf{B}$ and the harmonic scalar B_0 are governed by equations (2.2.8), (2.2.5), and (2.2.6), respectively. In the present case there are functions of only two coordinates. When using this solution it should be borne in mind that, in a system of curvilinear coordinates, the components of the harmonic vector $\mathbf{B}$ do not satisfy the Laplace equation. Making use of a well-known identity in vector analysis [18], the components of $\mathbf{B}$ will be found from the vector equation

$$\nabla^2 \mathbf{B} = \operatorname{grad} \operatorname{div} \mathbf{B} - \operatorname{rot} \operatorname{rot} \mathbf{B} = 0. \qquad (6.1.2)$$

Below we will derive the formulae needed for the study of the axisymmetric problem of thermoelasticity in cylindrical and spherical coordinates.

Cylindrical coordinates. When the state of stress is axisymmetric, the displacement u_θ, the strains $\epsilon_{r\theta}, \epsilon_{\theta z}$, and the stresses $\sigma_{r\theta}, \sigma_{\theta z}$ vanish (see Section 2.6).

The components u_r, u_z of the displacement vector in the directions of the

157

unit vectors e_r, e_z (see Fig. 5) have the form

$$u_r = u_r^{(T)} + u_r^*,$$
$$u_z = u_z^{(T)} + u_z^*,$$

(6.1.3)

where

$$u_r^{(T)} = \frac{\partial \Phi}{\partial r}, \quad u_z^{(T)} = \frac{\partial \Phi}{\partial z},$$

(6.1.4)

$$u_r^* = 4(1 - \nu)B_r - \frac{\partial}{\partial r}(rB_r + zB_z + B_0),$$

(6.1.5)

$$u_z^* = 4(1 - \nu)B_z - \frac{\partial}{\partial z}(rB_r + zB_z + B_0).$$

In the present case the Poisson equation (2.2.8) for the scalar function Φ assumes the form

$$\frac{\partial^2 \Phi}{\partial r^2} + \frac{1}{r}\frac{\partial \Phi}{\partial r} + \frac{\partial^2 \Phi}{\partial z^2} = \frac{1 + \nu}{1 - \nu}\alpha_T(T - T_0),$$

(6.1.6)

where T_0 is the temperature of the body in the stress—free state.

The function B_r, B_z in solution (6.1.4) are the components of the harmonic vector $\mathbf{B}$ in the directions of the unit vectors e_r and e_z (Fig. 5).

Replacing the vector operators in (6.1.2) by the expressions (2.6.1) to (2.6.3) and taking account of the fact that all derivatives with respect to θ vanish, we obtain for B_r and B_z the following governing equations

$$\frac{\partial^2 B_r}{\partial r^2} + \frac{1}{r}\frac{\partial B_r}{\partial r} - \frac{B_r}{r^2} + \frac{\partial^2 B_r}{\partial z^2} = 0,$$

(6.1.7)

$$\frac{\partial^2 B_z}{\partial r^2} + \frac{1}{r}\frac{\partial B_z}{\partial r} + \frac{\partial^2 B_z}{\partial z^2} = 0.$$

(6.1.8)

It should be noted that equation (6.1.7) for B_r is not the Laplace equation.

In cylindrical coordinates the Laplace equation (2.2.6) for the harmonic scalar B_0 assumes the form

$$\frac{\partial^2 B_0}{\partial r^2} + \frac{1}{r}\frac{\partial B_0}{\partial r} + \frac{\partial^2 B_0}{\partial z^2} = 0.$$

(6.1.9)

158

$$\epsilon_r = \epsilon_r^{(T)} + \epsilon_r^*,$$

$$\cdots\cdots\cdots\cdots \qquad (6.1.10)$$

$$\epsilon_{rz} = \epsilon_{rz}^{(T)} + \epsilon_{rz}^*;$$

$$\sigma_r = \sigma_r^{(T)} + \sigma_r^*,$$

$$\cdots\cdots\cdots\cdots \qquad (6.1.11)$$

$$\sigma_{rz} = \sigma_{rz}^{(T)} + \sigma_{rz}^*,$$

where

$$\epsilon_r^{(T)} = \frac{\partial^2 \Phi}{\partial r^2}, \ \ \epsilon_\theta^{(T)} = \frac{1}{r}\frac{\partial \Phi}{\partial r}, \ \ \epsilon_z^{(T)} = \frac{\partial^2 \Phi}{\partial z^2}, \ \ \epsilon_{rz}^{(T)} = \frac{\partial^2 \Phi}{\partial r \partial z}; \qquad (6.1.12)$$

$$\epsilon_r^* = \frac{\partial u_r^*}{\partial r}, \ \ \epsilon_\theta^* = \frac{1}{r}u_r^*, \ \ \epsilon_z^* = \frac{\partial u_z^*}{\partial z}, \ \ \epsilon_{rz}^* = \frac{1}{2}\left(\frac{\partial u_r^*}{\partial z} + \frac{\partial u_z^*}{\partial r}\right); \quad (6.1.13)$$

$$\sigma_r^{(T)} = 2\mu\left(\frac{\partial^2 \Phi}{\partial r^2} - \nabla_1^2 \Phi\right), \ \ \sigma_\theta^{(T)} = 2\mu\left(\frac{1}{r}\frac{\partial \Phi}{\partial r} - \nabla_1^2 \Phi\right),$$

$$\sigma_z^{(T)} = 2\mu\left(\frac{\partial^2 \Phi}{\partial z^2} - \nabla_1^2 \Phi\right), \ \ \sigma_{rz}^{(T)} = 2\mu\frac{\partial^2 \Phi}{\partial r \partial z}, \qquad (6.1.14)$$

$$\nabla_1^2 = \frac{\partial^2 \Phi}{\partial r^2} + \frac{1}{r}\frac{\partial \Phi}{\partial r} + \frac{\partial^2 \Phi}{\partial z^2};$$

$$\sigma_r^* = 2\mu\left(\epsilon_r^* + \frac{\nu}{1-2\nu}e^*\right), \ \ \sigma_\theta^* = 2\mu\left(\epsilon_\theta^* + \frac{\nu}{1-2\nu}e^*\right),$$

$$\sigma_z^* = 2\mu\left(\epsilon_z^* + \frac{\nu}{1-2\nu}e^*\right), \ \ \sigma_{rz}^* = 2\mu\epsilon_{rz}^*, \qquad (6.1.15)$$

$$e^* = \epsilon_r^* + \epsilon_\theta^* + \epsilon_z^*.$$

Spherical coordinates. When the state of stress is axisymmetric, the components $\epsilon_{r\theta}$, $\epsilon_{\theta\varphi}$ of the strain, and the stresses $\sigma_{r\theta}$, $\sigma_{\theta\varphi}$ all vanish (see Section 2.6).

The non—zero components of the displacement vector have the form

159

$$u_r = u_r^{(T)} + u_r^*,$$

$$u_\varphi = u_\varphi^{(T)} + u_\varphi^*,$$

(6.1.16)

where

$$u_r^{(T)} = \frac{\partial \Phi}{\partial r}, \quad u_\varphi^{(T)} = \frac{1}{r} \frac{\partial \Phi}{\partial \varphi};$$

(6.1.17)

$$u_r^* = 4(1 - \nu)B_r - \frac{\partial}{\partial r}(rB_r + B_0),$$

(6.1.18)

$$u_\varphi^* = 4(1 - \nu)B_\varphi - \frac{1}{r} \frac{\partial}{\partial \varphi}(rB_r + B_0).$$

Here B_r and B_φ are the components of **B** in the directions of the unit vectors $\mathbf{e}_r$ and $\mathbf{e}_\varphi$ (see Fig. 7).

With expression (2.6.10) for the Laplace operator in spherical coordinates, the equation governing the thermoelastic potential Φ is found to be

$$\frac{1}{r^2} \frac{\partial}{\partial r} \left(r^2 \frac{\partial \Phi}{\partial r} \right) + \frac{1}{r^2 \sin \varphi} \frac{\partial}{\partial \varphi} \left(\sin \varphi \frac{\partial \Phi}{\partial \varphi} \right) = \frac{1+\nu}{1-\nu} \alpha_T (T - T_0).$$ (6.1.19)

In order to formulate the equations for B_r and B_φ, we again make use of (6.1.2). Replacing the vector operators in it by the formulae (2.6.7) to (2.6.9), we obtain the following equations

$$\frac{\partial e_B}{\partial r} - \frac{1}{r \sin \varphi} \frac{\partial}{\partial \varphi}(\sin \varphi \omega_B) = 0,$$

(6.1.20)

$$\frac{\partial e_B}{\partial \varphi} + \frac{\partial}{\partial r}(r\omega_B) = 0,$$

where

$$e_B = \operatorname{div} \mathbf{B} = \frac{1}{r} \left[\frac{1}{r} \frac{\partial}{\partial r}(r^2 B_r) + \frac{1}{\sin \varphi} \frac{\partial}{\partial \varphi}(\sin \varphi B_\varphi) \right],$$

(6.1.21)

$$\omega_B = \operatorname{rot}_\theta \mathbf{B} = \frac{1}{r} \left[\frac{\partial (rB_\varphi)}{\partial r} - \frac{\partial B_r}{\partial \varphi} \right]$$

Equations (6.1.20) for e_B and ω_B are coupled.

160

By means of some simple transformations, we can reduce equations (6.1.20) to two independent equations in e_B and ω_B.

Taking the divergence of equation (6.1.2) and using the identities

$$\text{div grad } (\ ) = \nabla^2 (\ ),$$

$$\text{div rot } (\ ) = 0,$$

it is found that e_B is an harmonic function satisfying the equation

$$\nabla^2 e_B = \frac{1}{r^2} \frac{\partial}{\partial r} \left(r^2 \frac{\partial e_B}{\partial r} \right) + \frac{1}{r^2 \sin \varphi} \frac{\partial}{\partial \varphi} \left(\sin \varphi \frac{\partial e_B}{\partial \varphi} \right) = 0. \quad (6.1.22)$$

Application of the operator rot ( ) to (6.1.2) yields the following equation for the function ω_B:

$$r \frac{\partial^2}{\partial r^2} (r\omega_B) + \frac{\partial}{\partial \varphi} \left[\frac{1}{\sin \varphi} \frac{\partial}{\partial \varphi} (\sin \varphi \omega_B) \right] = 0. \quad (6.1.23)$$

The operator rot rot rot ( ) arising in the derivation of (6.1.23) could be calculated with the aid of formula (2.6.9) since rot grad ( ) vanishes identically.

When the solutions of equations (6.1.22, 23) have been found, equations (6.1.21) are first order equations for the determination of B_r and B_φ. The equation for the harmonic function B_0 appearing in the solution (6.1.18) is

$$\frac{1}{r^2} \frac{\partial}{\partial r} \left(r^2 \frac{\partial B_0}{\partial r} \right) + \frac{1}{r^2 \sin \varphi} \frac{\partial}{\partial \varphi} \left(\sin \varphi \frac{\partial B_0}{\partial \varphi} \right) = 0. \quad (6.1.24)$$

The strains and stresses are given by the formulae

$$\epsilon_r = \epsilon_r^{(T)} + \epsilon_r^*,$$

$$\dotfill \quad (6.1.25)$$

$$\epsilon_{r\varphi} = \epsilon_{r\varphi}^{(T)} + \epsilon_{r\varphi}^*;$$

$$\sigma_r = \sigma_r^{(T)} + \sigma_r^*,$$

$$\dotfill \quad (6.1.26)$$

$$\sigma_{r\varphi} = \sigma_{r\varphi}^{(T)} + \sigma_{r\varphi}^*,$$

where

161

$$\epsilon_r^{(T)} = \frac{\partial^2 \Phi}{\partial r^2} \ , \ \epsilon_\varphi^{(T)} = \frac{1}{r} \left(\frac{\partial \Phi}{\partial r} + \frac{1}{r} \frac{\partial^2 \Phi}{\partial \varphi^2} \right) ,$$

$$\epsilon_\theta^{(T)} = \frac{1}{r} \left(\frac{\partial \Phi}{\partial r} + \frac{1}{r} \frac{\partial \Phi}{\partial \varphi} \operatorname{ctg} \varphi \right) , \qquad (6.1.27)$$

$$\epsilon_{r\varphi}^{(T)} = \frac{1}{2} \left[\frac{\partial}{\partial r} \left(\frac{1}{r} \frac{\partial \Phi}{\partial \varphi} \right) + \frac{1}{r} \left(\frac{\partial^2 \Phi}{\partial r \partial \varphi} - \frac{1}{r} \frac{\partial \Phi}{\partial \varphi} \right) \right] ,$$

$$\epsilon_r^* = \frac{\partial u_r^*}{\partial r} \ , \ \epsilon_\varphi^* = \frac{1}{r} \left(u_r^* + \frac{\partial u_\varphi^*}{\partial \varphi} \right) ,$$

$$\epsilon_\theta^* = \frac{1}{r} \left(u_r^* + u_\varphi^* \operatorname{ctg} \varphi \right) , \qquad (6.1.28)$$

$$\epsilon_{r\varphi}^* = \frac{1}{2} \left[\frac{1}{r} \left(\frac{\partial u_r^*}{\partial \varphi} - u_\varphi^* \right) + \frac{\partial u_\varphi^*}{\partial r} \right] ;$$

$$\sigma_r^{(T)} = 2\mu \left[\frac{\partial^2 \Phi}{\partial r^2} - \nabla_1^2 \Phi \right] ,$$

$$\sigma_\varphi^{(T)} = 2\mu \left(\frac{1}{r} \frac{\partial \Phi}{\partial r} + \frac{1}{r^2} \frac{\partial^2 \Phi}{\partial \varphi^2} - \nabla_1^2 \Phi \right) ,$$

$$\sigma_\theta^{(T)} = 2\mu \left(\frac{1}{r} \frac{\partial \Phi}{\partial r} + \frac{1}{r^2} \frac{\partial \Phi}{\partial \varphi} \operatorname{ctg} \varphi - \nabla_1^2 \Phi \right) , \qquad (6.1.29)$$

$$\sigma_{r\varphi}^{(T)} = \mu \left[\frac{\partial}{\partial r} \left(\frac{1}{r} \frac{\partial \Phi}{\partial \varphi} \right) + \frac{1}{r} \left(\frac{\partial^2 \Phi}{\partial r \partial \varphi} - \frac{1}{r} \frac{\partial \Phi}{\partial \varphi} \right) \right] ,$$

$$\nabla_1^2 \Phi = \frac{\partial^2 \Phi}{\partial r^2} + \frac{2}{r} \frac{\partial \Phi}{\partial r} + \frac{1}{r^2} \frac{\partial \Phi}{\partial \varphi} \operatorname{ctg} \varphi + \frac{1}{r^2} \frac{\partial^2 \Phi}{\partial \varphi^2} ;$$

$$\sigma_r^* = 2\mu \left(\epsilon_r^* + \frac{\nu}{1 - 2\nu} e^* \right) ,$$

$$\sigma_\varphi^* = 2\mu \left(\epsilon_\varphi^* + \frac{\nu}{1 - 2\nu} e^* \right) ,$$

$$\sigma_\theta^* = 2\mu \left(\epsilon_\theta^* + \frac{\nu}{1 - 2\nu} e^* \right),$$

$$\sigma_{r\varphi}^* = 2\mu \epsilon_{r\varphi}^*;$$

$$e^* = \epsilon_r^* + \epsilon_\varphi^* + \epsilon_\theta^*. \tag{6.1.30}$$

In the rest of this Chapter examples illustrating the general solution (6.1.1) will be described. We will show how to calculate the thermal stresses in a finite cylinder (Section 6.2) and in a hollow sphere (Section 6.3) when the temperature field is prescribed.

6.2. Thermal stresses in finite cylinder

Let us consider the determination of the thermal stresses in a solid cylinder of radius r_2 and length $2l$ caused by axisymmetric heating which produces a temperature field $T \equiv T(r, z)$ symmetric with respect to both the z-axis and the plane $z = 0$ (see Fig. 24).

The cylindrical surface $r = r_2$ and the faces are stress free.

The problem of the unsteady heat conduction in a finite cylinder was treated in Section 3.7.

At each instant of time the temperature field in the cylinder can be approximated by the expression

$$T(r, z) - T_0 = \sum_{n=0}^{\infty} a_n(r) \cos k_n z, \tag{6.2.1}$$

where T_0 is the initial temperature corresponding to the stress–free state in the cylinder. The Fourier coefficients are given by the formulae

$$a_0(r) = \frac{1}{l} \int_0^l [T(r, z) - T_0] dz, \tag{6.2.2}$$

$$a_n(r) = \frac{2}{l} \int_0^l [T(r, z) - T_0] \cos k_n z dz,$$

$$k_n = \frac{\pi n}{l} \quad (n = 1, 2, \dots).$$

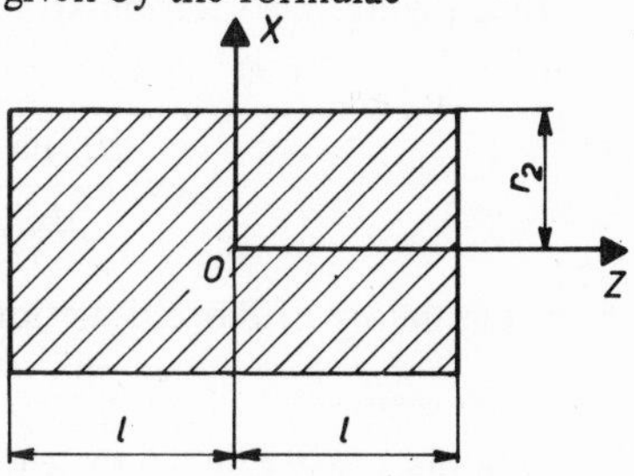

Fig. 24.

163

Having a known temperature field, the thermoelastic potential satisfying equation (6.1.6) will be chosen in the form

$$\Phi(r, z) = \frac{1 + \nu}{1 - \nu} \alpha_T \sum_{n=0}^{\infty} b_n(r) \cos k_n z. \qquad (6.2.3)$$

Substitution of expressions (6.2.1), (6.2.3) into equation (6.1.6) yields the following equations for the determination of the functions $b_n(r)$

$$r \frac{d}{dr}\left[r \frac{db_n(r)}{dr} \right] - k_n^2 r^2 b_n(r) = r^2 a_n(r) \qquad (6.2.4)$$

$$(n = 0, 1, \dots).$$

When $n = 0$ ($k_n = 0$), equation (6.2.4) yields

$$b_0(r) = \int_0^r \frac{1}{r} \int_0^r r a_0(r)\, dr\, dr. \qquad (6.2.5)$$

When $n \geqslant 1$, the homogeneous form of (6.2.4) is the Bessel equation of zeroth order. The non–homogeneous equation can then be solved by the method of variation of parameters. This yields the particular solution[1]

$$b_n(r) = I_0(k_n r) \int r K_0(k_n r) a_n(r)\, dr -$$

$$- K_0(k_n r) \int r I_0(k_n r) a_n(r)\, dr \qquad (6.2.6)$$

$$(n = 1, 2, \dots).$$

In deriving the solution (6.2.6) use has been made of the well–known relation

$$I_0(x) \frac{dK_0(x)}{dx} - K_0(x) \frac{dI_0(x)}{dx} = -\frac{1}{x} \qquad (6.2.7)$$

from the theory of Bessel functions.

---

1) In this Chapter we use the notation and formulae for Bessel functions introduced in Chapter III.

The displacements and stresses calculated by means of (6.1.4), (6.1.14) from the thermoelastic potential (6.2.3) are

$$u_r^{(T)} = \frac{1+\nu}{1-\nu}\alpha_T \frac{db_0(r)}{dr} + \frac{1+\nu}{1-\nu}\alpha_T \sum_{n=1}^{\infty} \frac{db_n(r)}{dr} \cos k_n z,$$

$$u_z^{(T)} = -\frac{1+\nu}{1-\nu}\alpha_T \sum_{n=1}^{\infty} k_n b_n(r) \sin k_n z; \qquad (6.2.8)$$

$$\frac{\sigma_r^{(T)}}{2\mu} = \frac{1+\nu}{1-\nu}\alpha_T \left[\frac{d^2 b_0(r)}{dr^2} - a_0(r) \right] + \frac{1+\nu}{1-\nu}\alpha_T \times$$

$$\times \sum_{n=1}^{\infty} \left[\frac{d^2 b_n(r)}{dr^2} - a_n(r) \right] \cos k_n z,$$

$$\frac{\sigma_\theta^{(T)}}{2\mu} = \frac{1+\nu}{1-\nu}\alpha_T \left[\frac{1}{r}\frac{db_0(r)}{dr} - a_0(r) \right] + \frac{1+\nu}{1-\nu}\alpha_T \times \qquad (6.2.9)$$

$$\times \sum_{n=1}^{\infty} \left[\frac{1}{r}\frac{db_n(r)}{dr} - a_n(r) \right] \cos k_n z,$$

$$\frac{\sigma_z^{(T)}}{2\mu} = -\frac{1+\nu}{1-\nu}\alpha_T \sum_{n=1}^{\infty} [k_n^2 b_n(r) + a_n(r)] \cos k_n z,$$

$$\frac{\sigma_{rz}^{(T)}}{2\mu} = -\frac{1+\nu}{1-\nu}\alpha_T \sum_{n=1}^{\infty} k_n \frac{db_n(r)}{dr} \sin k_n z.$$

We now turn to the construction of general solutions of the homogeneous equations for the present problem.

When the temperature field is symmetric with respect to the plane $z = 0$, the general solution (6.1.5) must obviously satisfy the conditions

$$u_r^*(-z) = u_r^*(z), \quad u_z^*(-z) = -u_z^*(z). \qquad (6.2.10)$$

We will split up the solution (6.1.5) into the two parts:

165

$$u_r^* = u_r^I + u_r^{II},$$

$$u_z^* = u_z^I + u_z^{II}. \tag{6.2.11}$$

The first part with superscript I will be constructed so that arbitrary stress boundary conditions can be satisfied on the cylinder $r = r_2$; the stresses corresponding to this solution must be in the form of complete orthogonal series on the interval $-l \leqslant z \leqslant l$. The functions B_r and B_0 in (6.1.5) will be chosen in the forms

$$B_r = g_0(r) + \sum_{n=1}^{\infty} g_n(r) \cos k_n z,$$

$$B_0 = h_0(r) + \sum_{n=1}^{\infty} h_n(r) \cos k_n z. \tag{6.2.12}$$

These must satisfy (6.1.7) and (6.1.9), respectively. Further, the function B_z can in this case be set equal to zero:

$$B_z = 0. \tag{6.2.13}$$

Substitution of expressions (6.2.12) into equations (6.1.7) and (6.1.9) yields the following system of equations for the determination of $g_0(r)$, $h_0(r)$, $g_n(r)$, and $h_n(r)$:

$$\frac{d^2 g_0(r)}{dr^2} + \frac{1}{r}\frac{dg_0(r)}{dr} - \frac{g_0(r)}{r^2} = 0,$$

$$\frac{d^2 h_0(r)}{dr^2} + \frac{1}{r}\frac{dh_0(r)}{dr} = 0, \tag{6.2.14}$$

$$\frac{d^2 g_n(r)}{dr^2} + \frac{1}{r}\frac{dg_n(r)}{dr} - \left(\frac{1}{r^2} + k_n^2\right) g_n(r) = 0,$$

$$\frac{d^2 h_n(r)}{dr^2} + \frac{1}{r}\frac{dh_n(r)}{dr} - k_n^2 h_n(r) = 0 \tag{6.2.15}$$

$$(n = 1, 2, \dots).$$

The general solution of these equations has the form

$$g_0(r) = \alpha_0 r + \alpha_0' \frac{1}{r}, \quad h_0(r) = \beta_0 + \beta_0' \ln r,$$

$$g_n(r) = \alpha_n I_1(k_n r) + \alpha_n' K_1(k_n r), \quad (6.2.16)$$

$$h_n(r) = \beta_n I_0(k_n r) + \beta_n' K_0(k_n r)$$

$$(n = 1, 2, \ldots),$$

where $\alpha_0, \ldots, \beta_n'$ are arbitrary constants.

Since the cylinder is solid, we must set

$$\alpha_0' = 0, \ldots, \beta_n' = 0. \quad (6.2.17)$$

In view of (6.2.17), the formulae (6.2.12) and (6.1.5) yield

$$u_r^{\mathrm{I}} = 2(1 - 2\nu)\alpha_0 r + \sum_{n=1}^{\infty} \left\{ \alpha_n \left[4(1 - \nu)I_1(k_n r) - k_n r I_0(k_n r) \right] - \right.$$

$$\left. - \beta_n k_n I_1(k_n r) \right\} \cos k_n z, \quad (6.2.18)$$

$$u_z^{\mathrm{I}} = \sum_{n=1}^{\infty} \left[\alpha_n k_n r I_1(k_n r) + \beta_n k_n I_0(k_n r) \right] \sin k_n z.$$

When constructing the second particular solution u_r^{II}, u_z^{II}, we can set

$$B_r = 0. \quad (6.2.19)$$

Similar arguments lead to the representation of the harmonic functions B_z and B_0 in the form

$$B_z = p_0(z) + \sum_{j=1}^{\infty} p_j(z) J_0(\lambda_j r),$$

$$(6.2.20)$$

$$B_0 = q_0(z) + \sum_{j=1}^{\infty} q_j(z) J_0(\lambda_j r),$$

The values λ_j in (6.2.20) are roots of the transcendental equation

$$J_1(\lambda r_2) = 0. \quad (6.2.21)$$

167

This guarantees the orthogonality of the functions

$$J_0(\lambda_j r) \text{ and } J_1(\lambda_j r) = -\frac{1}{\lambda_j} \frac{dJ_0(\lambda_j r)}{dr}$$

and is a necessary condition for the expansion of an arbitrary function in a series of the functions $J_0(\lambda_j r)$ and $J_1(\lambda_j r)$ on the interval $0 \leqslant r \leqslant r_2$.

Substitution of expressions (6.2.20) into equations (6.1.8) and (6.1.9) yields

$$\frac{d^2 p_0(z)}{dz^2} = 0, \qquad \frac{d^2 q_0(z)}{dz^2} = 0, \qquad (6.2.22)$$

$$\frac{d^2 p_j(z)}{dz^2} - \lambda_j^2 p_j(z) = 0, \qquad \frac{d^2 q_j(z)}{dz^2} - \lambda_j^2 q_j(z) = 0. \qquad (6.2.23)$$

In view of condition (6.2.11), the solutions of equations (6.2.22) and (6.2.23) will be chosen in the form

$$p_0(z) = \gamma_0 z, \qquad q_0(z) = \delta_0,$$

$$p_j(z) = \gamma_j \operatorname{sh} \lambda_j z, \quad q_j(z) = \delta_j \operatorname{ch} \lambda_j z \qquad (6.2.24)$$

$$(j = 1, 2, \ldots),$$

where $\gamma_0, \delta_0, \gamma_j, \delta_j$ are constants of integration.

These solutions for B_z and B_0 enable one to write the second part of the solution in the form

$$u_r^{II} = \sum_{j=1}^{\infty} \left\{ \gamma_j \lambda_j z \operatorname{sh} \lambda_j z + \delta_j \lambda_j \operatorname{ch} \lambda_j z \right\} J_1(\lambda_j r),$$

$$u_z^{II} = 2(1 - 2\nu)\gamma_0 z + \sum_{j=1}^{\infty} \left\{ \gamma_j [(3 - 4\nu) \operatorname{sh} \lambda_j z - \right. \qquad (6.2.25)$$

$$\left. - \lambda_j z \operatorname{ch} \lambda_j z] - \delta_j \lambda_j \operatorname{sh} \lambda_j z \right\} J_0(\lambda_j r).$$

Substitution of expressions (6.2.18) and (6.2.25) into equations (6.2.11) furnishes the following general solution of the homogeneous equations for the displacements

$$u_r^* = 2(1 - 2v)\alpha_0 r + \sum_{n=1}^{\infty} \Big\{ \alpha_n \left[4(1 - v) I_1(k_n r) - k_n r I_0(k_n r) \right] -$$

$$-\beta_n k_n I_1(k_n r) \Big\} \cos k_n z + \sum_{j=1}^{\infty} \Big\{ \gamma_j \lambda_j \ \text{sh} \ \lambda_j z + \delta_j \lambda_j \ \text{ch} \ \lambda_j z) J_1(\lambda_j r) \Big\},$$

$$(6.2.26)$$

$$u_z^* = 2(1 - 2v)\gamma_0 z + \sum_{n=1}^{\infty} \left[\alpha_n k_n r I_1(k_n r) + \beta_n k_n I_0(k_n r) \right] \sin k_n z +$$

$$+ \sum_{j=1}^{\infty} \Big\{ \gamma_j \left[(3 - 4v) \ \text{sh} \ \lambda_j z - \lambda_j z \ \text{ch} \ \lambda_j z \right] - \delta_j \lambda_j \ \text{sh} \ \lambda_j z \Big\} J_0(\lambda_j r).$$

The corresponding stresses obtained from formulae (6.1.13) and (6.1.15) are

$$\frac{\sigma_r^*}{2\mu} = 2\alpha_0 + 2v\gamma_0 + \sum_{n=1}^{\infty} \Bigg\{ \alpha_n \left[-4(1 - v) \frac{1}{r} I_1(k_n r) - k_n^2 r I_1(k_n r) + \right.$$

$$+ \left. (3 - 2v) k_n I_0(k_n r) \right] + \beta_n k_n \left[\frac{1}{r} I_1(k_n r) - k_n I_0(k_n r) \right] \Bigg\} \cos k_n z -$$

$$- \sum_{j=1}^{\infty} (\gamma_j \lambda_j z \ \text{sh} \ \lambda_j z + \delta_j \lambda_j \ \text{ch} \ \lambda_j z) \frac{J_1(\lambda_j r)}{r} + \sum_{j=1}^{\infty} \Big\{ \gamma_j (\lambda_j^2 z \ \text{sh} \ \lambda_j z +$$

$$+ 2v\lambda_j \ \text{ch} \ \lambda_j z) + \delta_j \lambda_j^2 \ \text{ch} \ \lambda_j z \Big\} J_0(\lambda_j r),$$

$$\frac{\sigma_\theta^*}{2\mu} = 2\alpha_0 + 2v\gamma_0 + \sum_{n=1}^{\infty} \Bigg\{ \alpha_n \left[4(1 - v) \frac{1}{r} I_1(k_n r) - (1 - 2v) k_n I_0(k_n r) \right] -$$

$$-\beta_n k_n \frac{1}{r} I_1(k_n r) \Bigg\} \cos k_n z + \sum_{j=1}^{\infty} (\gamma_j \lambda_j z \ \text{sh} \ \lambda_j z + \delta_j \lambda_j \ \text{ch} \ \lambda_j z) \times$$

$$\times \frac{J_1(\lambda_j r)}{r} + 2v \sum_{j=1}^{\infty} \gamma_j \lambda_j \ \text{ch} \ \lambda_j z J_0(\lambda_j r), \qquad (6.2.27)$$

$$\frac{\sigma_z^*}{2\mu} = 2(1-\nu)\gamma_0 + 4\nu\alpha_0 + \sum_{n=1}^{\infty} \Big\{ \alpha_n [k_n^2 r I_1(k_n r) + 2\nu k_n I_0(k_n r)] +$$

$$+ \beta_n k_n^2 I_0(k_n r) \Big\} \cos k_n z + \sum_{j=1}^{\infty} \Big\{ \gamma_j [2(1-\nu)\lambda_j \operatorname{ch} \lambda_j z - \lambda_j^2 z \operatorname{sh} \lambda_j z] -$$

$$- \delta_j \lambda_j^2 \operatorname{ch} \lambda_j z \Big\} J_0(\lambda_j r),$$

$$\frac{\sigma_{rz}^*}{2\mu} = \sum_{n=1}^{\infty} \Big\{ \alpha_n k_n [-2(1-\nu) I_1(k_n r) + k_n r I_0(k_n r)] +$$

$$+ \beta_n k_n^2 I_1(k_n r) \Big\} \sin k_n z + \sum_{j=1}^{\infty} \Big\{ \gamma_j \lambda_j [\lambda_j z \operatorname{ch} \lambda_j z - (1-2\nu) \operatorname{sh} \lambda_j z] +$$

$$+ \delta_j \lambda_j^2 \operatorname{sh} \lambda_j z \Big\} J_1(\lambda_j r).$$

Expressions (6.2.27) for the components of the stress tensor contain sufficient functional freedom in order to satisfy arbitrary boundary conditions that are symmetric with respect to the plane $z = 0$.

When the surfaces $r = r_2$ and $z = \pm l$ of the cylinder are stress free, the boundary conditions are

$$\text{when} \quad r = r_2 \quad \sigma_r^* + \sigma_r^{(T)} = 0, \quad \sigma_{rz}^* + \sigma_{rz}^{(T)} = 0,$$
$$\text{when} \quad z = \pm l \quad \sigma_z^* + \sigma_z^{(T)} = 0, \quad \sigma_{rz}^* + \sigma_{rz}^{(T)} = 0. \tag{6.2.28}$$

Substitution of the solutions of the homogeneous equations for the stresses (6.2.27) into the boundary conditions (6.2.28) yields the following system of functional equations for the determination of the constants $\alpha_0, \gamma_0, \alpha_n, \beta_n, \gamma_j, \beta_j$:

$$\frac{1}{2\mu}(\sigma_r^* + \sigma_r^{(T)})_{r=r_2} = 2\alpha_0 + 2\nu\gamma_0 + \sum_{n=1}^{\infty} \Big\{ \alpha_n \Big[-4(1-\nu)\frac{1}{r_2} I_1(k_n r_2) -$$

$$- k_n^2 r_2 I_1(k_n r_2) + (3-2\nu)k_n I_0(k_n r_2) \Big] + \beta_n k_n \Big[\frac{1}{r_2} I_1(k_n r) -$$

$$-k_n I_0(k_n r_2) \Big] \Big\} \cos k_n z + \sum_{j=1}^{\infty} \Big\{ \gamma_j [\lambda_j^2 z \, \mathrm{sh} \, \lambda_j z + 2\nu\lambda_j \, \mathrm{ch} \, \lambda_j z] +$$

$$+ \delta_j \lambda_j^2 \, \mathrm{ch} \, \lambda_j z \Big\} J_0(\lambda_j r_2) + \frac{1}{2\mu} (\sigma_r^{(T)})_{r=r_2} = 0, \qquad (6.2.29)$$

$$\frac{1}{2\mu} (\sigma_z^* + \sigma_z^{(T)})_{z=\pm l} = 2(1-\nu)\gamma_0 + 4\nu\alpha_0 + \sum_{n=1}^{\infty} (-1)^n \Big\{ \alpha_n [k_n^2 r I_1(k_n r) +$$

$$+ 2\nu k_n I_0(k_n r)] + \beta_n k_n^2 I_0(k_n r) \Big\} + \sum_{j=1}^{\infty} \Big\{ \gamma_j [2(1-\nu)\lambda_j \, \mathrm{ch} \, \lambda_j l -$$

$$- \lambda_j^2 l \, \mathrm{sh} \, \lambda_j l] - \delta_j \lambda_j^2 \, \mathrm{ch} \, \lambda_j l \Big\} J_0(\lambda_j r) + \frac{1}{2\mu} (\sigma_z^{(T)})_{z=\pm l} = 0;$$

$$\frac{1}{2\mu} (\sigma_{rz}^* + \sigma_{rz}^{(T)})_{r=r_2} = \sum_{n=1}^{\infty} \Big\{ \alpha_n k_n [-2(1-\nu)I_1(k_n r_2) + k_n r_2 I_0(k_n r_2)] +$$

$$+ \beta_n k_n^2 I_1(k_n r_2) \Big\} \sin k_n z + \frac{1}{2\mu} (\sigma_{rz}^{(T)})_{r=r_2} = 0, \qquad (6.2.30)$$

$$\frac{1}{2\mu} (\sigma_{rz}^* + \sigma_{rz}^{(T)})_{z=\pm l} = \pm \sum_{n=1}^{\infty} \Big\{ \gamma_j \lambda_j [\lambda_j l \, \mathrm{ch} \, \lambda_j l - (1-2\nu) \, \mathrm{sh} \, \lambda_j l] +$$

$$+ \delta_j \lambda_j^2 \, \mathrm{sh} \, \lambda_j l \Big\} J_1(\lambda_j r) + \frac{1}{2\mu} (\sigma_{rz}^{(T)})_{z=\pm l} = 0.$$

The boundary conditions for the shear stresses (6.2.30) yield the following relation between the unknown constants

$$\beta_n k_n^2 = -\alpha_n k_n \left[-2(1-\nu) + k_n r_2 \frac{I_0(k_n r_2)}{I_1(k_n r_2)} \right] -$$

$$- \frac{1+\nu}{1-\nu} \alpha_T k_n \frac{db_n}{dr} (r_2) \frac{1}{I_1(k_n r_2)}, \qquad (6.2.31)$$

$$\delta_j \lambda_j^2 = -\gamma_j \lambda_j [-(1-2\nu) + \lambda_j l \, \mathrm{ctg} \, \lambda_j l].$$

171

In virtue of the known expansions

$$\operatorname{ch} \lambda_j z = \frac{\operatorname{sh} \lambda_j l}{\lambda_j l} + \frac{2\lambda_j \operatorname{sh} \lambda_j l}{l} \sum_{n=1}^{\infty} (-1)^n \frac{\cos k_n z}{k_n^2 + \lambda_j^2},$$

$$\lambda_j z \operatorname{sh} \lambda_j z = \operatorname{ch} \lambda_j l - \frac{\operatorname{sh} \lambda_j l}{\lambda_j l} + \left(\frac{2\lambda_j \operatorname{sh} \lambda_j l}{l} + 2\lambda_j^2 \operatorname{ch} \lambda_j l \right) \times \qquad (6.2.32)$$

$$\times \sum_{n=1}^{\infty} (-1)^n \frac{\cos k_n z}{k_n^2 + \lambda_j^2} - \frac{4\lambda_j^3 \operatorname{sh} \lambda_j l}{l} \sum_{n=1}^{\infty} (-1)^n \frac{\cos k_n z}{(k_n^2 + \lambda_j^2)^2}$$

and the first of expressions (6.2.9) for the stress $\sigma_r^{(T)}$, the first functional equation in system (6.2.29) is found to reduce in the interval $-l \leqslant z \leqslant l$ to the equivalent algebraic equations

$$2\alpha_0 + 2\nu\gamma_0 = -C_0, \qquad (6.2.33)$$

$$\alpha_n k_n^2 r_2 I_1(k_n r_2) \left[\frac{I_0^2(k_n r_2)}{I_1^2(k_n r_2)} - \frac{2(1-\nu)}{k_n^2 r_2^2} - 1 \right] =$$

$$= -\sum_{j=1}^{\infty} (-1)^n \gamma_j J_0(\lambda_j r_2) \frac{4k_n^2 \lambda_j^2 \operatorname{sh} \lambda_j l}{l(k_n^2 + \lambda_j^2)^2} - C_n, \qquad (6.2.34)$$

where

$$C_0 = -\frac{1+\nu}{1-\nu} \alpha_T \left[\frac{d^2 b_0}{dr^2}(r_2) - a_0(r_2) \right],$$

$$\qquad (6.2.35)$$

$$C_n = -\frac{1+\nu}{1-\nu} \alpha_T \left\{ \frac{d^2 b_n}{dr^2}(r_2) - k_n \frac{db_n}{dr}(r_2) \left[\frac{I_0(k_n r_2)}{I_1(k_n r_2)} - \frac{1}{k_n r_2} \right] - a_n(r_2) \right\}.$$

Similarly the expansions

$$I_0(k_n r) = 2 \frac{I_1(k_n r_2)}{k_n r_2} + \frac{2k_n}{r_2} I_1(k_n r_2) \sum_{j=1}^{\infty} \frac{J_0(\lambda_j r)}{(k_n^2 + \lambda_j^2) J_0(\lambda_j r_2)}, \quad (6.2.36)$$

$$k_n r I_1(k_n r) = -4 \frac{I_1(k_n r_2)}{k_n r_2} + 2I_0(k_n r_2) + 2k_n^2 I_0(k_n r_2) \times$$

$$\times \sum_{j=1}^{\infty} \frac{J_0(\lambda_j r)}{(k_n^2 + \lambda_j^2) J_0(\lambda_j r_2)} - \frac{4k_n^2}{r_2} I_1(k_n r_2) \sum_{j=1}^{\infty} \frac{J_0(\lambda_j r)}{(k_n^2 + \lambda_j^2)^2 J_0(\lambda_j r_2)} :$$

$$\frac{1}{2\mu}(\sigma_z^{(T)})_{z=\pm l} = D_0 + \sum_{j=1}^{\infty} D_j J_0(\lambda_j r), \qquad (6.2.37)$$

where

$$D_0 = \frac{2}{r_2^2} \int_0^{r_2} (\sigma_z^{(T)})_{z=\pm l}\, r\, dr,$$

$$D_j = \frac{2}{r_2^2 J_0^2(\lambda_j r_2)} \int_0^{r_2} (\sigma_z^{(T)})_{z=\pm l}\, r J_0(\lambda_j r)\, dr,$$

reduce .the second functional equation in (6.2.29) in the interval $0 \leqslant r \leqslant r_2$ to the algebraic equations

$$2(1 - \nu)\gamma_0 + 4\nu\alpha_0 = -D_0, \qquad (6.2.38)$$

$$\gamma_j \lambda_j \left(\operatorname{ch} \lambda_j l + \frac{\lambda_j l}{\operatorname{sh} \lambda_j l} \right) = - \sum_{n=1}^{\infty} (-1)^n \alpha_n \frac{4k_n^2 \lambda_j^2 I_1(k_n r_2)}{r_2(k_n^2 + \lambda_j^2)^2 J_0(\lambda_j r_2)} - D_j. \quad (6.2.39)$$

The system of two equations (6.2.33) and (6.2.38) for the determination of γ_0 and α_0 corresponds to the elementary solution of the static problem for a finite cylinder [26].

We now examine the infinite system of linear algebraic equations (6.2.34), (6.2.39) for the unknowns α_n and γ_j.

Introducing the new variables X_n, Y_j

$$4(-1)^n \alpha_n k_n^2 \frac{I_1(k_n r_2)}{r_2} = X_n,$$

$$4 J_0(\lambda_j r_2) \gamma_j \lambda_j^2 \frac{\operatorname{sh} \lambda_j l}{l} = -Y_j,$$

we can reduce these algebraic equations to the more convenient form

$$Y_j = \frac{1}{s_j} \sum_{n=1}^{\infty} X_n \frac{\lambda_j^2}{(k_n^2 + \lambda_j^2)^2} + \frac{D_j J_0(\lambda_j r_2)}{s_j},$$

$$\quad (6.2.41)$$

$$X_n = \frac{1}{t_n} \sum_{j=1}^{\infty} Y_j \frac{k_n^2}{(k_n^2 + \lambda_j^2)^2} - \frac{C_n(-1)^n}{t_n},$$

where

$$s_j = \frac{l \left[\operatorname{ch} \lambda_j l + \dfrac{\lambda_j l}{\operatorname{sh} \lambda_j l} \right]}{4 \lambda_j \operatorname{sh} \lambda_j l},$$

$$\quad (6.2.42)$$

$$t_n = \frac{r_2^2}{4} \left[\frac{I_0^2(k_n r_2)}{I_1^2(k_n r_2)} - 1 - \frac{2(1-\nu)}{k_n^2 r_2^2} \right].$$

We now consider the infinite sums in (6.2.41). Since the series (6.2.32) and (6.2.36) are uniformly convergent, we have the equalities

$$\frac{1}{s_j} \sum_{n=1}^{\infty} \frac{\lambda_j^2}{(k_n^2 + \lambda_j^2)^2} = 1 - \frac{1}{2\lambda_j^2 s_j},$$

$$\quad (6.2.43)$$

$$\frac{1}{t_n} \sum_{j=1}^{\infty} \frac{k_n^2}{(k_n^2 + \lambda_j^2)^2} = 1 - \frac{1+\nu}{2k_n^2 t_n}.$$

It can be shown that the functions

$$\varphi_j = \frac{1}{2\lambda_j^2 s_j},$$

$$\quad (6.2.44)$$

$$\psi_n = \frac{1+\nu}{2k_n^2 t_n}$$

are positive definite and none of them becomes equal to unity for all values $j = 1, 2, \ldots$; $n = 1, 2, \ldots$. This fact means that the system of equations (6.2.41) is regular [13].

In order that the regular infinite system has a bounded solution, the nonhomogeneous terms must satisfy special conditions; they must vanish with increasing index at the same rate as the functions φ_j and ψ_n. For system

174

(6.2.41) these conditions are satisfied if

$$C_n = O\left(\frac{1}{n^2}\right),$$

$$D_j = O\left(\frac{1}{\lambda^{3/2}}\right).$$

(6.2.45)

For the temperature fields considered, these conditions usually hold.

When the estimates (6.2.45) are satisfied, the method of reduction [13] can be used to obtain approximate values for a finite number of the unknowns X_n, Y_j in the regular infinite system (6.2.41).

On the basis of the results in [19], the method of reduction can be greatly improved. Then it can be shown that for system (6.2.41) the following so—called asymptotic law holds

$$\lim_{n\to\infty} X_n = \lim_{j\to\infty} Y_j = K.$$

(6.2.46)

Setting

$$Y_{N+1} = Y_{N+2} = \ldots, \quad X_{N+1} = X_{N+2} = \ldots$$

for sufficiently large N, system (6.2.41) can be replaced by the finite system of $2(N+1)$ equations

$$Y_j = \frac{1}{s_j} \sum_{n=1}^{N} X_n \frac{\lambda_j^2}{(k_n^2 + \lambda_j^2)^2} + X_{N+1}\left[1 - \varphi_j - \sum_{n=1}^{N} \frac{\lambda_j^2}{(k_n^2 + \lambda_j^2)^2}\right] + \frac{D_j J_0(\lambda_j r_2)}{s_j},$$

$$X_n = \frac{1}{t_n} \sum_{j=1}^{N} Y_j \frac{k_n^2}{(k_n^2 + \lambda_j^2)^2} + Y_{N+1}\left[1 - \psi_n - \sum_{j=1}^{N} \frac{k_n^2}{(k_n^2 + \lambda_j^2)^2}\right] - \frac{C_n(-1)^n}{t_n}.$$

(6.2.47)

This method allows us to considerably increase the accuracy in finding the first N unknowns in the infinite system (6.2.41). At the same time an approximate value of K is found. The value of K can be taken equal to one of the numbers Y_{N+1} or X_{N+1}.

Other methods (based on St.—Venant's principle or the method of homogeneous solutions) were used in [41, 67] to study thermoelastic problems for finite cylinders.

175

6.3. Thermal stresses in a hollow sphere

In this section we consider the thermal stresses in a hollow sphere when the temperature field $T(r, \varphi)$ is axisymmetric. It will be assumed that the sphere is unconstrained and that the inner surface $r = r_1$ and the outer surface $r = r_2$ are stress free (see Fig. 25).

First we shall determine a particular solution of equation (6.1.19) for the thermoelastic displacement potential Φ.

The homogeneous form of (6.1.19) is the Laplace equation in spherical coordinates. As is well known, its solution can be found in the form of an expansion in the terms

$$\text{const } r^n P_n(\cos \varphi),$$

where n are integers (positive or negative), and $P_n(\cos \varphi)$ is the Legendre polynomial of degree n.

The polynomial $P_n(\cos \varphi)$ is a solution of the equation [46]

$$\frac{d^2 P_n(\cos \varphi)}{d\varphi^2} + \text{ctg } \varphi \, \frac{dP_n(\cos \varphi)}{d\varphi} + n(n + 1) P_n(\cos \varphi) = 0. \quad (6.3.1)$$

For integral values of n, the Legendre polynomials form a complete orthogonal system of functions in the interval $0 \leqslant \varphi \leqslant \pi$, i.e.

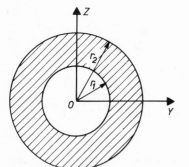

$$\int_0^\pi P_n(\cos \varphi) P_m(\cos \varphi) \sin \varphi d\varphi =$$

$$= \begin{cases} 0 & \text{when } n \neq m, \\[2mm] \dfrac{2}{2n + 1} & \text{when } n = m. \end{cases} \quad (6.3.2)$$

Fig. 25.

It is proved in [22] that the expansion of a function in a series of Legendre polynomials has the same properties as a Fourier series. In order to construct a particular solution of equation (6.1.9), we represent the temperature $T(r, \varphi) - T_0$ by the expansion

$$T(r, \varphi) - T_0 = \sum_{n=0}^{\infty} a_n(r) P_n(\cos \varphi). \tag{6.3.3}$$

The coefficients are given by

$$a_n(r) = \frac{2n+1}{2} \int_0^{\pi} [T(r, \varphi) - T_0] P_n(\cos \varphi) \sin \varphi \, d\varphi. \tag{6.3.4}$$

We seek the particular solution of equation (6.1.19) in the form

$$\Phi(r, \varphi) = \sum_{n=0}^{\infty} b_n(r) P_n(\cos \varphi). \tag{6.3.5}$$

Substitution of expansions (6.3.3) and (6.3.5) into equation (6.3.1) yields the following equation for the determination of the unknown functions $b_n(r)$:

$$\frac{d}{dr}\left(r^2 \frac{db_n}{dr} \right) - n(n+1)b_n = \frac{1+\nu}{1-\nu} \alpha_T r^2 a_n(r). \tag{6.3.6}$$

Since the general solution of the homogeneous form of equation (6.3.6) is $C_1 r^n + C_2 r^{-n-1}$, where C_1 and C_2 are arbitrary constants, the particular solution of the nonhomogeneous equation (6.3.6) found by the method of variation of parameters can be written as

$$b_n(r) = \frac{1+\nu}{1-\nu} \frac{\alpha_T}{2n+1} \left[r^n \int r^{1-n} a_n(r) \, dr - r^{-n-1} \int r^{n+2} a_n(r) \, dr \right]. \tag{6.3.7}$$

In the case of steady heat exchange without heat sources, the expression for the temperature field is the solution of the Laplace equation in spherical coordinates. This is given by the expression

$$T(r, \varphi) - T_0 = \sum_{n=0}^{\infty} (\alpha_n r^n + \beta_n r^{-n-1}) P_n(\cos \varphi), \tag{6.3.8}$$

where the coefficients α_n and β_n can be regarded as known. From case to case, they are determined by the prescribed conditions concerning the heat exchange.

The particular solution for the $b_n(r)$ in (6.3.7) now assumes the form

177

$$b_n(r) = \frac{1 + \nu}{1 - \nu} \alpha_T \left[\frac{\alpha_n}{2(2n + 3)} r^{n+2} - \frac{\beta_n}{2(2n - 1)} r^{-n+1} \right]. \quad (6.3.9)$$

Having the particular integral (6.3.5) for the thermoelastic displacement potential $\Phi(r, \varphi)$, we can determine the corresponding particular solutions for the stresses and strains by means of (6.1.27) and (6.1.29). In the calculations, use can be made of equation (6.3.1).

Below we quote the results of the calculations for the stresses in the case of the temperature field (6.3.3):

$$\frac{\sigma_r^{(T)}}{2\mu} = -\frac{1}{r} \sum_{n=0}^{\infty} \left[2 \frac{db_n(r)}{dr} - \frac{n(n+1) b_n(r)}{r} \right] P_n(\cos \varphi),$$

$$\frac{\sigma_\varphi^{(T)}}{2\mu} = -\frac{1}{r^2} \sum_{n=0}^{\infty} \left\{ r \frac{d}{dr} \left[r \frac{db_n(r)}{dr} \right] P_n(\cos \varphi) + b_n(r) \frac{dP_n(\cos \varphi)}{d\varphi} \operatorname{ctg} \varphi \right\},$$

$$\qquad\qquad\qquad\qquad (6.3.10)$$

$$\frac{\sigma_\theta^{(T)}}{2\mu} = -\frac{1}{r^2} \sum_{n=0}^{\infty} \left\{ r \frac{d}{dr} \left[r \frac{db_n(r)}{dr} \right] P_n(\cos \varphi) - n(n+1) b_n(r) P_n(\cos \varphi) - \right.$$

$$\left. - b_n(r) \frac{dP_n(\cos \varphi)}{d\varphi} \operatorname{ctg} \varphi \right\},$$

$$\frac{\sigma_{r\varphi}^{(T)}}{2\mu} = \frac{1}{r} \sum_{n=1}^{\infty} \left[\frac{db_n(r)}{dr} - \frac{b_n(r)}{r} \right] \frac{dP_n(\cos \varphi)}{d\varphi};$$

in the case of the steady temperature field (6.3.8):

$$\frac{\sigma_r^{(T)}}{2\mu} = \frac{(1 + \nu)\alpha_T}{2(1 - \nu)} \sum_{n=0}^{\infty} \left(\frac{n^2 - n - 4}{2n + 3} \alpha_n r^n - \frac{n^2 + 3n - 2}{2n - 1} \beta_n r^{-n-1} \right) P_n(\cos \varphi),$$

$$\frac{\sigma_\varphi^{(T)}}{2\mu} = -\frac{(1 + \nu)\alpha_T}{2(1 - \nu)} \sum_{n=0}^{\infty} \left[\left(\frac{(n + 2)^2}{2n + 3} \alpha_n r^n - \frac{(n - 1)^2}{2n - 1} \beta_n r^{-n-1} \right) P_n(\cos \varphi) + \right.$$

$$\left. + \left(\frac{\alpha_n r^n}{2n + 3} - \frac{\beta_n r^{-n-1}}{2n - 1} \right) \frac{dP_n(\cos \varphi)}{d\varphi} \operatorname{ctg} \varphi \right], \quad (6.3.11)$$

$$\frac{\sigma_\theta^{(T)}}{2\mu} = -\frac{(1+\nu)\alpha_T}{2(1-\nu)} \sum_{n=0}^{\infty} \left[\left(\frac{3n+4}{2n+3} \alpha_n r^n + \frac{3n-1}{2n-1} \beta_n r^{-n-1} \right) P_n(\cos\varphi) - \right.$$

$$\left. - \left(\frac{\alpha_n r^n}{2n+3} - \frac{\beta_n r^{-n-1}}{2n-1} \right) \frac{dP_n(\cos\varphi)}{d\varphi} \operatorname{ctg}\varphi \right],$$

$$\frac{\sigma_{r\varphi}^{(T)}}{2\mu} = \frac{(1+\nu)\alpha_T}{2(1-\nu)} \sum_{n=1}^{\infty} \left(\frac{n+1}{2n+3} \alpha_n r^n + \frac{n}{2n-1} \beta_n r^{-n-1} \right) \frac{dP_n(\cos\varphi)}{d\varphi}.$$

When the sphere is solid, we must set $\beta_n = 0$ in expressions (6.3.11). When, on the other hand, spherical coordinates are used in a half-space, one must set $\alpha_n = 0$.

Now we turn to the determination of the solutions u_r^* and u_φ^*. We will begin by finding the functions e_B and ω_B. These are expressed through the formulae (6.1.21) in terms of B_r and B_φ, and the latter functions are solutions of equations (6.1.22) and (6.1.23).

Using separation of variables, we find that the solution of equation (6.1.22) can be represented as the sum of the terms

$$e_{Bn} = C_n' r^n P_n(\cos\varphi), \tag{6.3.12}$$

and the solution of equation (6.1.23) as the sum of the terms

$$\omega_{Bn} = D_n' r^n \frac{dP_n(\cos\varphi)}{d\varphi}. \tag{6.3.13}$$

The constants C_n' and D_n' are not independent since e_{Bn} and ω_{Bn} are related through equation (6.1.20).

Substitution of the expressions for e_{Bn} and ω_{Bn} into these equations yields the relations

$$C_n' = -(n+1)D_n'. \tag{6.3.14}$$

Replacing the functions e_{Bn}, ω_{Bn} in equations (6.1.21) by their expressions (6.3.12), (6.3.13) and bearing in mind relation (6.3.14), we obtain the following system of equations for the determination of B_{rn}, $B_{\varphi n}$

$$\frac{1}{r}\frac{\partial}{\partial r}(r^2 B_{rn}) + \frac{1}{\sin\varphi}\frac{\partial}{\partial\varphi}(\sin\varphi B_{\varphi n}) = -(n+1)D_n' r^{n+1} P_n(\cos\varphi),$$

$$\frac{\partial(rB_{\varphi n})}{\partial r} - \frac{\partial B_{rn}}{\partial \varphi} = D'_n r^{n+1} \frac{dP_n(\cos \varphi)}{d\varphi}. \tag{6.3.15}$$

A particular solution of this system of equations is

$$B_{rn} = -(n+1)A_n r^{n+1} P_n(\cos \varphi), \quad B_{\varphi n} = A_n r^{n+1} \frac{dP_n(\cos \varphi)}{d\varphi}, \tag{6.3.16}$$

where the new constant of integration is defined by

$$A_n = \frac{D'_n}{2n+3}.$$

Because of the functional freedom contained in solution (6.1.18), the general solution of the system of equations (6.3.15) is not needed; the corresponding particular integral can be incorporated in the function B_0. This function will be represented as the sum of the terms

$$B_{0n} = -B_n r^n P_n(\cos \varphi). \tag{6.3.17}$$

Substituting expressions (6.3.16), (6.3.17), for B_r, B_φ, and B_0 into (6.1.18) and summing over integral values of n from $-\infty$ to $+\infty$ and taking account of the recurrence relations $P_n(\cos \varphi) = P_{-(n+1)}(\cos \varphi)$, we obtain

$$u_r^* = \sum_{n=0}^{\infty} [(n+1)(n-2+4\nu)A_n r^{n+1} + nB_n r^{n-1} +$$

$$+ n(n+3-4\nu)C_n r^{-n} - (n+1)D_n r^{-n-2}]P_n(\cos \varphi),$$

$$\tag{6.3.18}$$

$$u_\varphi^* = \sum_{n=0}^{\infty} [(n+5-4\nu)A_n r^{n+1} + B_n r^{n-1} +$$

$$+ (4-n-4\nu)C_n r^{-n} + D_n r^{-n-2}] \frac{dP_n(\cos \varphi)}{d\varphi}.$$

where we have introduced the constants $C_n = A_{-n-1}, D_n = B_{-n-1}$.
Formulae (6.1.28), (6.1.30) now yield the stresses

$$\frac{\sigma_r^*}{2\mu} = \sum_{n=0}^{\infty} [(n+1)(n^2-n-2-2\nu)A_n r^n + n(n-1)B_n r^{n-2} -$$

180

$$-n(n^2 + 3n - 2\nu)C_n r^{-n-1} + (n+1)(n+2)D_n r^{-n-3}] P_n(\cos\varphi),$$

$$\frac{\sigma_\varphi^*}{2\mu} = -\sum_{n=0}^{\infty} \left\{ [(n+1)(n^2 + 4n + 2 + 2\nu)A_n r^n + n^2 B_n r^{n-2} - \right.$$

$$-n(n^2 - 2n - 1 + 2\nu)C_n r^{-n-1} + (n+1)^2 D_n r^{-n-3}] P_n(\cos\varphi) +$$

$$+ [(n+5-4\nu)A_n r^n + B_n r^{n-2} + (4-n-4\nu)C_n r^{-n-1} +$$

$$\left. + D_n r^{-n-3}] \frac{dP_n(\cos\varphi)}{d\varphi} \operatorname{ctg}\varphi \right\},$$

$$\frac{\sigma_\theta^*}{2\mu} = \sum_{n=0}^{\infty} \left\{ [(n+1)(n-2-2\nu-4n\nu)A_n r^n + n B_n r^{n-2} + \right.$$

$$\text{(6.3.19)}$$

$$+ n(n+3-4n\nu-2\nu)C_n r^{-n-1} - (n+1)D_n r^{-n-3}] P_n(\cos\varphi) +$$

$$+ [(n+5-4\nu)A_n r^n + B_n r^{n-2} + (4-n-4\nu)C_n r^{-n-1} +$$

$$\left. + D_n r^{-n-3}] \frac{dP_n(\cos\varphi)}{d\varphi} \operatorname{ctg}\varphi \right\},$$

$$\frac{\sigma_{r\varphi}^*}{2\mu} = \sum_{n=1}^{\infty} [(n^2 + 2n - 1 + 2\nu)A_n r^n + (n-1)B_n r^{n-2} +$$

$$+ (n^2 - 2 + 2\nu)C_n r^{-n-1} - (n+2)D_n r^{-n-3}] \frac{dP_n(\cos\varphi)}{d\varphi}.$$

The constants of integration A_n, B_n, C_n, and D_n are determined from the conditions that the surfaces $r = r_1, r_2$ are stress free, i.e.

$$\sigma_r^* + \sigma_r^{(T)} = 0 \quad \text{when} \quad r = r_1, r = r_2.$$

$$\sigma_{r\varphi}^* + \sigma_{r\varphi}^{(T)} = 0 \quad \text{when} \quad r = r_1, r = r_2.$$

$$\text{(6.3.20)}$$

We will consider the cases $n = 0$, $n = 1$, and $n \geqslant 2$ separately.

When $n = 0$, we have $dP_0/d\varphi \equiv 0$, and according to (6.3.11), (6.3.19) $\sigma_{r\varphi} \equiv 0$. The other stresses are functions of r alone. Moreover, $\sigma_\varphi = \sigma_\theta$. Of the four constants of integration there remain only two, namely A_0 and D_0. They are determined by the two algebraic equations

$$2(1+\nu)A_0 - 2D_0 r_1^{-3} = -\frac{2}{r_1}\frac{db_0}{dr}(r_1),$$

$$2(1+\nu)A_0 - 2D_0 r_2^{-3} = -\frac{2}{r_2}\frac{db_0}{dr}(r_2). \qquad (6.3.21)$$

Hence

$$A_0 = \frac{1}{(1+\nu)(r_1^3 - r_2^3)}\left[r_2^2\frac{db_0}{dr}(r_2) - r_1^3\frac{db_0}{dr}(r_1)\right],$$

$$D_0 = \frac{1}{r_1^3 - r_2^3}r_1^2 r_2^2\left[r_1\frac{db_0}{dr}(r_2) - r_2\frac{db_0}{dr}(r_1)\right]. \qquad (6.3.22)$$

In the case of a steady temperature field, it follows from (6.3.9) that

$$b_0(r) = \frac{(1+\nu)\alpha_T}{2(1-\nu)}\left(\frac{\alpha_0}{3}r^2 + \beta_0 r\right),$$

which yields the stresses

$$\sigma_r = -4\mu\left[\frac{1}{r}\frac{db_0(r)}{dr} + (1+\nu)A_0 - \frac{1}{r^3}D_0\right],$$

$$\sigma_\varphi = \sigma_\theta = -2\mu\left[\frac{d^2 b_0(r)}{dr^2} + \frac{1}{r}\frac{db_0(r)}{dr} + 2(1+\nu)A_0 + \frac{2D_0}{r^3}\right]. \qquad (6.3.23)$$

We now determine the solution for a solid sphere for the case where the temperature field $T(r)$ has central symmetry. On the basis of formulae (6.3.6) and (6.3.10) we find

$$\sigma_r^{(T)} = -2\mu\frac{1+\nu}{1-\nu}\alpha_T\frac{2}{r^3}\int_0^r r^2 T(r)dr = -\frac{4\mu}{3}\frac{1+\nu}{1-\nu}\alpha_T T_*(r),$$

$$\qquad (6.3.24)$$

$$\sigma_\varphi^{(T)} = \sigma_\theta^{(T)} = \frac{2\mu}{3}\frac{1+\nu}{1-\nu}\alpha_T[T_*(r) - 3T(r)],$$

where $T_* = \frac{3}{r^3}\int_0^r r^2 T(r)dr$ is the mean temperature of the sphere of radius r.

Adding to solution (6.3.24) the expression for the equilibrium state of stress:

$$\sigma_r = \sigma_\varphi = \sigma_\theta = \frac{4\mu}{3}\frac{1+\nu}{1-\nu}\alpha_T T_*(r_2),$$

we obtain the well-known solution for the thermoelastic problem for a solid sphere in the case of central symmetry in the absence of stresses on the surface [41]

$$\sigma_r = \frac{4\mu}{3}\frac{1+\nu}{1-\nu}\alpha_T\,[T_*(r_2) - T_*(r)],$$

$$\sigma_\varphi = \sigma_\theta = \frac{2\mu}{3}\frac{1+\nu}{1-\nu}\alpha_T\,[2T_*(r_2) + T_*(r) - 3T(r)].$$

(6.3.25)

In the case $n = 1$ the coefficients of B_1 in equations (6.3.19) vanish. For the determination of the remaining three constants A_1, C_1, and D_1 we have the system of four algebraic equations

$$-4(1+\nu)r_1 A_1 - \frac{2(2-\nu)}{r_1^2}C_1 + \frac{6}{r_1^4}D_1 = \frac{2}{r_1}\left[\frac{db_1}{dr}(r_1) - \frac{b_1(r_1)}{r_1}\right] = \sigma_1,$$

$$2(1+\nu)r_1 A_1 - \frac{1-2\nu}{r_1^2}C_1 - \frac{3}{r_1^4}D_1 = \frac{1}{r_1}\left[\frac{b_1(r_1)}{r_1} - \frac{db_1}{dr}(r_1)\right] = \tau_1,$$

(6.3.26)

$$-4(1+\nu)r_2 A_1 - \frac{2(2-\nu)}{r_2^2}C_1 + \frac{6}{r_2^4}D_1 = \frac{2}{r_2}\left[\frac{db_1}{dr}(r_2) - \frac{b_1(r_2)}{r_2}\right] = \sigma_2,$$

$$2(1+\nu)r_2 A_1 - \frac{1-2\nu}{r_2^2}C_1 - \frac{3}{r_2^4}D_1 = \frac{1}{r_2}\left[\frac{b_1(r_2)}{r_2} - \frac{db_1}{dr}(r_2)\right] = \tau_2,$$

The existence of a solution of system (6.3.26) requires that the (4×4)-determinant of the coefficients and the right-hand sides should vanish. In the present case this determinant has the value

$$\Delta = \frac{36(r_2^5 - r_1^5)}{r_1^6 r_2^6}(1 - \nu^2)\,[r_1^2(\sigma_1 + 2\tau_1) - r_2^2(\sigma_2 + 2\tau_2)] \quad (6.3.27)$$

For the particular values of the right-hand sides of (6.3.26), this determinant vanishes.

It is to be noted that the existence of a solution to equations (6.3.26) becomes obvious, if we set $C_1 = 0$. The system of four equations (6.3.26) then reduces to a system of two equations for the constants A_1 and D_1.

The solution of (6.3.26) can then be written

$$C_1 = 0, A_1 = \frac{\left[r_2 \dfrac{db_1}{dr}(r_2) - b_1(r_2)\right] r_2^2 - \left[r_1 \dfrac{db_1}{dr}(r_1) - b_1(r_1)\right] r_1^2}{2(1 + \nu)(r_1^5 - r_2^5)},$$

$$D_1 = \frac{r_1^4 r_2^4}{3(r_1^5 - r_2^5)} \left\{ \frac{r_1}{r_2} \left[\frac{db_1}{dr}(r_2) - \frac{b_1(r_2)}{r_2} \right] - \frac{r_2}{r_1} \left[\frac{db_1}{dr}(r_1) - \frac{b_1(r_1)}{r_1} \right] \right\}.$$
(6.3.28)

It can be proved that the determinant of the system of four algebraic equations is nonzero for each $n \geqslant 2$.

Thus, the thermoelastic problem for the axisymmetric deformation of a sphere can be regarded as solved. This problem has been considered by a number of authors [66, 68].

Chapter VII

DYNAMIC AND COUPLED PROBLEMS OF THERMOELASTICITY

7.1. Preliminaries

When the unsteady heat exchange produces high rates of temperature change, it is necessary to take account of the dynamic effects caused by the motion of the particles of the solid during the rapid thermal expansion. We are then confronted with the dynamic problem of thermoelasticity.

The displacement formulation of the dynamic problem of thermoelasticity leads to the solution of the first of equations (1.6.8), in which the temperature field T can be regarded as known from the solution of the corresponding unsteady problem of heat conduction (Chapter III). In order to obtain the general solution of this equation in the form (1.6.9), we must study the wave equations (1.6.14) and (1.6.15).

Here we limit consideration to the simplest dynamic problems of thermoelasticity connected with the estimation of the dynamic effects in one–dimensional problems of heat exchange: The Problem of thermal shock on the surface of a half–space in Section 7.2, and on the surface of a rectangular plate in Section 7.3. The studies of these and related dynamic problems of thermoelasticity carried out in [41] and elsewhere show that significant dynamic effects can arise only when there is an instantaneous change in the surface temperature or in the temperature of the surrounding medium.

Actual, fast–acting, unsteady heat exchange is accompanied by a change in temperature in a very short, but finite, interval of time, during which the dynamic effects are greatly reduced.

The foregoing facts have given rise to the opinion that when studying the thermal stresses in a machine component there is in general no practical value in considering the dynamic stresses and that the quasi–static formulation can be used to determine the thermal stresses during unsteady heat exchange. The study of the dynamic problem of thermoelasticity is however necessary in recent developments concerned with the operation of new components subjected to the action of pulses of heat fluxes. In such cases it is important to study the conditions under which thermoelastic stress waves arise and propagate in the components.

Recently, new ways have been suggested for studying thermoelastic problems in which account is taken of the interaction between the fields of strain and temperature [52, 58, 59].

The laws of thermodynamics state that a change in strain in an elastic solid is accompanied by a change in its temperature which gives rise to a heat flux that in its turn leads to an increase in entropy of the thermodynamic system and, consequently, to a thermoelastic dissipation of energy. This process is described by the differential equations (1.6.8).

The determination of the general solution (1.6.9) of the system of equations (1.6.8) leads to the solution of equation (1.6.13) for the scalar potential Φ and equation (1.6.11) for the vector potential $\mathbf{A}$.

When studying the propagation of irrotational waves, we must set $\mathbf{A} = 0$ in solution (1.6.9).

Choosing the solution for Φ in the form

$$\Phi = \varphi(x, y, z)\, e^{pt}, \tag{7.1.1}$$

we find for φ the equation

$$(\nabla^2 + \delta_1^2)(\nabla^2 + \delta_2^2)\varphi = 0, \tag{7.1.2}$$

where

$$\delta_1^2, \delta_2^2 = -\frac{p^2}{2c_1^2}\left\{\left(1 + \frac{1+\epsilon}{\Omega'}\right) \pm \left[1 - \frac{2(1-\epsilon)}{\Omega'} + \left(\frac{1+\epsilon}{\Omega'}\right)^2\right]^{\frac{1}{2}}\right\}. \tag{7.1.3}$$

The notation in (7.1.3) is

$$\epsilon = \frac{T_0(3\lambda + 2\mu)^2 \alpha_T^2}{\rho c_1^2 C_\epsilon}, \quad \Omega' = \frac{ap}{c_1^2}. \tag{7.1.4}$$

If it is assumed that there is no thermoelastic coupling ($\epsilon = 0$) and that the waves are sinusoidal with frequency $\omega/2\pi$, where $p = i\omega$, then equation (7.1.3) yields

$$\delta_1^2 = \frac{\omega^2}{c_1^2}, \quad \delta_2^2 = -\frac{i\omega}{a}. \tag{7.1.5}$$

Consequently, equation (7.1.2) described the propagation of two types of waves: those associated with δ_1 are close to the pure elastic waves, and

186

and those associated with δ_2 have the character of a purely thermal wave.

On the basis of equations (7.1.1) and (7.1.2), the general solution of equation (1.6.13) can be represented in the form

$$\Phi = \sum_{j=1}^{2} \varphi_j e^{pt}, \tag{7.1.6}$$

where φ_j satisfy the equation

$$(\nabla^2 + \delta_j^2)\varphi_j = 0, \quad j = 1, 2. \tag{7.1.7}$$

Thus, in the case of irrotational motion ($\mathbf{A} = 0$), the general solution of the coupled thermoelastic problem (1.6.9) can in view of equations (7.1.6) and (1.6.10) be represented in the form

$$\mathbf{u} = \sum_{j=1}^{2} \operatorname{grad} \varphi_j e^{pt}, \tag{7.1.8}$$

$$T - T_0 = -\frac{\rho c_1^2}{(3\lambda + 2\mu)\alpha_T} \sum_{j=1}^{2} \left(\frac{p^2}{c_1^2} + \delta_j^2 \right) \varphi_j e^{pt}.$$

Since

$$\epsilon_{kk} = \operatorname{div} \mathbf{u} = \sum_{j=1}^{2} \nabla^2 \varphi_j e^{pt} = -\sum_{j=1}^{2} \delta_j^2 \varphi_j e^{pt}, \tag{7.1.9}$$

and using formula (7.1.9), we find from (1.6.3) the following solutions for the stresses

$$\sigma_{kl} = 2\mu \left[\epsilon_{kl} + \delta_{kl} \sum_{j=1}^{2} \left(\delta_j^2 + \frac{\rho p^2}{2\mu} \right) \varphi_j e^{pt} \right], \tag{7.1.10}$$

where δ_{kl} is the Kronecker delta.

In Section 7.4 we shall illustrate the theory by considering plane dilatational waves in an infinite continuum.

In Section 7.5 we shall use the full solution (1.6.9) with both the potential and solenoidal parts. There we shall study the influence of thermoelastic energy dissipation on the propagation of longitudinal waves in an infinite, solid cylinder.

187

7.2. Thermal stresses in an elastic half—space due to a thermal shock on the boundary

The problem of thermal shock on the surface of a half—space is one of the first dynamic problems of thermoelasticity to be studied in detail.

This problem was first treated by Danilovskaya [8, 9].

Let the initial temperature of the half—space $x \geqslant 0$ be T_0. At time $t = 0$ the temperature of the surrounding medium is suddenly increased by an amount ϑ. On the boundary of the half—space there is a convective heat exchange.

The unsteady temperature field $T(x, t)$ in the half—space is governed by equations (3.1.3) and (3.1.8). In the present one—dimensional case these reduce to

$$\frac{\partial^2 T}{\partial x^2} = \frac{1}{a} \frac{\partial T}{\partial t} \tag{7.2.1}$$

with the boundary conditions

$$T = T_0 \qquad \text{when} \quad t = 0, \tag{7.2.2}$$

$$\frac{\partial T}{\partial x} - \frac{\alpha}{\lambda_T}(T - \vartheta) = 0 \quad \text{when} \quad x = 0. \tag{7.2.3}$$

After applying the Laplace transform (3.6.3) to equation (7.2.1) and condition (7.2.3), the problem can be stated in the form

$$\frac{d^2 T^*}{dx^2} - \frac{s}{a}\left(T^* - \frac{1}{s}T_0\right) = 0 \tag{7.2.4}$$

with the condition

$$\frac{dT^*}{dx} - \frac{\alpha}{\lambda_T}\left(T^* - \frac{1}{s}T_0 - \frac{\vartheta - T_0}{s}\right) = 0 \quad \text{when} \quad x = 0. \tag{7.2.5}$$

The solution of equation (7.2.4) satisfying the condition (7.2.5) and the condition that T^* remains bounded as $x \to \infty$ is

$$T^* - \frac{1}{s}T_0 = \frac{\gamma(\vartheta - T_0)e^{-x\sqrt{\frac{s}{a}}}}{s\left(\gamma + \sqrt{\frac{s}{a}}\right)}, \tag{7.2.6}$$

where $\gamma = \dfrac{\alpha}{\lambda_T}$ (α is the surface transfer coefficient, and λ_T is the coefficient of thermal conductivity).

Passing from the transfer T^* (back to the original function T as explained in [27], we find

$$T - T_0 = (\vartheta - T_0) \left[\operatorname{erfc} \frac{x}{2\sqrt{at}} - \exp(\gamma x + \gamma^2 at)\operatorname{erfc}\left(\frac{x}{2\sqrt{at}} + \gamma\sqrt{at}\right) \right],$$
(7.2.7)

where

$$\operatorname{erfc} u = 1 - \operatorname{erf} u,$$

$\operatorname{erf} u = \dfrac{2}{\sqrt{\pi}} \displaystyle\int\limits_0^u e^{-u^2}\, du$ is the Gauss error integral, and exp denotes the exponential function.

When $\gamma = \dfrac{\alpha}{\lambda_T} \to \infty$, it is seen from condition (7.2.3) that the surface temperature instantaneously attains the temperature ϑ of the surrounding medium. In this case solution (7.2.7) assumes the form

$$T - T_0 = (\vartheta - T_0)\operatorname{erfc}\frac{x}{2\sqrt{at}}.$$
(7.2.8)

We now turn to the solution of the one–dimensional dynamic problem of thermoelasticity in which the displacements $v = w = 0$ and all derivates with respect to y and z are zero. Thus

$$\epsilon_y = \epsilon_z = \epsilon_{xy} = \epsilon_{xz} = \epsilon_{yz} = 0.$$

From relations (1.5.13) we have

$$\sigma_y = \sigma_z = \frac{\nu}{1-\nu}\sigma_x - \frac{1}{1-\nu}\alpha_T E(T - T_0),$$
(7.2.9)

$$\epsilon_x = \frac{(1+\nu)(1-2\nu)}{(1-\nu)E}\sigma_x + \frac{1+\nu}{1-\nu}\alpha_T(T - T_0),$$
(7.2.10)

and from the first equation of motion (1.2.15) we obtain

$$\frac{\partial \sigma_x}{\partial x} = \rho \frac{\partial^2 u}{\partial t^2}. \qquad (7.2.11)$$

Differentiating both sides of equation (7.2.11) with respect to x and replacing the derivative $\partial u/\partial x$ by expression (7.2.10) for ϵ_x, we find the following equation of motion

$$\frac{\partial^2 \sigma_x}{\partial x^2} - \frac{1}{c_1^2} \frac{\partial^2 \sigma_x}{\partial t^2} = \frac{1+\nu}{1-\nu} \rho \alpha_T \frac{\partial^2 T}{\partial t^2}, \qquad (7.2.12)$$

where $c_1^2 = \dfrac{\lambda + 2\mu}{\rho} = \dfrac{E(1-\nu)}{(1+\nu)(1-2\nu)\rho}$ is the velocity of propagation of elastic longitudinal waves.

We seek the solution of equation (7.2.12) for the following initial and boundary conditions

$$\sigma_x = \frac{\partial \sigma_x}{\partial t} = 0 \quad \text{when} \quad t = 0, \qquad (7.2.13)$$

$$\sigma_x = 0 \qquad \text{when} \quad x = 0. \qquad (7.2.14)$$

By means of the Laplace transform (7.2.12) is reduced to the ordinary differential equation

$$\frac{d^2 \sigma_x^*}{dx^2} - \frac{s^2}{c_1^2} \sigma_x^* = \frac{1+\nu}{1-\nu} \rho \alpha_T s^2 \left(T^* - \frac{1}{s} T_0 \right) \qquad (7.2.15)$$

and (7.2.14) transforms into the boundary condition

$$\sigma_x^* = 0 \quad \text{when} \quad x = 0. \qquad (7.2.16)$$

Substitution of the transformed temperature (7.2.6) into equation (7.2.15) yields

$$\frac{d^2 \sigma_x^*}{dx^2} - \frac{s^2}{c_1^2} \sigma_x^* = \frac{(1+\nu)\, \rho \alpha_T \gamma (\vartheta - T_0) s}{(1-\nu) \left(\gamma + \sqrt{\dfrac{s}{a}} \right)} e^{-x\sqrt{\frac{s}{a}}}. \qquad (7.2.17)$$

The solution of equation (7.2.17) with the boundary condition (7.2.16) and the condition that σ_x^* remains bounded as $x \to \infty$ has the form

190

$$\sigma_x^* = \frac{E\alpha_T(\vartheta - T_0)}{(1-2\nu)\left(s - \dfrac{c_1^2}{a}\right)\left(1 + \sqrt{\dfrac{s}{a\gamma^2}}\right)}\left(e^{-\frac{xs}{c_1}} - e^{-x\sqrt{\frac{s}{a}}}\right). \quad (7.2.18)$$

In order to facilitate the transformation back to the original function, we write this expression in the form

$$\sigma_x^* = \frac{E\alpha_T(\vartheta - T_0)}{1 - 2\nu}\,\gamma a^{3/2}\left[\frac{1}{2c_1(c_1 + a\gamma)} \cdot \frac{1}{\sqrt{s} - \dfrac{c_1}{\sqrt{a}}} + \right.$$

$$\left. + \frac{1}{2c_1(c_1 - a\gamma)}\frac{1}{\sqrt{s} + \dfrac{c_1}{\sqrt{a}}} + \frac{1}{a^2\gamma^2 - c_1^2}\frac{1}{\sqrt{s} + \gamma\sqrt{a}}\right]\left(e^{-\frac{xs}{c_1}} - e^{-x\sqrt{\frac{s}{a}}}\right).$$

$$(7.2.19)$$

Using the theorem on time-lag and the table of transforms given in [27], we find

$$\sigma_x = \sigma_x' + \begin{cases} 0 & \text{when} \quad t < \dfrac{x}{c_1}, \\[3mm] \sigma_x'' & \text{when} \quad t > \dfrac{x}{c_1}, \end{cases} \quad (7.2.20)$$

where

$$\sigma_x' = -\frac{E\alpha_T(\vartheta - T_0)}{1 - 2\nu}\left\{\frac{1}{2\left(1 + \dfrac{c_1}{a\gamma}\right)}\,\exp\left[\frac{c_1^2}{a}\left(t - \frac{x}{c_1}\right)\right] \times \right.$$

$$\times \operatorname{erfc}\left(\frac{x}{2\sqrt{at}} - c_1\sqrt{\frac{t}{a}}\right) - \frac{1}{2\left(1 - \dfrac{c_1}{a\gamma}\right)}\exp\left[\frac{c_1^2}{a}\left(t + \frac{x}{c_1}\right)\right] \times$$

$$\times \operatorname{erfc}\left(\frac{x}{2\sqrt{at}} + c_1\sqrt{\frac{t}{a}}\right) - \frac{1}{1 - \dfrac{c_1^2}{a^2\gamma^2}}\,\exp(\gamma x + \gamma^2 at) \times$$

$$\left. \times \operatorname{erfc}\left(\frac{x}{2\sqrt{at}} + \gamma\sqrt{at}\right)\right\}, \quad (7.2.21)$$

$$\sigma_x'' = \frac{E\alpha_T(\vartheta - T_0)}{1 - 2\nu} \frac{1}{1 - \dfrac{c_1^2}{a^2\gamma^2}} \left\{ \exp\left[\frac{c_1^2}{a}\left(t - \frac{x}{c_1}\right)\right] \left[1 - \frac{c_1}{a\gamma} \times \right.\right.$$

$$\left.\left. \times \, \mathrm{erf}\sqrt{\frac{c_1^2}{a}\left(t - \frac{x}{c_1}\right)}\right] - \exp\left[a\gamma^2\left(t - \frac{x}{c_1}\right)\right] \mathrm{erfc}\left[\gamma\sqrt{a\left(t - \frac{x}{c_1}\right)}\right]\right\}.$$

In the case where the surface temperature jumps instantaneously from T_0 to $\vartheta = T$, i.e. $\gamma = (\alpha/\lambda_T) \to \infty$, the function (7.2.21) in solution (7.2.20) becomes

$$\sigma_x' = -\frac{1}{2}Ke^{\frac{c_1^2 t}{a}}\left[e^{-\frac{c_1 x}{a}}\,\mathrm{erfc}\left(\frac{x}{2\sqrt{at}} - c_1\sqrt{\frac{t}{a}}\right) - \right.$$

$$\left. - e^{\frac{c_1 x}{a}}\,\mathrm{erfc}\left(\frac{x}{2\sqrt{at}} + c_1\sqrt{\frac{t}{a}}\right)\right], \tag{7.2.22}$$

$$\sigma_x'' = K \exp\left[\frac{c_1^2}{a}\left(t - \frac{x}{c_1}\right)\right],$$

where

$$K = \frac{E\alpha_T(T - T_0)}{1 - 2\nu}.$$

Having the value of σ_x, we can determine the normal stresses σ_y and σ_z by means of formula (7.2.9).

If the inertia force in equation (7.2.11) is omitted, i.e. if we set $\partial^2 u/\partial t^2 = 0$, it follows from the boundary condition (7.2.14) and formula (7.2.9) that the solution of the present problem in the quasi—linear formulation is

$$\sigma_x = 0, \quad \sigma_y = \sigma_z = -\frac{E\alpha_T(T - T_0)}{1 - \nu}. \tag{7.2.23}$$

On considering formulae (7.2.9) and (7.2.23), we come to the conclusion that the solution of the dynamic problem (7.2.20) coincides with the solution in the quasi—static formulation for all those cases in which $\sigma_x = 0$, namely in the whole region $x \geqslant 0$ when $t = 0$, and on the surface $x = 0$ when $t > 0$.

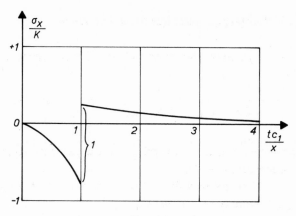

Fig. 26.

Danilovskaya studied the variation of the dynamic stress σ_x in a fixed section $\xi = xc_1/a$.

For α/λ_T infinite, Fig. 26 shows the graph of the relative stress σ_x/K, where $K = E\alpha_T(T - T_0)/(1 - 2\nu)$, versus the dimensionless time tc_1/x in the section $\xi = 1$. The dynamic stress decreases from zero at $t = 0$ to the negative value σ_x' at time $t = x/c_1$. At this instant the longitudinal wave of stress σ_x'', travelling from the surface $x = 0$ into the half–space with velocity c_1, reaches the section $\xi = 1$ and produces a discontinuous jump in the stress σ_x to the positive value $\sigma_x'' = E\alpha_T(T - T_0)/(1 - 2\nu)$. After this the dynamic stress quickly decreases to zero, like the quasi–static stress.

When $\alpha/\lambda_T < \infty$, the way in which the dynamic stress σ_x changes depends on the parameter $\beta = c_1/\alpha\gamma = c_1\lambda_T/a\alpha$.

For small values of the parameter, i.e. $\beta \ll 1$, the stress decreases from zero to some negative value, then changes smoothly to the positive region, and subsequently decreases rapidly to zero.

For large values of the parameter, i.e. $\beta \gg 1$, the stress σ_x increases in the positive region, reaches a maximum, and then rapidly drops to zero.

A study of the thermal shock on the surface of a half–space with finite rate of change of temperature was made in [41].

It has been established that the dynamic effect is greatly decreased if the change of surface temperature occurs not instantaneously but in a small, finite interval of time. For example, even for the extremely short duration of heating of $t_0 = 10^{-12}$ sec., the maximum dynamic stress shown in Fig. 26 is reduced to 86%.

193

7.3. Vibration of rectangular plate due to thermal shock

Let us consider a freely supported rectangular plate occupying the region (see Fig. 27)

$$-a \leqslant x \leqslant a, \quad -b \leqslant y \leqslant b, \quad -\frac{h}{2} \leqslant z \leqslant \frac{h}{2}.$$

It will be supposed that the surface $z = h/2$ is suddenly subjected to the heat flux[1] of intensity $q' = -q$.

Further, it will be assumed that the lower surface $z = -h/2$ and the edges $x = \pm a$, $y = \pm b$ are ideally heat insulated.

A study of the dynamic behaviour of a plate during a sudden change of temperature of its surface was made in [53].

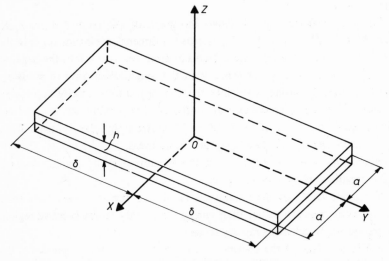

Fig. 27.

Under the above conditions of heat exchange, the unsteady temperature field will depend only on the coordinate z and the time t.

On the basis of equations (3.1.3), (3.1.6), and (3.1.7), the unsteady heat

---

1) The positive direction of the heat flux vector q coincides with the direction of the outward normal to the surface.

conduction problem in the present case is described by the equation[1]

$$\frac{\partial^2 T}{\partial z^2} = \frac{1}{a'} \frac{\partial T}{\partial t} \tag{7.3.1}$$

the initial condition

$$T = T_0 \quad \text{when} \quad t = 0 \tag{7.3.2}$$

and the boundary conditions

$$\lambda_T \frac{\partial T}{\partial z} = q' = -q \quad \text{when} \quad z = \frac{h}{2}, \tag{7.3.3}$$

$$\frac{\partial T}{\partial z} = 0 \qquad \text{when} \quad z = -\frac{h}{2}. \tag{7.3.4}$$

The solution of this problem found by means of Laplace transformations in the book [57] has the form

$$T - T_0 = \frac{q'h}{\lambda_T} \left[\frac{\beta t}{\pi^2} + \frac{12z^2 + 12hz - h^2}{24h^2} - \right.$$

$$\left. - \frac{2}{\pi^2} \sum_{n=1}^{\infty} \frac{(-1)^n}{n^2} e^{-n^2 \beta t} \cos \frac{n\pi}{2} \left(\frac{2z}{h} + 1 \right) \right], \tag{7.3.5}$$

where

$$\beta = \frac{a' \pi^2}{h^2}.$$

Using the well—known equation for the thermoelastic bending of a plate [15]

$$\nabla^2 \nabla^2 w - \frac{q_z}{D_M} + (1 + \nu) \nabla^2 \kappa_T = 0 \tag{7.3.6}$$

and replacing in accordance with d'Alemberts' principle the intensity of the

---

[1] Here the coefficient of heat conduction is denoted by a' to avoid confusion with the breadth 2a of the plate.

surface forces by the inertia forces $-\rho h\, \partial^2 w/\partial t^2$, we obtain the following equation of motion

$$\nabla^2 \nabla^2 w + \rho \frac{h}{D_M} \frac{\partial^2 w}{\partial t^2} + (1 + \nu) \nabla^2 \kappa_T = 0, \qquad (7.3.7)$$

where

$$\kappa_T = \frac{12}{h^3} \int\limits_{-h/2}^{h/2} z\alpha_T (T - T_0)\, dz, \qquad (7.3.8)$$

α_T — is the coefficient of linear expansion, and $D_M = Eh^3/12(1 - \nu^2)$ is the flexural rigidity.

The solution of equation (7.3.7) must satisfy the following initial and boundary conditions[1]

$$w = 0, \quad \frac{\partial w}{\partial t} = 0 \qquad\qquad \text{when} \quad t = 0, \qquad (7.3.9)$$

$$w = 0, \quad \frac{\partial^2 w}{\partial x^2} + (1 + \nu)\kappa_T = 0 \quad \text{when} \quad x = \pm a, \qquad (7.3.10)$$

$$w = 0, \quad \frac{\partial^2 w}{\partial y^2} + (1 + \nu)\kappa_T = 0 \quad \text{when} \quad y = \pm b. \qquad (7.3.11)$$

Substitution of expression (7.3.5) into formula (7.3.8) yields the purely thermal strain κ_T:

$$\kappa_T = \frac{q'\alpha_T}{2\lambda_T} \left(1 - \frac{96}{\pi^4} \sum_{n=1,3,\ldots}^{\infty} \frac{1}{n^4} e^{-n^2\beta t} \right). \qquad (7.3.12)$$

Since the strain κ_T is independent of the coordinates x and y, we have

$$\nabla^2 \kappa_T = 0. \qquad (7.3.13)$$

In view of equation (7.3.13), we can rewrite equation (7.3.7) in the form

---

1) The boundary conditions (7.3.10), (7.3.11) are the expressions in polar coordinates of the boundary conditions (5.16) in the book [15].

196

$$\nabla^2\nabla^2 w + \frac{\rho h}{D_M}\frac{\partial^2 w}{\partial t^2} = 0. \tag{7.3.14}$$

The solution of (7.3.14) may be represented as the sum of a quasi–static part w_I and a dynamic part w_{II}:

$$w = w_I + w_{II}. \tag{7.3.15}$$

The quasi–static part w_I must satisfy the equation

$$\nabla^2\nabla^2 w_I = 0 \tag{7.3.16}$$

with the boundary conditions (7.3.10) and (7.3.11) in which w is to be replaced by w_I.

Substituting solution (7.3.15) into equation (7.3.14) and taking account of equation (7.3.16), we obtain the following equation for the dynamic part of the solution:

$$\nabla^2\nabla^2 w_{II} + \kappa^2\left(\frac{\partial^2 w_{II}}{\partial t^2} + \frac{\partial^2 w_I}{\partial t^2}\right) = 0, \tag{7.3.17}$$

where

$$\kappa^2 = \frac{\rho h}{D_M}.$$

Since the quasi–static part w_I satisfies all the boundary conditions (7.3.10), (7.3.11) for the plate, the dynamic part of the solution must satisfy the initial conditions

$$w_{II} = 0, \quad \frac{\partial w_{II}}{\partial t} = 0 \quad \text{when} \quad t = 0 \tag{7.3.18}$$

and the homogeneous boundary conditions

$$w_{II} = 0 \quad \nabla^2 w_{II} = 0 \quad \text{when} \quad x = \pm a, \quad y = \pm b. \tag{7.3.19}$$

The solution of equation (7.3.16) will be chosen in the form

$$w_I = -\frac{1}{2}(1 + \nu)\kappa_T(x^2 + y^2) + w_I' + w_I'', \tag{7.3.20}$$

where the functions w_I' and w_I'' are biharmonic functions subjected to the boundary conditions

$$w_I' = 0, \quad \frac{\partial^2 w_I'}{\partial x^2} = 0 \qquad\qquad \text{when} \quad x = \pm a, \quad (7.3.21)$$

$$w_I' = \frac{1}{2}(1+\nu)\kappa_T(b^2 + x^2), \quad \frac{\partial^2 w_I'}{\partial y^2} = 0 \quad \text{when} \quad y = \pm b, \quad (7.3.22)$$

$$w_I'' = \frac{1}{2}(1+\nu)\kappa_T(a^2 + y^2), \quad \frac{\partial^2 w_I''}{\partial x^2} = 0 \quad \text{when} \quad x = \pm a, \quad (7.3.23)$$

$$w_I'' = 0, \quad \frac{\partial^2 w_I''}{\partial y^2} = 0 \qquad\qquad \text{when} \quad y = \pm b. \quad (7.3.24)$$

With these boundary conditions for w_I' and w_I'', the boundary conditions for w_I are all satisfied.

The expressions for the biharmonic functions will be chosen in the form

$$w_I' = \sum_{n=1,3,\ldots} (A_n \operatorname{ch} \alpha_n y + \alpha_n y B_n \operatorname{sh} \alpha_n y) \cos \alpha_n x,$$

$$w_I'' = \sum_{n=1,3,\ldots} (C_n \operatorname{ch} \beta_n x + \beta_n x D_n \operatorname{sh} \beta_n x) \cos \beta_n y, \qquad (7.3.25)$$

where

$$\alpha_n = \frac{n\pi}{2a}, \quad \beta_n = \frac{n\pi}{2b}.$$

The expression for w_I' automatically satisfies condition (7.3.21), and the expression for w_I'' automatically satisfies condition (7.3.24).

In order to satisfy the remaining boundary conditions, we expand in Fourier series the following quantities appearing in the boundary conditions (7.3.22) and (7.3.23):

$$-\frac{1}{2}(1+\nu)\kappa_T(b^2 + x^2) = \sum_{n=1,3,\ldots} a_n \cos \alpha_n x,$$

$$-\frac{1}{2}(1+\nu)\kappa_T(a^2 + y^2) = \sum_{n=1,3,\ldots} b_n \cos \beta_n x, \qquad (7.3.26)$$

where

$$a_n = -\frac{(1+\nu)\kappa_T}{\alpha_n a}\left(a^2+b^2-\frac{2}{\alpha_n^2}\right)\sin\frac{n\pi}{2},$$

$$b_n = -\frac{(1+\nu)\kappa_T}{\beta_n b}\left(a^2+b^2-\frac{2}{\beta_n^2}\right)\sin\frac{n\pi}{2}. \tag{7.3.27}$$

Substituting expressions (7.3.25) and (7.3.26) into the boundary conditions (7.3.22) and (7.3.23), we find the constants

$$A_n = \frac{-a_n}{\mathrm{ch}^2\alpha_n b}\left(\mathrm{ch}\,\alpha_n b+\frac{\alpha_n b}{2}\,\mathrm{sh}\,\alpha_n b\right),$$

$$B_n = \frac{a_n}{2\,\mathrm{ch}\,\alpha_n b},$$

$$C_n = \frac{-b_n}{\mathrm{ch}^2\beta_n a}\left(\mathrm{ch}\,\beta_n a+\frac{\beta_n a}{2}\,\mathrm{sh}\,\beta_n a\right), \tag{7.3.28}$$

$$D_n = \frac{b_n}{2\,\mathrm{ch}\,\beta_n a}.$$

Now we turn to the determination of the dynamic part of the solution. Conditions (7.3.19) are satisfied if the dynamic part of the solution is chosen in the form

$$w_{II} = \sum_{n=1,3,\ldots}\sum_{m=1,3,\ldots} q_{nm}(t)\cos\alpha_n x\cos\beta_m y. \tag{7.3.29}$$

When function w_I in expression (7.3.20) is represented by the double trigonometric series

$$w_I = \kappa_T\sum_{n=1,3,\ldots}\sum_{m=1,3,\ldots} k_{nm}\cos\alpha_n x\cos\beta_m y, \tag{7.3.30}$$

where

$$k_{nm} = -\frac{16(1+\nu)(-1)^{\frac{n+m}{2}}}{\pi^2 nm(\alpha_n^2+\beta_m^2)},$$

and the series (7.3.29), (7.3.30) are substituted into equation (7.3.17), we obtain the following differential equation for the determination of the coefficients q_{nm}:

$$\frac{\partial^2 q_{nm}}{\partial t^2} + \omega_{nm}^2 q_{nm} + k_{nm} \frac{\partial^2 \kappa_T}{\partial t^2} = 0,$$

where

$$\omega_{nm} = \frac{\alpha_n^2 + \beta_m^2}{\kappa}.$$

(7.3.31)

The initial conditions are

$$q_{nm} = 0, \quad \frac{\partial q_{nm}}{\partial t} = 0 \quad \text{when} \quad t = 0.$$

(7.3.32)

With initial conditions (7.3.32) and the relation

$$\kappa_T(0) = 0,$$

the Laplace transformation of equation (7.3.31) yield the following algebraic equation in the transform q_{nm}^*:

$$(s^2 + \omega_{nm}^2) q_{nm}^* + k_{nm} \left[s^2 \kappa_T^* - \frac{d\kappa_T}{dt}(0) \right] = 0.$$

(7.3.33)

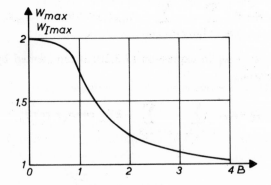

Fig. 28.

Taking account of expression (7.3.12) for κ_T and the relation

$$\frac{d\kappa_T}{dt}(0) = \frac{q'\alpha_T}{2\lambda_T}\frac{96\beta}{\pi^4}\sum_{n=1,3,\dots}\frac{1}{n^2} = \frac{6q'\beta\alpha_T}{\pi^2\lambda_T},$$

when calculating the inverse transformation, we finally obtain the dynamic part of the solution in the form

$$\omega_{II} = \frac{6q'\beta\alpha_T}{\lambda_T\pi^2}\sum_{n=1,3,\dots}\sum_{m=1,3,\dots}\left\{k_{nm}\left[\frac{1}{\omega_{nm}}\sin\omega_{nm}t - \right.\right.$$

$$-\frac{8\beta}{\pi^2}\sum_{j=1,3,\dots}\frac{1}{j^4\beta^2+\omega_{nm}^2}\left(\cos\omega_{nm}t+\frac{\omega_{nm}}{\beta}\frac{1}{j^2}\sin\omega_{nm}t-e^{-j^2\beta t}\right)\left.\left.\right]\right\} \times$$

$$\times \cos\alpha_n x \cos\beta_m y. \tag{7.3.34}$$

Boley and Barber [53] calculated the relative maximum dynamic bending deflection in the centre of the plate and the greatest quasi–static deflection $w_{max}/w_{I\,max}$ for different values of parameter

$$B = \frac{h}{2a\sqrt{a}}\sqrt[4]{\frac{D_M}{\rho h}}$$

and the ratio a/b.

Figure 28 shows the ration $w_{max}/w_{I\,max}$ versus the parameter B for a beam $(a/b = 0)$.

Similar curves are obtained for the values $0 < a/b < 1$.

The above results indicate that the dynamic effect increases as parameter B decreases. When $B \to 0$, the ratio $w_{max}/w_{I\,max}$ tends to 2.

7.4. Plane dilatational waves in an infinite continuum

We consider a plane dilatational wave of angular frequency ω in an infinite thermoelastic medium. It will be assumed that φ_j in solution (7.1.6) depends only on the coordinate x, i.e. $\varphi_j = \varphi_j(x)$. Then equation (7.1.7) becomes

$$\left(\frac{d^2}{dx^2} + \delta_j^2\right)\varphi_j = 0, \tag{7.4.1}$$

which has the solution

$$\varphi_j = C_j'' e^{\pm i\delta_j x}. \tag{7.4.2}$$

Substituting (7.4.2) into (7.1.8) and setting $p = i\omega$, we find the solution

$$u_x = \sum_{j=1}^{2} C_j' \exp\left[i(\pm \delta_j x + \omega t)\right], \tag{7.4.3}$$

$$u_y = u_z = 0,$$

where δ_j is defined by (7.1.3) after replacing p by $i\omega$, and $C_j' = \pm i\delta_j C_j''$ ($j = 1, 2$).

Now we will examine the propagation of the predominantly elastic wave associated with δ_1.

The value of δ_1 is determined by the formula

$$\delta_1^2 = \frac{\omega^2}{2c_1^2}\left\{\left(1 + \frac{1+\epsilon}{i\Omega}\right)\left[1 - \frac{2(1-\epsilon)}{i\Omega} + \left(\frac{1+\epsilon}{i\Omega}\right)^2\right]^{\frac{1}{2}}\right\}, \tag{7.4.4}$$

where

$$\Omega = \frac{a\omega}{c_1^2}.$$

The dimensionless coefficient Ω is very small for most materials encountered in technology. In the following we will assume that $\Omega \ll 1$. Then expanding (7.4.4) in a series of powers of Ω, we find after some calculation that

$$\delta_1 = m_1 + il_1, \tag{7.4.5}$$

where

$$m_1 = \frac{\omega}{c_s}\left[1 + \frac{\epsilon(4 - 3\epsilon)}{8(1 + \epsilon)^4}\Omega^2\right], \tag{7.4.6}$$

$$l_1 = -\frac{\epsilon\omega\Omega}{2c_s(1 + \epsilon)^2}; \tag{7.4.7}$$

$$c_s = c_1(1 + \epsilon)^{\frac{1}{2}}.$$

The quantity c_s is the adiabatic phase velocity of irrotational waves in an infinite medium. The physical meaning of c_s will be explained in the following.

Setting $\alpha = \lambda_T/c_\epsilon = 0$ for an adiabatic process and recalling the notation (7.1.4) for ϵ, from (1.6.13) we obtain the wave equation

$$\nabla^2 \Phi - \frac{1}{c_S^2} \frac{\partial^2 \Phi}{\partial t^2} = 0,$$

where the adiabatic velocity c_S is connected with the propagation velocity $c_1 = c_T$ of dilatational waves through relation (7.4.7). This same result is obtained by substitution in the expression

$$c_S^2 = \frac{\lambda_a + 2\mu}{\rho}$$

of value (1.5.29) for the Lamé constant λ_a in the case of adiabatic strain.

Substituting (7.4.5) into solution (7.4.3) with $j = 1$ and choosing the minus sign in front of m_1, which corresponds to the propagation of a wave in the direction of the positive x-axis, the solution for the displacement connected with a predominantly elastic wave is

$$u_x = [C_1 \sin(\omega t - m_1 x) + C_2 \cos(\omega t - m_1 x)]\, e^{l_1 x}, \qquad (7.4.8)$$

where

$$C_1 = iC_1', \quad C_2 = C_1'.$$

The coefficient l_1 is negative; the amplitude of the waves in a heat-conducting medium is therefore attenuated according to an exponential law. The phase velocity of propagation of such waves is

$$v = \frac{\omega}{m_1}.$$

Substituting the value of m_1 and using the fact that $\epsilon \ll 1$ for most materials, we find the following approximation for the phase velocity

$$v = c_S \left(1 + \frac{\epsilon \Omega^2}{2}\right)^{-1} = c_S \left(1 - \epsilon \frac{\Omega^2}{2}\right) \qquad (7.4.9)$$

We shall now determine the relative energy dissipation $\Delta W/W$ for the present type of waves. Here, ΔW is the energy dissipated during one cycle of stress and W is the maximum value of the elastic strain energy attained during the cycle.

By u_1 and u_2 we denote two subsequent maximum displacements on one side of the equilibrium position.

When the relative energy dissipation is small compared with unity, one can write

$$\frac{\Delta W}{W} = \frac{u_1^2 - u_2^2}{u_1^2} \approx \frac{2(u_1 - u_2)}{u_2} \approx 2 \ln \frac{u_1}{u_2}.$$

It follows from (7.4.8) that

$$\frac{u_1}{u_2} = e^{-l_1 L},$$

where

$$L = \frac{v \, 2\pi}{\omega} = \frac{2\pi}{m_1},$$

In view of (7.4.6) one then obtains

$$\frac{\Delta W}{W} = -\frac{4\pi l_1}{m_1} = \frac{2\pi\epsilon\Omega}{(1 + \epsilon)^2}. \qquad (7.4.10)$$

7.5. Longitudinal waves in an infinite solid cylinder

In this section we consider the influence of the thermoelastic energy dissipation on the propagation of longitudinal waves in an infinite solid cylinder.

In the present problem, the general solution (1.6.9) for the displacements consists of an irrotational and a solenoidal part.

The irrotational part can be determined by the method explained in Section 7.4.

Assuming that the motion is axisymmetric and confined to the planes rz, the scalar potential will be written in terms of cylindrical coordinates, i.e. $\varphi_j = \varphi_j \, (r, z)$. Equation (7.1.7) then becomes

$$\left(\frac{\partial^2}{\partial r^2} + \frac{1}{r} \frac{\partial}{\partial r} + \frac{\partial^2}{\partial z^2} + \delta_j^2 \right) \varphi_j = 0. \qquad (7.5.1)$$

Applying the method of separation of variables (see Section 3.7), for the solid cylinder we obtain the solution

$$\varphi_j = C_j J_0(h_j r) e^{i\gamma z}, \tag{7.5.2}$$

where $J_0(x)$ is the Bessel function of order zero and first kind. Moreover we have introduced the notation

$$h_j^2 = \delta_j^2 - \gamma^2.$$

Substitution of solution (7.5.2) into (7.1.6) yields

$$\Phi = \sum_{j=1}^{2} C_j J_0(h_j r) e^{i\gamma z + pt}. \tag{7.5.3}$$

Turning now to the solenoidal part of the solution, we note that the vector $\nabla^2 A$ can be calculated from formula (6.1.2) after replacing B by A. Without loss of generality it can be assumed [18] that

$$\text{div } A = 0, \tag{7.5.4}$$

where A is called the vector potential.

Taking account of (2.6.3), (7.5.4), and the fact that not only $\text{rot}_\theta A$ but all derivatives with respect to θ vanish, we find

$$\nabla^2 A = -\text{rot}\left[-e_r \frac{\partial A_\theta}{\partial z} + e_z \frac{1}{r} \frac{\partial (rA_\theta)}{\partial r} \right] =$$
$$= e_\theta \left\{ \frac{\partial}{\partial r} \left[\frac{1}{r} \frac{\partial}{\partial r} (rA_\theta) \right] + \frac{\partial^2 A_\theta}{\partial z^2} \right\}. \tag{7.5.5}$$

In view of equation (7.5.5), the vector equation (1.6.11) yields the following scalar equation for the determination of A_θ:

$$\left(\frac{\partial^2}{\partial r^2} + \frac{1}{r} \frac{\partial}{\partial r} - \frac{1}{r^2} + \frac{\partial^2}{\partial z^2} - \frac{1}{c_2^2} \frac{\partial^2}{\partial t^2} \right) A_\theta = 0. \tag{7.5.6}$$

The solution of (7.5.6) for a solid cylinder is

$$A_\theta = iC J_1(kr) e^{i\gamma z + pt}, \tag{7.5.7}$$

where $J_1(x)$ is the Bessel function of first order and first kind. The parameter k is given by

$$k^2 = -\frac{p^2}{c_2^2} - \gamma^2.$$

Now we substitute solutions (7.5.3), (7.5.7) into (1.6.9). Making use of (2.6.3) and the formula for the derivative of Bessel functions, since $A_r = A_z = 0$ we find

$$u_r = -\left[\sum_{j=1}^{2} C_j h_j J_1(h_j r) - C\gamma J_0(kr) \right] e^{i\gamma z + pt},$$

$$u_\theta = 0, \tag{7.5.8}$$

$$u_z = i\left[\sum_{j=1}^{\infty} C_j \gamma J_0(h_j r) + Ck J_0(kr) \right] e^{i\gamma z + pt}.$$

Since there are no thermal effects associated with longitudinal waves, the expression for the temperature field is given by formula (7.1.9):

$$T - T_0 = -\frac{\rho c_1^2}{(3\lambda + 2\mu)\alpha_T} \sum_{j=1}^{2} C_j \left(\frac{p^2}{c_1^2} + \delta_j^2 \right) J_0(h_j r) e^{i\gamma z + pt}. \tag{7.5.9}$$

The components of the stress tensor on the surfaces $r = $ const are given by (7.1.10) in the form

$$\sigma_r = 2\mu\left\{ \sum_{j=1}^{2} C_j \left[\frac{h_j}{r} J_1(h_j r) + \left(\gamma^2 + \frac{p^2}{2c_2^2} \right) J_0(h_j r) \right] + \right.$$

$$\left. + \gamma C \left[k J_0(kr) - \frac{1}{r} J_1(kr) \right] \right\} e^{i\gamma z + pt}, \tag{7.5.10}$$

$$\sigma_{rz} = -i\mu\left[2\gamma \sum_{j=1}^{2} C_j h_j J_1(h_j r) + C(k^2 - \gamma^2) J_1(kr) \right] e^{i\gamma z + pt},$$

$$\sigma_{r\theta} = 0.$$

In order to have a unique solution of the present problem, it is necessary to satisfy boundary conditions not only for the stresses but also for the heat exchange on the surface of the cylinder.

Let us assume that the surface $r = r_2$ of the cylinder is stress free and thermally insulated.

With the boundary conditions

$$\sigma_r = 0, \quad \sigma_{rz} = 0, \quad \frac{\partial T}{\partial r} = 0 \quad \text{when} \quad r = r_2, \qquad (7.5.11)$$

the equations for period waves $(p = i\omega)$ are

$$C_1 \left[\frac{h_1}{r_2} J_1(h_1 r_2) + \left(\gamma^2 - \frac{\omega^2}{2c_2^2} \right) J_0(h_1 r_2) \right] + C_2 \left[\frac{h_2}{r_2} J_1(h_2 r_2) + \right.$$

$$\left. + \left(\gamma^2 - \frac{\omega^2}{2c_2^2} \right) J_0(h_2 r_2) \right] + C\gamma \left[k J_0(kr_2) - \frac{1}{r_2} J_1(kr_2) \right] = 0,$$

$$\hspace{10cm} (7.5.12)$$

$$C_1 2\gamma h_1 J_1(h_1 r_2) + C_2 2\gamma h_2 J_1(h_2 r_2) + C(k^2 - \gamma^2) J_1(kr_2) = 0,$$

$$C_1 h_1 \left(\frac{\omega^2}{c_1^2} - \delta_1^2 \right) J_1(h_1 r_2) + C_2 \left(\frac{\omega^2}{c_1^2} - \delta_2^2 \right) J_1(h_2 r_2) = 0.$$

Let the radius r_2 of the cylinder be so small that $h_j r_2$ $(j = 1, 2)$ and kr_2 are small compared with one, i.e. the wavelength is large in comparison with the radius of the cylinder. Then

$$J_0(h_j r_2) \approx J_0(kr_2) \approx 1,$$

$$J_1(h_j r_2) \approx \frac{1}{2} h_j r_2, \quad J_1(kr_2) \approx \frac{1}{2} kr_2.$$

Substituting these approximate values into the system of equations (7.5.12) and setting the determinant of this system equal to zero, we find the following frequency equation

$$h_1^2 \left(\frac{\omega^2}{c_1^2} - \delta_1^2 \right) \left[\left(\frac{h_2^2}{2} + \gamma^2 - \frac{\omega^2}{2c_2^2} \right) (k^2 - \gamma^2) - \gamma^2 h_2^2 \right] -$$

$$- h_2^2 \left(\frac{\omega^2}{c_1^2} - \delta_2^2 \right) \left[\left(\frac{h_1^2}{2} + \gamma^2 - \frac{\omega^2}{2c_2^2} \right) (k^2 - \gamma^2) - \gamma^2 h_1^2 \right] = 0. \ (7.5.13)$$

In view of the relations

$$\frac{h_j^2}{2} + \gamma^2 - \frac{\omega^2}{2c_2^2} = \frac{\delta_j^2}{2} + \frac{\gamma^2}{2} - \frac{\omega^2}{2c_2^2}$$

$$k^2 - \gamma^2 = \frac{\omega^2}{c_2^2} - 2\gamma^2, \quad \gamma^2 h_j^2 = \gamma^2 \delta_j^2 - \gamma^4 \quad (j = 1, 2),$$

the frequency equation (7.5.13) assumes the form

$$\left(\gamma^2 - \frac{\omega^2}{c_0^2}\right)\left(\gamma^2 + \frac{i\omega^2}{\Omega c_1^2}\right) + \frac{i\omega^2}{\Omega c_0^2}\frac{\epsilon}{(e^2 - 1)}\left(3\gamma^2 - \frac{\omega^2}{c_2^2}\right) = 0. \quad (7.5.14)$$

where

$$\epsilon = \frac{T_0(3\lambda + 2\mu)^2 \alpha_T^2}{\rho c_1^2 c_\epsilon}, \quad \Omega = \frac{a\omega}{c_1^2},$$

$$e^2 = \frac{c_1^2}{c_2^2} = \frac{\lambda + \mu}{\mu}, \quad c_0^2 = \frac{E}{\rho}. \quad (7.5.15)$$

In the absence of thermal effects ($\epsilon = 0$), the phase velocity of propagation of longitudinal waves is equal to $v = \omega/\gamma = c_0$, i.e. the velocity of propagation of longitudinal waves in a bar according to the elementary theory.

The fact that equation (7.5.14) is complex indicates that the amplitude of the waves is attenuated as they propagate.

The roots of equation (7.5.14) are

$$\gamma_1^2, \gamma_2^2 = \frac{\omega^2}{2c_0^2}\left\{\left(1 - \frac{\alpha}{\Omega_1}\right) \pm \left[1 + \frac{\beta}{\Omega_1} + \left(\frac{\alpha}{\Omega_1}\right)^2\right]^{1/2}\right\}, \quad (7.5.16)$$

where

$$\alpha = i\alpha_1 \Omega_1, \quad \alpha_1 = \frac{1}{\Omega_1}[1 + (1 + k')\sigma],$$

$$\beta = i(4\beta_1 - 2\alpha_1)\Omega_1, \quad \beta_1 = \frac{1}{\Omega_1}(1 + \sigma), \quad (7.5.17)$$

$$\Omega_1 = \Omega\frac{c_1^2}{c_0^2}, \quad k' = \frac{1 - 2\nu}{2(1 + \nu)}, \quad \sigma = 2(1 - \nu)\epsilon.$$

It is easily shown that the roots (7.5.16) correspond to waves of two types. The waves associated with γ_1^2 are similar to purely elastic waves, and those associated with γ_2^2 have the nature of purely thermal waves.

We will limit consideration to the purely elastic waves.

Assuming that $\Omega \ll 1$, we obtain

$$\gamma_1^2 = \left(\frac{\omega}{c_0}\right)^2 (\psi_1 - i\psi_2), \qquad (7.5.18)$$

where

$$\psi_1 = \frac{\beta_1}{\alpha_1} \left[1 - \frac{1}{\alpha_1^2} \left(1 - \frac{\beta_1}{\alpha_1} \right) \left(1 - \frac{2\beta_1}{\alpha_1} \right) \right],$$

$$\psi_2 = \frac{1}{\alpha_1} \frac{\beta_1}{\alpha_1} \left(1 - \frac{\beta_1}{\alpha_1} \right). \qquad (7.5.19)$$

If we now set

$$\gamma_1 = \gamma_r + i\gamma_i,$$

where γ_r and γ_i are real valued, and denote the phase velocity by

$$V = \frac{\omega}{\gamma_r c_0}, \qquad (7.5.20)$$

equation (7.5.18) goes over into the form

$$V^2 \equiv (1 - \tau^2) \psi_1^{-1}, \qquad (7.5.21)$$

where $\tau = \gamma_i/\gamma_r$, satisfies the algebraic equations

$$\tau^2 - \frac{2\psi_1}{\psi_2} \tau - 1 = 0. \qquad (7.5.22)$$

The negative root of this equation corresponding to spatially attenuated waves is

$$\tau = -\frac{\psi_2}{2\psi_1}. \qquad (7.5.23)$$

Substituting the value (7.5.23) into equation (7.5.21), when $\Omega \ll 1$ and $\epsilon \ll 1$, we obtain the following expression for the dimensionless phase velocity

$$V = V_S \left[1 - \frac{(1 - \nu)(1 - 2\nu)}{2(1 + \nu)} \epsilon \Omega_1^2 \right], \qquad (7.5.24)$$

where $V_s = (\alpha_1/\beta_1)^{1/2}$ is the dimensionless phase velocity of dilational waves in a bar when the process is adiabatic.

The velocity V_s can be found by solving the present problem with $\alpha = \lambda_T/c_\epsilon = 0$.

Appendix

SOME ASPECTS OF THERMO–ELASTIC STABILITY

A.1. Introduction

The theory of thermo–elastic stability is part of the general theory of elastic stability, which is concerned with problems in which the effect of the loading depends on the deformation. The buckling of a beam column under axial forces provides an example from this theory. In a consistent linear theory of elasticity the effects of the loading have to be disregarded, as the deflections and loadings are assumed there to be infinitesimally small and these effects are of the second order. It seems that several authors of well–known books on the linear theory of elasticity, e.g. [A1], [A2], [A3], have, like the author of the present book, adopted this point of view. Consequently they make no reference to buckling phenomena and so exclude many problems of practical interest. It is the purpose of this appendix to examine some problems of instability under thermal forces.

It is obvious that our considerations have to be based on the non–linear theory of elasticity. Non–linearity may occur in three different ways:
(a) the relations between the strains and the derivatives of the displacements are non–linear.
(b) undeformed and deformed area elements are different,
(c) the stress–strain relations are non–linear.

Although it is possible to formulate a completely general theory of stability, in which the different aspects of nonlinearity are taken into account [A4], [A5], practical results are mainly obtained by reducing the problems to partial nonlinearity [A6]. In our discussion we shall retain only some non–linear terms in the strain tensor.

Partial nonlinearity cannot lead to a consistent theory. We neglect some second order terms and retain others. It has to be assumed that the neglected terms are very small. Comparison with experimental results of those obtained by the theory of stability supports these assumptions. With these assumptions, the theory may be built into a consistent one. Sometimes we shall have to make some further simplifying assumptions.

In this appendix Young's modulus E and Poisson's ratio ν will be assumed to be independent of the temperature. In some special problems the coefficient of thermal conductivity λ_T and the coefficient of thermal expansion α_T will also be assumed to be constant.

The phenomena of elastic instability, in the form of buckling, mainly occur in slender bodies, such as beams, plates and shells. Here we shall limit our considerations to the case of thermal instability of plates. Beam problems are included in the discussion of the infinite strip.

The treatment is based on the investigation of the behaviour of a plate subjected to the combined action of forces, acting in the plane of the plate and perpendicular to it.

A.2. Basic equations

The basic equations are derived by means of a variational principle for the specific free energy F, defined in (1.5.9) by

$$F = \frac{\lambda}{2} \epsilon_{kk}^2 + \mu \epsilon_{ij} \epsilon_{ij} - (3\lambda + 2\mu) \alpha_T \epsilon_{kk} (T - T_0) + F_0, \quad i, j, k = 1, 2, 3.$$

$$(A.2.1)$$

A thin plate may be considered to be in a plane state of stress if it is subjected to the combined action of forces, acting in, and perpendicular to, the plane of the plate. According to (4.1.5) the stresses σ_z, σ_{xz}, σ_{yz} vanish

$$\sigma_z = \sigma_{xz} = \sigma_{yz} = 0. \tag{A.2.2}$$

We next express the specific free energy F by means of E and ν, related to the Lamé constants through the equations (1.5.14)

$$\lambda = \frac{\nu E}{(1 + \nu)(1 - 2\nu)} \ ; \quad \mu = \frac{E}{2(1 + \nu)} \ ,$$

and further use the definitions of (4.1.4)

$$E_1 = \frac{E}{1 - \nu^2} \ ; \quad \alpha_{T1} = \alpha_T (1 + \nu).$$

We eliminate the strains $\epsilon_z, \epsilon_{xz}, \epsilon_{yz}$ by means of (A.2.2) and obtain

212

$$F = \tfrac{1}{2}E_1 \left[(1-v)\,\epsilon_{ij}\epsilon_{ij} + v\epsilon_{kk}^2 - 2\alpha_{T1}\epsilon_{kk}(T-T_0) - \frac{\alpha_{T1}^2}{1-2v}(T-T_0)^2 \right] + F_0,$$

$$i,j,k = 1,2. \qquad (A.2.3)$$

The stress—strain relations for the plane problem may be found by (1.5.7)

$$\sigma_{ij} = \frac{\partial F}{\partial \epsilon_{ij}},$$

from which it follows that

$$\sigma_{ij} = E_1 \left[(1-v)\,\epsilon_{ij} + \delta_{ij}\left\{ v\epsilon_{kk} - \alpha_{T1}(T-T_0) \right\} \right]. \qquad (A.2.4)$$

In the classical linear theory the strain—deformation relations are given by (1.6.4)

$$\epsilon_{ij} = \tfrac{1}{2}(u_{i,j} + u_{j,i}),$$

where $u_i = u_i\,(x,y,z)$. If the plate is only slightly stretched and bent the displacements may be represented by

$$u_i = u_i^{(0)}\,(x,y) - zw_{,i}, \qquad i = 1,2, \qquad (A.2.5)$$

where $u_i^{(0)}\,(x,y)$ is the displacement of the mid—plane and w is the deflection.

In the following we omit the superscript$^{(0)}$ and write u_i for the displacement in the mid—plane. From (A.2.5) we find that

$$\epsilon_{ij} = \tfrac{1}{2}(u_{i,j} + u_{j,i}) - zw_{,ij}. \qquad (A.2.6)$$

A theory based on the expression (A.2.6) can never predict instability phenomena. Bending and stretching are simply superimposed. If (A.2.6) is supplied with the term $\tfrac{1}{2}w_{,i}w_{,j}$, which is comparable with the $u_{i,j}$ terms and which occurs in the complete (non—linear) expressions for ϵ_{ij}, we have

$$\epsilon_{ij} = \tfrac{1}{2}(u_{i,j} + u_{j,i}) + \tfrac{1}{2}w_{,i}w_{,j} - zw_{,ij}, \qquad i,j = 1,2. \qquad (A.2.7)$$

On the basis of (A.2.7) an interaction of bending and compression (stretching) forces will occur.

The middle surface forces N_{ij} and the moments M_{ij} are defined by

$$N_{ij} = \int_{-h/2}^{h/2} \sigma_{ij} dz \qquad \text{(A.2.8)}$$

and

$$M_{ij} = \int_{-h/2}^{h/2} z\sigma_{ij} dz, \qquad \text{(A.2.9)}$$

respectively. After substituting (A.2.7) into (A.2.4) and integrating, we obtain the equations

$$N_{ij} = D_N \left[\frac{1-\nu}{2} \left\{ (u_{i,j} + u_{j,i}) + w_{,i}w_{,j} \right\} \right.$$
$$\left. + \delta_{ij}(\nu u_{k,k} + \tfrac{1}{2}\nu w_{,k}w_{,k} - \epsilon_{T1}) \right], \qquad \text{(A.2.10)}$$

$$M_{ij} = -D_M \left[(1-\nu)w_{,ij} + \delta_{ij}(\nu w_{,kk} + \kappa_{T1}) \right], \qquad \text{(A.2.11)}$$

in which the abbreviations

$$D_N = \frac{Eh}{1-\nu^2}, \quad D_M = \frac{Eh^3}{12(1-\nu^2)}, \qquad \text{(A.2.12)}$$

and

$$\epsilon_{T1} = (1+\nu)\epsilon_T = \frac{1+\nu}{h} \int_{-h/2}^{h/2} \alpha_T(T-T_0)dz, \qquad \text{(A.2.13)}$$

$$\kappa_{T1} = (1+\nu)\kappa_T = \frac{12(1+\nu)}{h^3} \int_{-h/2}^{h/2} \alpha_T(T-T_0)zdz, \qquad \text{(A.2.14)}$$

are introduced.

The specific free energy $\bar{F}$ per unit surface area may be found from

$$\bar{F} = \int_{-h/2}^{h/2} F dz. \qquad \text{(A.2.15)}$$

The integration (A.2.15) can easily be carried out under the assumption (A.2.7).

214

The result is the equation

$$\bar{F} = \bar{F}_1 + \bar{F}_2 + \bar{F}_3 \tag{A.2.16}$$

in which

$$\bar{F}_1 = \tfrac{1}{2}D_N \left[(1 - v)\,(u_{i,j} + \tfrac{1}{2}w_{,i}w_{,j})\,(u_{i,j} + \tfrac{1}{2}w_{,i}w_{,j}) \right.$$
$$\left. + v(u_{k,k} + \tfrac{1}{2}w_{,k}w_{,k})^2 - 2\epsilon_{T1}(u_{k,k} + \tfrac{1}{2}w_{,k}w_{,k}) \right], \tag{A.2.17}$$

$$\bar{F}_2 = \tfrac{1}{2}D_M \left[(1 - v)\,w_{,ij}w_{,ij} + vw_{,kk}^2 + 2\kappa_{T1}\,w_{,kk} \right], \tag{A.2.18}$$

$$\bar{F}_3 = \int\limits_{-h/2}^{h/2} \left[F_0 - \frac{\alpha_{T1}^2}{1 - 2v}(T - T_0)^2 \right] dz. \tag{A.2.19}$$

For the derivation of the basic equations, $\bar{F}_3$ is insignificant. With (A.2.10) and (A.2.11) some other expressions for $\bar{F}_1$ and $\bar{F}_2$ may be found. We have

$$\bar{F}_1 = \tfrac{1}{4}N_{ij} \left[(u_{i,j} + u_{j,i}) + w_{,i}w_{,j} \right] - \tfrac{1}{4}D_N\epsilon_{T1} \left[u_{k,k} + w_{,k}w_{,k} \right], \tag{A.2.20}$$

which also can be written as

$$\bar{F}_1 = \frac{1}{2D_N} \left[\frac{N_{ij}N_{ij}}{1 - v} - \frac{vN_{kk}^2}{1 - v^2} \right] - D_N \frac{\epsilon_{T1}^2}{1 + v}, \tag{A.2.21}$$

and

$$\bar{F}_2 = -\tfrac{1}{2}M_{ij}w_{,ij} + \tfrac{1}{2}D_M\kappa_{T1}\,w_{,kk}, \tag{A.2.22}$$

which is equivalent to

$$\bar{F}_2 = \frac{1}{2D_M} \left[\frac{M_{ij}M_{ij}}{1 - v} - \frac{vM_{kk}^2}{1 - v^2} \right] - D_M \frac{\kappa_{T1}^2}{1 + v}. \tag{A.2.23}$$

The basic equations are derived from the variational principle

$$\delta \int\limits_{\Omega} (\bar{F} - pw)\,d\Omega = 0, \tag{A.2.24}$$

subjected to the independent variations δu_i and δw. In (A.2.24) p is the surface load, while the integration extends over the surface Ω of the mid—plane. We impart to the plate the virtual displacements δu_{ij} at constant w and find

215

$$\delta \int_\Omega \bar{F}_1 d\Omega = 0 = \int_\Omega N_{ij} \delta u_{i,j} d\Omega = \int_\Omega (N_{ij} \delta u_i)_{,j} d\Omega - \int_\Omega N_{ij,j} \delta u_i d\Omega =$$

$$= \int_L N_{ij} n_j \delta u_i ds - \int_\Omega N_{ij,j} \delta u_i d\Omega, \qquad (A.2.25)$$

by the application of the divergence theorem. In this expression s denotes the coordinate along the boundary **L**.

Equation (A.2.25) can only be satisfied if

$$N_{ij,j} = 0, \quad \text{on } \Omega, \qquad (A.2.26)$$

while on the boundary L

$$\delta u_i = 0 \quad \text{or} \quad N_{ij} n_j = 0 \qquad (A.2.27)$$

must hold. The first equation of the pair (A.2.27) corresponds to a restrained, the second to a free part of the edge.

Next we keep u_i constant and vary **w**. We have

$$\delta \int_\Omega (\bar{F}_1 + \bar{F}_2 - pw) d\Omega = 0 =$$

$$= \int_\Omega N_{ij} w_{,i} \delta w_{,j} d\Omega - \int_\Omega M_{ij} \delta w_{,ij} d\Omega - \int_\Omega p \delta w d\Omega$$

$$= \int_\Omega (N_{ij} w_{,i} \delta w)_{,j} d\Omega - \int_\Omega N_{ij,j} w_{,i} \delta w d\Omega$$

$$- \int_\Omega N_{ij} w_{,ij} \delta w d\Omega - \int_\Omega (M_{ij} \delta w_{,i})_{,j} d\Omega +$$

$$+ \int_\Omega M_{ij,j} \delta w_{,i} d\Omega - \int_\Omega p \delta w d\Omega =$$

$$= \int_L N_{ij} n_j w_{,i} \delta w ds - \int_\Omega N_{ij} w_{,ij} \delta w d\Omega - \int_L M_{ij} n_j \delta w_{,i} ds +$$

216

$$+ \int_{\Omega} (M_{ij,j}\delta w)_{,i} d\Omega - \int_{\Omega} M_{ij,ij}\delta w d\Omega - \int_{\Omega} p\delta w d\Omega =$$

$$= - \int_{\Omega} [M_{ij,ij} + N_{ij}w_{,ij} + p]\delta w d\Omega +$$

$$+ \int_{L} N_{ij}n_j w_{,i}\delta w ds - \int_{L} M_{ij}n_j\delta w_{,i}ds + \int_{L} M_{ij,j}n_i\delta w ds = 0, \quad \text{(A.2.28)}$$

where again the divergence theorem has been applied.

The expression (A.2.28) has to be satisfied for all admissible δw, so we conclude that

$$M_{ij,ij} + N_{ij}w_{,ij} + p = 0, \quad \text{on } \Omega, \quad \text{(A.2.29)}$$

while at the boundary the equation

$$\int_{L} (N_{ij}n_j w_{,i} + M_{ij,j}n_i)\delta w ds - \int_{L} M_{ij}n_j\delta w_{,i}ds = 0 \quad \text{(A.2.30)}$$

must hold. We next transform the second integral of (A.2.30). We have

$$- \int_{L} M_{ij}n_j\delta w_{,i}ds = - \int_{L} M_n \delta \frac{\partial w}{\partial n} ds + \int_{L} \frac{\partial M_{ns}}{\partial s}\delta w ds, \quad \text{(A.2.31)}$$

for a sufficiently smooth boundary, where $\frac{\partial}{\partial n}$ and $\frac{\partial}{\partial s}$ denote derivatives in the (outward) normal and tangential direction of the boundary respectively, while M_n is the normal component of the moment and M_{ns} the twisting moment, all per unit length. The term $N_{ij}n_j w_{,i}$ in (A.2.30) denotes an apparent shear force. For some boundary conditions it is exactly zero, sometimes it is very small. We shall neglect this term. The normal shear force is given by the equation $Q_n = M_{ij,j}n_i$, while the reduced shear force is defined $\bar{Q}_n = Q_n + \frac{\partial M_{ns}}{\partial s}$. With this notation and assumption, (A.2.30) becomes

$$\int_{L} (\bar{Q}_n \delta w - M_n \delta \frac{\partial w}{\partial n}) ds = 0. \quad \text{(A.2.32)}$$

The identity (A.2.32) is satisfied for the most important boundary conditions. For a clamped edge we have

$$w = \frac{\partial w}{\partial n} = 0, \tag{A.2.33}$$

for a simply supported edge

$$w = M_n = 0, \tag{A.2.34}$$

while at a free edge we have

$$\bar{Q}_n = M_n = 0. \tag{A.2.35}$$

It may be of some interest to state explicitly the expressions for M_n and $\bar{Q}_n$. We have

$$M_n = -D_M \left[\frac{\partial^2 w}{\partial n^2} + \nu \left(\frac{\partial^2 w}{\partial s^2} + \frac{1}{R} \frac{\partial w}{\partial n} \right) + \kappa_{T1} \right], \tag{A.2.36}$$

$$\bar{Q}_n = -D_M \left[\frac{\partial}{\partial n} \nabla^2 w + (1-\nu) \frac{\partial}{\partial s} \left(\frac{\partial^2 w}{\partial n \partial s} - \frac{1}{R} \frac{\partial w}{\partial s} \right) + \frac{\partial \kappa_{T1}}{\partial n} \right], \tag{A.2.37}$$

where R is the radius of curvature of the boundary.

The equation for the deflection is obtained from (A.2.29) by using (A.2.11). We find that

$$D_M \nabla^2 \nabla^2 w - N_{ij} w_{,ij} + D_M \nabla^2 \kappa_{T1} + p = 0. \tag{A.2.38}$$

The equations (A.2.26) are identically satisfied if N_{ij} can be expressed in terms of an Airy function A:

$$N_{11} = \frac{\partial^2 A}{\partial y^2}, \quad N_{22} = \frac{\partial^2 A}{\partial x^2}, \quad N_{12} = -\frac{\partial^2 A}{\partial x \partial y}. \tag{A.2.39}$$

The function A has to satisfy the equation

$$\nabla^2 \nabla^2 A + \frac{Eh}{1+\nu} \nabla^2 \epsilon_{T1} = Eh \left[\left(\frac{\partial^2 w}{\partial x \partial y} \right)^2 - \frac{\partial^2 w}{\partial x^2} \cdot \frac{\partial^2 w}{\partial y^2} \right]. \tag{A.2.40}$$

The equations (A.2.38) to (A.2.40) form a complete set of (non−linear) equations for the unknowns w, A, N_{11}, N_{22}, N_{12}. This system has to be

218

solved under suitable boundary conditions.

In table AI we collect some important combinations of boundary conditions

deflection	mid—plane deformation	symbol
clamped	restrained	
	unrestrained	
supported	restrained	
	unrestrained	
free	restrained	
	unrestrained	

Table AI

A.3. General Solutions

In all cases to be considered the temperature field $(T - T_0)$ will be known, so that κ_{T1} and ϵ_{T1} can be calculated. We then have to solve the equations (A.2.38) to (A.2.40) for w and N_{ij}. In many situations of practical interest the right hand side of (A.2.40) is equal to zero, or may be neglected. Then N_{ij} can be determined independently of w as the equations are uncoupled. In particular, this is the case with the determination of the buckling forces. In the prebuckling state w is equal to zero if p is equal to zero. In the postbuckling state large deflections will occur and the equation (A.2.40) must be solved in its complete form.

In this appendix the determination of the buckling forces will be based upon (A.2.38) and

$$\nabla^2\nabla^2 A + \frac{Eh}{1+\nu}\nabla^2\epsilon_{T1} = 0, \qquad (A.3.1)$$

while postbuckling behaviour will be discussed by means of (A.2.38) and (A.2.26). As has already been pointed out in §4.1, the equation (A.3.1) may be written in the form

$$\nabla^2 [\nabla^2 A + Eh\, \epsilon_T] = 0, \tag{A.3.2}$$

which can be split into two equations

$$\nabla^2 A^{(T)} = -Eh\, \epsilon_T \tag{A.3.3}$$

and

$$\nabla^2 \nabla^2 A^* = 0. \tag{A.3.4}$$

The middle—plane forces derived from (A.3.3) and (A.3.4) may be written in the form

$$N_{ij} = N_{ij}^{(T)} + N_{ij}^*. \tag{A.3.5}$$

For $T = T_0$, we have $\epsilon_T = 0$ and the buckling forces are independent of T. This case is insignificant for the theory of thermal buckling.

We also may split the equation (A.2.38) by introducing $w^{(T)}$ and w^*, which satisfy

$$w = w^{(T)} + w^*, \tag{A.3.6}$$

and

$$\nabla^2 \nabla^2 w^{(T)} - \frac{N_{ij}}{D_M}\, w_{,ij}^{(T)} + \nabla^2 \kappa_{T1} = 0, \tag{A.3.7}$$

$$\nabla^2 \nabla^2 w^* - \frac{N_{ij}}{D_M}\, w_{,ij}^* + \frac{p}{D_M} = 0. \tag{A.3.8}$$

In this way the effects of the bending loads $D_M \nabla^2 \kappa_{T1}$ and p are separated.

We assume the temperature difference to be given in the form $\lambda(T - T_0)$, where λ is a parameter which increases from zero to a critical value λ_{cr}. We further assume that N_{ij} has the form $\lambda N_{ij}^{(0)}$, which means that the vorly mide-plane forces are temperature and reaction forces. $N_{ij}^{(0)}$ of course satisfies the equation (A.3.1) with $\lambda = 1$. For every small values of λ, (A.3.7) may be approximated by

$$\nabla^2 \nabla^2 w^{(T)} = -\nabla^2 \kappa_{T1}, \tag{A.3.9}$$

the usual bending equation. If λ increases, we have to take into account the

220

complete equation (A.3.7), while buckling occurs at the least value of λ for which the homogeneous equation

$$\nabla^2 \nabla^2 w(T) = \lambda \frac{N_{ij}^{(0)}}{D_M} w_{,ij}^{(T)} \qquad (A.3.10)$$

has a non–trivial solution.

We remark that the buckling value λ_{cr} can only be determined by (A.3.10) if N_{ij} is independent of w, as has been assumed in the derivation of (A.3.1).

In many cases it is not possible to solve the eigenvalue problem (A.3.10) in closed form, due to the fact that the forces $N_{ij}^{(0)}$ are not constant. We shall have to consider some methods for the determination of an appropriate solution (compare the discussion in [A7]). We therefore consider the solutions of the equation

$$\nabla^2 \nabla^2 \psi_k - \lambda_k^4 \psi_k = 0, \qquad (A.3.11)$$

defined in the same domain and satisfying the same homogeneous boundary conditions as w (we drop the superscript$^{(T)}$). The set of solutions ψ_k forms (for the usual boundary conditions) an orthonormal system. To prove this, we multiply (A.3.11) by ψ_l, multiply the equation (A.3.11) for ψ_l by ψ_k, substract the results and integrate. We obtain

$$\int_\Omega [\psi_k \nabla^2 \nabla^2 \psi_l - \psi_l \nabla^2 \nabla^2 \psi_k] d\Omega - (\lambda_k^4 - \lambda_l^4) \int_\Omega \psi_k \psi_l d\Omega = 0. \qquad (A.3.12)$$

As in our derivation of (A.2.32), we can prove that the first integral is equal to

$$\int_\Omega [\psi_k \bar{Q}_n^{(\psi_l)} - \psi_l \bar{Q}_n^{(\psi_k)} - \frac{\partial \psi_k}{\partial n} M_n^{(\psi_l)} + \frac{\partial \psi_l}{\partial n} M_n^{(\psi_k)}] d\Omega, \qquad (A.3.13)$$

where the reduced shear forces $\bar{Q}_n^{(\psi)}$ and bending moments $M_n^{(\psi)}$ associated with the defection ψ have been introduced. This integral vanishes because of the boundary conditions. So we find for $\lambda_k \neq \lambda_l$

$$\int_\Omega \psi_k \psi_l d\Omega = 0. \qquad (A.3.14)$$

It can be proved that all λ_k are different. After normalization we have

$$\int_{\Omega} \psi_k \psi_l \, d\Omega = \delta_{kl}. \qquad (A.3.15)$$

We represent w by a series of the form

$$w = \sum_{k=1}^{\infty} a_k \psi_k \qquad (A.3.16)$$

and substitute this series into (A.3.10). With the aid of the expressions (A.3.11) and (A.3.15) we obtain

$$a_k + \frac{\lambda}{D_M} \frac{1}{\lambda_k^4} \sum_{l=1}^{\infty} a_l b_{lk} = 0, \quad k = 1, 2, \ldots, \infty, \qquad (A.3.17)$$

– an infinite series of algebraic equations for a_k with b_{lk} defined by

$$b_{lk} = \int_{\Omega} N_{ij}^{(0)} (\psi_k)_{,i} (\psi_l)_{,j} \, d\Omega - \int_{L} N_{ij}^{(0)} n_j (\psi_l)_{,i} \psi_k \, ds. \quad (A.3.18)$$

In (A.3.18) the second integral will often be neglected.

The least eigenvalue λ in the equation (A.3.10) may also be determined approximately by means of Rayleigh's method. To this end we write (A.3.10) in the form

$$M_{ij,ij} + \lambda N_{ij}^{(0)} w_{,ij} = 0, \qquad (A.3.19)$$

multiply this expression by w and integrate over the domain. Neglecting the integral

$$\int_{L} N_{ij}^{(0)} n_j w_{,i} w \, ds,$$

we find that the least eigenvalue is given by the equation.

$$\lambda = \frac{\displaystyle\int_{\Omega} M_{ij} w_{,ij} \, d\Omega}{\displaystyle\int_{\Omega} N_{ij}^{(0)} w_{,i} w_{,j} \, d\Omega} . \qquad (A.3.20)$$

222

It appears that if κ_{T1} is equal to zero and $N_{ij}^{(0)}$ is independent of $w_{,j}$, which is the case before buckling, the equation (A.3.20) is equivalent to

$$\lambda = \frac{-\bar{F}_2}{\bar{F}_1}, \tag{A.3.21}$$

from which the important conclusion

$$\delta\lambda = -\frac{\bar{F}_1\delta\bar{F}_2 - \bar{F}_2\delta\bar{F}_1}{\bar{F}_1^2} = -\frac{1}{\bar{F}_1}\delta(\bar{F}_2 + \lambda\bar{F}_1) = 0 \tag{A.3.22}$$

follows. The equation (A.3.22) expresses the fact, that the critical value of λ is a stationary one.

The problem has been reduced to the determination of an extremum of

$$\lambda = \frac{-\displaystyle\int_\Omega [(1-\nu)w_{,ij}w_{,ij} + \nu w_{,kk}^2]\,d\Omega}{\displaystyle\int_\Omega N_{ij}^{(0)}w_{,i}w_{,j}\,d\Omega} \tag{A.3.23}$$

in an appropriate class of competing test functions w.

A.4. The uniform infinite strip

We consider the stability of an infinite strip, occupying the region of space $0 \leqslant x \leqslant l$, $-\infty < y < \infty$, $-h/2 \leqslant z \leqslant h/2$, under the action of thermal forces (cf. fig. A1).

We assume that the temperature field and the stress and deformation field are independent of the coordinate y, while the load p and the displacement v will be taken equal to zero. So we have

$$\frac{\partial}{\partial y} = 0, \qquad p = 0, \qquad v = 0. \tag{A.4.1}$$

It is obvious from (A.2.10) that the last condition of (A.4.1) can only satisfied if appropriate forces N_{ij} have been applied at $y \to \pm\infty$.

With some little modifications the strip analysis may be applied to the case of the buckling of a beam. The equations (A.2.38) and (A.2.26) become

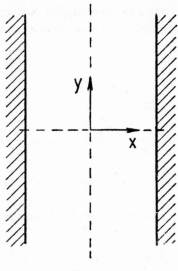

Fig. A1.

for this case

$$\frac{d^4w}{dx^4} - \frac{N_x}{D_M}\frac{d^2w}{dx^2} = -\frac{d^2}{dx^2}\kappa_{T1},$$ (A.4.2)

and

$$\frac{dN_x}{dx} = 0.$$ (A.4.3)

We limit the discussion to the boundary value problem of the simply support-ed plate, so the equations

$$w = 0; \quad M_n = \frac{d^2w}{dx^2} + \kappa_{T1} = 0$$ (A.4.4)

have to be satisfied when $x = 0, l$.

We first consider the case of a prescribed constant compression force P acting along the boundary in the plane of the strip. We have

$$N_x = -P, \quad \text{when} \quad x = 0, l.$$ (A.4.5)

and it follows from (A.4.3) that $N_x = -P$ in the whole domain. The equation

224

(A.4.2) will be integrated twice. Resulting from the boundary conditions (A.4.4) the integration constants must be taken equal to zero and we obtain

$$\frac{d^2w}{dx^2} + k^2 w = -\kappa_{T1} \tag{A.4.6}$$

with

$$k^2 = \frac{P}{D_M}. \tag{A.4.7}$$

The solution of (A.4.6) is

$$w = \int_0^x \frac{\sin k(x-\xi)}{k} \kappa_{T1}(\xi)d\xi - \sin kx \int_0^l \frac{\sin k(l-\xi)}{k \sin kl} \kappa_{T1}(\xi)d\xi. \tag{A.4.8}$$

From (A.4.8) we conclude that w tends to infinity if

$$\sin kl = 0, \quad \text{or} \quad k = n\frac{\pi}{l}, \tag{A.4.9}$$

so the critical compression force is

$$P = \frac{\pi^2}{l^2} D_M, \tag{A.4.10}$$

well known from classical theory.

We now proceed to the more interesting case of the restrained edge:

$$u = 0 \quad \text{when} \quad x = 0, \, l. \tag{A.4.11}$$

The equation (A.4.6) also holds for this problem, and we again introduce P by (A.4.5) and k by (A.4.7). The constant P is now an unknown. From the expression (A.2.10) we have

$$\frac{du}{dx} = -\frac{P}{D_N} - \frac{1}{2}\left(\frac{dw}{dx}\right)^2 + \epsilon_{T1}, \tag{A.4.12}$$

from which we derive

$$\int_0^l \left(\frac{dw}{dx}\right)^2 dx = 2\int_0^l \epsilon_{T1} dx - \frac{2Pl}{D_N}. \tag{A.4.13}$$

Before buckling occurs the deflection w is equal to zero and P is found from

$$P = \frac{D_N}{l} \int_0^l \epsilon_{T1}\, dx = D_N \bar{\epsilon}_{T1} \qquad (A.4.14)$$

where $\bar{\epsilon}_{T1}$ has been defined by

$$\bar{\epsilon}_{T1} = \frac{1}{l} \int_0^l \epsilon_{T1}\, dx = \frac{1+\nu}{hl} \int_0^l dx \int_{-h/2}^{h/2} \alpha_T (T - T_0)\, dz. \qquad (A.4.15)$$

If ϵ_{T1} is constant $\bar{\epsilon}_{T1}$ is equal to ϵ_{T1}.

Buckling occurs at the value $k = \pi/l$, from which the critical $\bar{\epsilon}_{T1}$ is obtained

$$(\bar{\epsilon}_{T1})_{cr} = \frac{D_M}{D_N} \cdot \frac{\pi^2}{l^2} = \frac{\pi^2}{12} \frac{h^2}{l^2}. \qquad (A.4.16)$$

Before we proceed to the discussion of the post—buckling behaviour, we first investigate the forms of ϵ_{T1} and κ_{T1}. In the absence of heat sources, the heat conduction equation is

$$\frac{\partial^2 T}{\partial x^2} + \frac{\partial^2 T}{\partial z^2} = 0, \qquad (A.4.17)$$

which has to be supplemented by boundary conditions. A solution with prescribed temperature at the boundaries can be represented by

$$T - T_0 = \sum_{k=1}^{\infty} f_k(z) \sin \frac{k\pi x}{l}, \qquad (A.4.18)$$

where the functions $f_k(z)$ are given by

$$f_k(z) = A_k \cosh \frac{k\pi z}{l} + B_k \sinh \frac{k\pi z}{l}. \qquad (A.4.19)$$

The constants A_k and B_k are determined from the surface temperatures. We find from (A.4.19) with constant α_T

$$\epsilon_{T1} = \frac{2(1+\nu)}{\pi} \frac{l}{h} \alpha_T \sum_{k=1}^{\infty} A_k \frac{\sinh \dfrac{k\pi h}{2l}}{k} \sin \frac{k\pi x}{l}, \qquad (A.4.20)$$

226

and

$$\kappa_{T1} = \frac{12(1+\nu)}{\pi} \frac{l}{h^3} \alpha_T \sum_{k=1}^{\infty} B_k \left(\frac{h \cosh\dfrac{k\pi h}{2l} - \dfrac{2\ell}{k\pi} \sinh\dfrac{k\pi h}{2l}}{k} \right) \sin\frac{k\pi x}{l}. \quad \text{(A.4.21)}$$

Substituting the expression (A.4.20) into (A.4.15) we find that $\bar{\epsilon}_{T1}$ can be represented by

$$\bar{\epsilon}_{T1} = \frac{2(1+\nu)}{\pi^2} \frac{l}{h} \alpha_T \sum_{k=1}^{\infty} A_k (1-(-1)^k) \frac{\sinh\dfrac{k\pi h}{2l}}{k^2}, \quad \text{(A.4.22)}$$

while κ_{T1} can be represented by

$$\kappa_{T1} = \sum_{n=1}^{\infty} m_n \sin\frac{n\pi x}{l}, \quad \text{(A.4.23)}$$

with

$$m_n = \frac{12(1+\nu)}{\pi} \frac{l}{h^3} \alpha_T B_n \frac{n \cosh\dfrac{n\pi h}{2\ell} - \dfrac{2l}{n\pi} \sinh\dfrac{n\pi h}{2l}}{n}. \quad \text{(A.4.24)}$$

The solution of (A.4.6) is obtained in the form

$$w = \sum_{n=1}^{\infty} w_n \sin\frac{n\pi x}{l}, \quad \text{(A.4.25)}$$

where

$$w_n = \frac{m_n}{\dfrac{n^2 \pi^2}{l^2} - k^2}. \quad \text{(A.4.26)}$$

Substituting from (A.4.25) into (A.4.13) we obtain

$$\frac{\pi^2}{4l^2} \sum_{n=1}^{\infty} \frac{m_n^2}{\left(\dfrac{n^2 \pi^2}{l^2} - k^2\right)^2} = \bar{\epsilon}_{T1} - k^2 \frac{D_M}{D_N}, \quad \text{(A.4.27)}$$

a transcendental equation for k. The series in (A.4.27) is a rapidly convergent one and we hope to obtain a good estimate for k^2 by considering only the first term. We then have

$$\frac{\pi^2}{4l^2} \frac{m_1^2}{\left(\dfrac{\pi^2}{l^2} - k^2\right)^2} = \overline{\epsilon}_{T1} - k^2 \frac{D_M}{D_N}. \qquad (A.4.28)$$

To simplify the discussion we transform the expression (A.4.28) by means of the abbreviations

$$p = 1 - \frac{k^2 l^2}{\pi^2}, \quad s = \frac{\overline{\epsilon}_{T1}}{(\overline{\epsilon}_{T1})_{cr}} - 1, \quad m^2 = \frac{m_1^2 l^2}{4\pi^2 (\overline{\epsilon}_{T1})_{cr}}, \qquad (A.4.29)$$

into

$$p^3 + p^2 s - m^2 = 0. \qquad (A.4.30)$$

The maximum deflection $w_{max} = \dfrac{m_1}{\dfrac{\pi^2}{l^2} - k^2}$, becomes in this notation

$$w_{max} = \frac{h}{\sqrt{3}} \frac{m}{p}. \qquad (A.4.31)$$

We write the equation (A.4.30) in the form

$$q^3 - 1/3\, s^2 q + (\frac{2}{27} s^3 - m^2) = 0, \qquad (A.4.32)$$

by putting $p = q - 1/3\, s$.

The expression (A.4.32) can further be simplified, if $s \neq 0$. With $q = 1/3\, sr$, the equation (A.4.32) becomes

$$(r-1)^2 (r+2) = \alpha \qquad (A.4.33)$$

where

$$\alpha = \frac{27 m^2}{s^3}. \qquad (A.4.34)$$

In this notation is

$$w_{\text{max}} = \sqrt{3}\,h\,\frac{m}{(r-1)s}. \tag{A.4.35}$$

The equation (A.4.33) has double roots if the discriminant D is equal to zero. D is defined for the equation of the third degree $x^3 + ax + b = 0$ by

$$D = -4a^3 - 27b^2. \tag{A.4.36}$$

If $D < 0$ only one root is real, while if $D > 0$ the three roots are all real [A8]. For the equation (A.4.33) D is zero if $\alpha = 0$ or $\alpha = 4$. For $\alpha = 4$ the double root is $r = -1$, while the single root is $r = 2$.

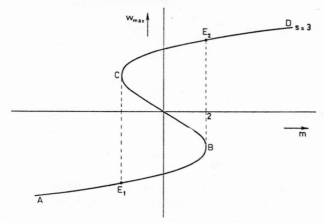

Fig. A2.

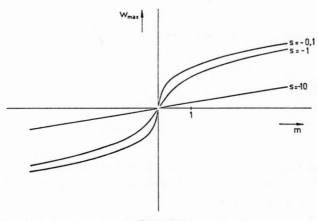

Fig. A3.

After the calculation of the roots of (A.4.33) for different combinations of m and s, the function w_{max} is determined from (A.4.35). In fig. A2 w_{max} is plotted as a function of m for constant $s > 0$, in fig. A3 for constant $s < 0$. Notice that for $s < -1$, k becomes imaginary.

In fig. A4 the deflection is shown as a function of s for constant $m > 0$

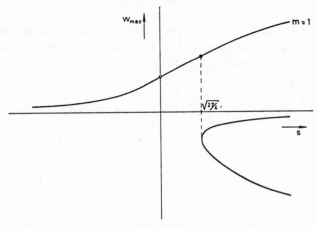

Fig. A4.

The asymptotic behaviour of w_{max} can easily be obtained from (A.4.33) to (A.4.35). If s constant and $|m|$ tends to infinity we have

$$w_{max} \approx \frac{h}{\sqrt{3}} m^{1/3}. \qquad (A.4.37)$$

If m is constant we find for very large $|s|$:

$$s \to -\infty \; : \; |w| \approx \frac{h}{\sqrt{3}} \frac{|m|}{|s|}, \qquad (A.4.38)$$

$$s \to +\infty \; : \; |w| \approx \frac{h}{\sqrt{3}} \sqrt{s}. \qquad (A.4.39)$$

We remark that $s < 0$, $\alpha < 0$ and $D < 0$, so only one deflection exists for all values of m, cf. fig. A2. This may be expected: stretching due to temperature decrease can never lead to instability.

The fig. A2 and A4 show some intervals, where three deflections exist. It may be expected that some of them are unstable. If in fig. A2 the value of

m is increased from $-\infty$ to $+\infty$ the deflection follows the curve AE_1BE_2D. If the loading is reversed, the curve DE_2CE_1A is traversed. In both loading cases a jump will occur, from B to E_2 and from C to E_1 respectively. The phenomenon described in this way is called 'snapping' and is well known in practice. If in fig. A4 the value of s is increased from $-\infty$ to $+\infty$ no jump will occur.

It is possible to investigate the stability of the equilibrium positions by means of the expressions (A.2.16) to (A.2.18). A stable equilibrium requires a relative minimum of the free energy functional. For the case under consideration the specific free energy $\bar{F}$ has the form

$$\bar{F} = \tfrac{1}{2} D_M \left(\left(\frac{\partial^2 w}{\partial x^2} \right)^2 + 2\kappa_{T1} \frac{\partial^2 w}{\partial x^2} \right) + \frac{1}{2D_N(1-\nu^2)} (N_x^2 + N_y^2 - 2\nu N_x N_y) - D_N \frac{\epsilon_{T1}^2}{1+\nu}.$$

With $\hspace{8cm}$ (A.4.40)

$$N_x = -P,$$

$$N_y = -\nu P - D_N(1-\nu)\epsilon_{T1},$$

the expression (A.4.40) may be written as

$$\bar{F} = \tfrac{1}{2} D_M \left(\left(\frac{\partial^2 w}{\partial x^2} \right)^2 + 2\kappa_{T1} \frac{\partial^2 w}{\partial x^2} \right) + \frac{1}{2D_N} P^2 - \tfrac{1}{2} D_N \epsilon_{T1}^2. \quad \text{(A.4.41)}$$

To simplify the analysis we restrict ourselves to the case ϵ_{T1} = constant. The energy functional becomes

$$\frac{\bar{F}}{D_M} = \tfrac{1}{2} \int_0^l (w'')^2 dx + \int_0^l \kappa_{T1} w'' dx + \tfrac{1}{2} l \left(\frac{D_N}{D_M} k^4 - \frac{D_N}{D_M} \epsilon_{T1}^2 \right) \quad \text{(A.4.42)}$$

from which after variation of w, subject to the condition

$$\int_0^l (w')^2 dx = 2l \left(\epsilon_{T1} - \frac{D_M}{D_N} k^2 \right), \hspace{3cm} \text{(A.4.43)}$$

we find the equation (A.4.2), as we should.

We eliminate κ_{T1} from (A.4.42) and (A.4.6) and obtain

231

$$\frac{\overline{\overline{F}}}{D_M} = -\tfrac{1}{2} \int_0^l (w'')^2 dx - \tfrac{1}{2}\ell \left[\left(3k^2 \sqrt{\frac{D_M}{D_N}} - \epsilon_{T1} \sqrt{\frac{D_N}{D_M}} \right) \cdot \left(k^2 \sqrt{\frac{D_M}{D_N}} - \epsilon_{T1} \sqrt{\frac{D_N}{D_M}} \right) \right] =$$

$$= -\tfrac{1}{2} \int_0^l (w'')^2 dx + \frac{\pi^2}{2} \frac{(\overline{\epsilon}_{T1})_{cr}}{l} ((p+s)(2-3p-s)). \qquad (A.4.44)$$

The integration in (A.4.44) can be easily carried out. The result is

$$\frac{\overline{\overline{F}}}{D_M} = \frac{\pi^2}{l} (\overline{\epsilon}_{T1})_{cr} \left[-\frac{9m^2}{(r-1)^2 s^2} + \frac{s}{6}(2+r)(2-sr) \right], \qquad (A.4.45)$$

which may be simplified to the final form

$$\frac{\overline{\overline{F}}}{D_M} = \frac{\pi^2}{6l}(\overline{\epsilon}_{T1})_{cr}. - s^2 r (r+2). \qquad (A.4.46)$$

From the expression (A.4.46) the second derivative of $\overline{\overline{F}}$ with respect to m at constant s may be calculated. It is found that

$$\frac{d^2}{dm^2}\left[\frac{\overline{\overline{F}}}{D_M} \frac{6l}{\pi^2} \frac{1}{(\overline{\epsilon}_{T1})_{cr}} \right] = -\frac{12}{s}\frac{1}{r+1}, \qquad (A.4.47)$$

from which the stability of the branches $AE_1 B$ and $DE_2 C$ in fig. A2 follows, since it may be proved that this expression is proportional to $-\dfrac{\partial w_{max}}{\partial m}$, while the parameter r varied continuously from infinity to -1. Along the branch BC we have $r < -1$. We conclude that the double roots of (A.4.33) are points of instability, while the single root represents a stable equilibrium position. The energy which is gained during the jump can easily be calculated. Finally, we notice that the point $w_{max} = 0$ represents a stable equilibrium position, if $m = 0$ and $s \leqslant 0$.

A.5. The circular plate without heat source

We next consider the circular plate and we shall limit the discussion to the case of a plate which is simply supported at the edge, while the radial displacement of the middle plane is restrained [A7]. We also limit the discussion to the case of cylindrical symmetry. The equation for the deflection

232

(A.2.38) becomes

$$\nabla^2 \nabla^2 w + \nabla^2 \kappa_{T1} = \frac{1}{D_M} \left(N_{rr} \frac{d^2 w}{dr^2} + N_{\theta\theta} \frac{1}{r} \frac{dw}{dr} \right), \qquad (A.5.1)$$

where ∇^2 has now the form

$$\nabla^2 = \frac{d^2}{dr^2} + \frac{1}{r} \frac{d}{dr}.$$

The equilibrium equation (A.2.26) is of the form

$$N_{rr,r} + \frac{N_{rr} - N_{\theta\theta}}{r} = 0, \qquad (A.5.2)$$

while the equations (A.2.10) become

$$N_{rr} = D_N(u_{,r} + v\frac{u}{r} + \tfrac{1}{2}(w_{,r})^2 - \epsilon_{T1}), \qquad (A.5.3)$$

$$N_{\theta\theta} = D_N(\frac{u}{r} + v(u_{,r} + \tfrac{1}{2}(w_{,r})^2) - \epsilon_{T1}), \qquad (A.5.4)$$

where u denotes the radial displacement.

By means of the equation (A.5.2) we can eliminate the force $N_{\theta\theta}$ in (A.5.1), to transform that equation to

$$\nabla^2 \nabla^2 w + \nabla^2 \kappa_{T1} = \frac{1}{D_M} \frac{1}{r} (-(r N_{rr} w_{,r}),_r),_r). \qquad (A.5.5)$$

If we eliminate $w_{,r}$ and $u_{,r}$ from (A.5.3) and (A.5.4), we have the equation

$$u = \frac{r}{Eh} [N_{\theta\theta} - v N_{rr}] + \frac{r}{1+v} \epsilon_{T1}.$$

Substituting $N_{\theta\theta}$ from (A.5.2) into this expression we find that

$$u = \frac{r}{Eh} ((r N_{rr}),_r - v N_{rr}) + \frac{r}{1+v} \epsilon_{T1}. \qquad (A.5.6)$$

If we substitute for u from (A.5.6) into (A.5.3), we find the equation which has to be satisfied by N_{rr}

$$r\frac{d^2N_{rr}}{dr^2} + 3\frac{dN_{rr}}{dr} + \frac{Eh}{1+\nu}\frac{d\epsilon_{T1}}{dr} + \frac{Eh}{2r}\left(\frac{dw}{dr}\right)^2 = 0. \qquad (A.5.7)$$

The heat–conduction equation is, in cylindrical coordinates,

$$\left(\frac{\partial^2}{\partial r} + \frac{1}{r}\frac{\partial}{\partial r} + \frac{\partial^2}{\partial z^2}\right)(T - T_0) = 0, \qquad (A.5.8)$$

under the assumption of the absence of heat sources.

The equation (A.5.8) can be solved under suitable boundary conditions, similar to the equation for the infinite strip (A.4.18). Much information however may be obtained even if we restrict the discussion to the simple solution

$$T - T_0 = p + qz, \qquad (A.5.9)$$

where p and q are constants to be determined from the boundary values on $z = \pm h/2$, which are in this problem independent of r. From (A.5.9) we see that ϵ_{T1} and κ_{T1} are constants.

Under these restrictions the problem is reduced to the determination of the solution of the equations

$$D_M\left(\frac{1}{r}(rw_{,r})_{,r}\right)_{,r} = N_{rr}w_{,r} \qquad (A.5.10)$$

$$r\left(\frac{1}{r}(r^2N_{rr})_{,r}\right)_{,r} + \frac{Eh}{2}(w_{,r})^2 = 0. \qquad (A.5.11)$$

For the boundary conditions we have

$$w = 0,$$

$$M_r = -D_M\left(\frac{d^2w}{dr^2} + \frac{\nu}{r}\frac{dw}{dr} + \kappa_{T1}\right) = 0 \quad \text{when} \quad r = R, \qquad (A.5.12)$$

and

$$u = 0 \quad \text{when} \quad r = R, \qquad (A.5.13)$$

if R is the radius of the circular plate.

At the centre of the plate, $r = 0$, the deflection w has to remain finite. The boundary condition (A.5.13) may be expressed in the form

$$(rN_{rr})_{,r} - \nu N_{rr} + \frac{Eh}{1+\nu}\epsilon_{T1} = 0 \quad \text{when} \quad r = R. \tag{A.5.14}$$

By the introduction of the quantities [A7]

$$\rho = \frac{r}{R}, \quad \varphi = \frac{1}{R}w_{,\rho}, \quad \psi = -\frac{rN_{rr}}{Ehr},$$

$$\tag{A.5.15}$$

$$k = 12(1-\nu^2)R^2, \quad \kappa = R\kappa_{T1}, \quad \epsilon = \frac{\epsilon_{T1}}{1+\nu},$$

the equations (A.5.10) and (A.5.11) are simplified and the following system is obtained

$$\varphi'' + \frac{1}{\rho}\varphi' - \frac{1}{\rho^2}\rho = -k\frac{\varphi\psi}{\rho}, \tag{A.5.16}$$

$$\psi'' + \frac{1}{\rho}\psi' - \frac{1}{\rho^2}\psi = \tfrac{1}{2}\frac{\varphi^2}{\rho}, \tag{A.5.17}$$

while the boundary conditions become

$$\varphi = \psi = 0, \quad \text{when} \quad \rho = 0,$$

$$\varphi' + \nu\varphi + \kappa = 0, \tag{A.5.18}$$

$$\psi' - \nu\psi - \epsilon = 0 \quad \text{when} \quad \rho = 1.$$

We introduce the new variables $\overline{\varphi}, \overline{\psi}$ by

$$\varphi = \overline{\varphi} + a\rho$$

$$\psi = \overline{\psi} + b\rho, \tag{A.5.19}$$

with

$$a = -\frac{\kappa}{1+\nu}, \quad b = \frac{\epsilon}{1-\nu}, \tag{A.5.20}$$

and obtain

$$\overline{\varphi}'' + \frac{1}{\rho}\overline{\varphi}' - \frac{1}{\rho^2}\overline{\varphi} = -k\frac{(\overline{\varphi}+a\rho)(\overline{\psi}+b\rho)}{\rho}$$

235

$$\bar{\psi}'' + \frac{1}{\rho}\bar{\psi}' - \frac{\bar{\psi}}{\rho^2} = \frac{1}{2}\frac{(\bar{\psi} + a\rho)^2}{\rho} . \tag{A.5.21}$$

The boundary conditions take the form

$$\bar{\varphi} = \bar{\psi} = 0, \quad \text{when} \quad \rho = 0,$$

$$\bar{\varphi}' + \nu\bar{\varphi} = 0, \tag{A.5.22}$$

$$\bar{\psi}' - \nu\bar{\psi} = 0, \quad \text{when} \quad \rho = 1.$$

We try to solve the system (A.5.21) by means of the following expansion into series of the variable ρ

$$\bar{\varphi} = \sum_{l=0}^{\infty} a_{2l}\,\rho^{2l+1},$$

$$\bar{\psi} = \sum_{l=0}^{\infty} b_{2l}\,\rho^{2l+1}. \tag{A.5.23}$$

Substituting the series (A.5.23) into the equations (A.5.21), and equating to zero the coefficients of the different powers of ρ, we arrive at the following formulae

$$4(l+1)(l+2)a_{2l+2} + k\left[\sum_{n=0}^{l} a_{2n}b_{2l-2n} + ba_{2l} + ab_{2l} + ab\delta_{l0}\right] = 0, \quad l = 0, 1, \ldots \tag{A.5.24}$$

$$4(l+1)(l+2)b_{2l+2} - \frac{1}{2}\left[\sum_{n=0}^{l} a_{2n}a_{2l-2n} + 2aa_{2l} + a^2\delta_{l0}\right] = 0, \quad l = 0, 1, \ldots$$

while the substitution into the boundary conditions (A.5.22) leads to:

$$\sum_{l=0}^{\infty} a_{2l}\,[2l+1+\nu] = 0,$$

$$\sum_{l=0}^{\infty} b_{2l}\,[2l+1-\nu] = 0, \tag{A.5.25}$$

236

We approximate the solution by retaining only the terms with $l = 0$, and $l = 1$. Then we find from (A.5.25) that a_2 and b_2 are given respectively by the equations

$$a_2 = -\frac{1+\nu}{3+\nu}a_0,$$

$$b_2 = -\frac{1-\nu}{3-\nu}b_0,$$

(A.5.26)

while the equations (A.5.24) may be restricted to $l = 0$, from which we deduce

$$\left. \begin{array}{l} -8\dfrac{1-\nu}{3-\nu}b_0 = \tfrac{1}{2}(a_0+a)^2, \\[2ex] -8\dfrac{1+\nu}{3+\nu}a_0 = -k(a_0+a)(b_0+b). \end{array} \right\}$$

(A.5.27)

Eliminating b_0 from (A.5.27) we find that

$$\bar{a}_0^3 + \bar{a}_0\left(-16\frac{1-\nu}{3-\nu}b + \frac{128}{k}\frac{1-\nu^2}{9-\nu^2}\right) - \frac{128}{k}\frac{1-\nu^2}{9-\nu^2}a = 0, \quad \text{(A.5.28)}$$

where $\bar{a}_0 = a_0 + a$.

This is an equation of the third degree, which is similar to the equation (A.4.28) of the strip. We consider some special cases

(1) if $a = 0$, then $\kappa_{T1} = 0$ and we have either

$$\bar{a}_0 = 0 \quad \text{or} \quad \bar{a}_0^2 + \left(-16\frac{1-\nu}{3-\nu}b + \frac{128}{k}\frac{1-\nu^2}{9-\nu^2}\right) = 0. \quad \text{(A.5.29)}$$

The second solution only exists for

$$b \geqslant \frac{8}{k}\frac{1+\nu}{3+\nu},$$

(A.5.30)

from which we derive the buckling value

$$(\epsilon_{T1})_{cr} = \frac{8}{k}(1-\nu^2)\frac{1+\nu}{3+\nu} - \frac{2}{3}\frac{1+\nu}{3+\nu}\frac{h^2}{R^2}.$$

(A.5.31)

237

and the critical temperature

$$(T - T_0)_{cr} = \frac{2}{3} \frac{1}{3 + \nu} \frac{1}{\alpha_T} \frac{h^2}{R^2} . \qquad (A.5.32)$$

After buckling we have

$$\bar{a}_0 = \pm 4 \sqrt{\frac{\alpha_T}{3 - \nu} (T - T_0)_{cr}} \qquad (A.5.33)$$

(2) If $b = 0$, we have $\epsilon_{T1} = 0$ and $D < 0$.

This is the case of bending under thermal forces. Only one deflection exists.

(3) In the general case we have, with the notation $\epsilon_{cr} = \dfrac{(\epsilon_{T1})_{cr}}{1 + \nu}$,

$$\bar{a}_0^3 + \bar{a}_0 \left(-16 \frac{1 - \nu}{3 - \nu} b + 16 \frac{\epsilon_{cr}}{3 - \nu} \right) - 16 \frac{\epsilon_{cr}}{3 - \nu} a = 0. \qquad (A.5.34)$$

The discriminant

$$D = -4 \left(-16 \frac{1 - \nu}{3 - \nu} b + 16 \frac{\epsilon_{cr}}{3 - \nu} \right)^3 - 27 \left(16 \frac{\epsilon_{cr}}{3 - \nu} a \right)^2 ,$$

becomes equal to zero for

$$\epsilon - \epsilon_{cr} = \tfrac{3}{4} \sqrt[3]{3 - \nu} (\epsilon_{cr} a)^{2/3}. \qquad (A.5.35)$$

The roots of (A.5.34), for which $D = 0$, are

$$\bar{a}_0^{(1)} = \bar{a}_0^{(2)} = -4 \sqrt{\frac{1}{3} \frac{1}{3 - \nu} (\epsilon - \epsilon_{cr})},$$

$$\bar{a}_0^{(3)} \qquad = 8 \sqrt{\frac{1}{3} \frac{1}{3 - \nu} (\epsilon - \epsilon_{cr})}. \qquad (A.5.36)$$

It is obvious that $D < 0$ if

$$\epsilon - \epsilon_{cr} < 0, \qquad (A.5.37)$$

which implies that buckling can only occur for a temperature which is higher than the critical temperature, given by (A.5.32). The dependence of $\bar{a}_0$ on a, at a constant value of ϵ, satisfying (A.5.37) is similar to the dependence of w_{max} on m as has been shown in fig. A3.

If

$$\epsilon - \epsilon_{cr} > 0, \qquad (A.5.38)$$

we introduce s and m by

$$s^2 = \frac{48}{3-\nu}(\epsilon - \epsilon_{cr}), \quad m = \frac{2}{27}s^2 + 16\frac{\epsilon_{cr}}{3-\nu}a, \qquad (A.5.39)$$

and we transform the equation (A.5.34) by putting $\bar{a}_0 = \dfrac{1}{3}sr$ into the equation

$$(r-1)^2\,(r+2) = \alpha = \frac{27m}{s^3}\,, \qquad (A.5.40)$$

similar, but not identical with (A.4.34).

In fig. A5 the function $\bar{a}_0$ has been plotted at a constant value of $s > 0$ in dependence of a.

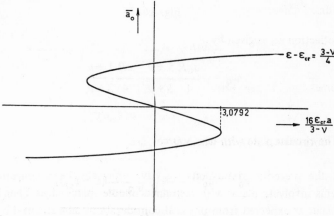

Fig. A5.

In fig. A6 the same function is shown for variable s at constant value of a. The function $\bar{a}_0$ is a measure for the deflection w_0 at the centre. For we have in the approximation under discussion

$$\varphi = a_0\left(\rho - \frac{1+\nu}{3+\nu}\rho^3\right) + a\rho$$

239

from which we derive

$$w = R \int_{1}^{\rho} \varphi d\rho = \frac{\bar{a}_0 R}{2} \left(\rho^2 - \frac{1+\nu}{3+\nu} \frac{\rho^4}{2} - \frac{5+\nu}{6+2\nu} \right) + \frac{aR}{2} \left(-\frac{1+\nu}{6+2\nu} + \frac{1+\nu}{3+\nu} \frac{\rho^4}{2} \right).$$

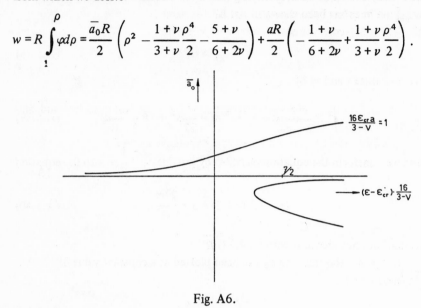

Fig. A6.

The deflection w_0 is given by

$$w_0 = -\frac{\bar{a}_0 R}{4} \frac{5+\nu}{3+\nu} - \frac{aR}{4} \frac{1+\nu}{3+\nu}.$$

A.6. The circular plate with heat source

In the preceding discussions we have especially been concerned with problems involving plates with restrained middle–plane edges. Then buckling may occur as expected from physical considerations and affirmed by mathematical analysis. We now investigate the problem of a circular plate which has a heat source at its centre, uniformly distributed over the thickness. It will appear that in this problem buckling also may occur, not only for the plate with restrained middle–plane edge, but also for the plate with unrestrained edge.

To keep the discussion short, we shall only consider the plate with clamped edges which is unrestrained in the middle–plane. We shall further limit ourselves to the case of circular symmetry. The discussion will be restricted to the determination of the buckling value of the source strength.

Post buckling behaviour will not be discussed.

The heat—conduction equation becomes here

$$\nabla^2 T = -\frac{Q}{\lambda_T} \delta(x) \delta(y), \qquad (A.6.1)$$

where Q denotes the source strength, λ_T the heat—conductivity and $\delta(x)$ Dirac's delta function.

A solution of (A.6.1) with the right singularity at $r = 0$ is

$$T - T_0 = C \log \rho, \qquad (A.6.2)$$

where

$$\rho = \frac{r}{R},$$

and

$$C = -\frac{Q}{2\pi\lambda_T h}. \qquad (A.6.3)$$

If we keep α_T constant and independent of the temperature, we find, from the expression (A.2.13), that

$$\epsilon_{T1} = -\frac{(1 + \nu)Q}{2\pi\lambda_T h} \alpha_T \log \rho. \qquad (A.6.4)$$

The equation (A.5.7) for N_{rr} has to be solved under the boundary condition $N_{rr} = 0$ when $r = R$. In the prebuckling state, we have $w = 0$ and (A.5.7) takes the form

$$\rho \frac{d^2 N_{rr}}{d\rho^2} + 3 \frac{dN_{rr}}{d\rho} - \frac{E\alpha_T Q}{2\pi\lambda_T} \frac{1}{\rho} = 0, \qquad (A.6.5)$$

with the solution

$$N_{rr} = \frac{E\alpha_T Q}{4\pi\lambda_T} \log \rho. \qquad (A.6.6)$$

From the equilibrium condition (A.5.2) we obtain

241

$$N_{\theta\theta} = \frac{E\alpha_T Q}{4\pi\lambda_T}(\log\rho + 1). \tag{A.6.7}$$

The basic equation for the deflection (A.5.5) now becomes

$$\nabla^2\nabla^2 w = \lambda\left(\log\rho\nabla^2 w + \frac{1}{\rho}\frac{\partial w}{\partial\rho}\right), \tag{A.6.8}$$

where the parameter

$$\lambda = \frac{E\alpha_T QR^2}{4\pi\lambda_T D_M}, \tag{A.6.9}$$

has been introduced.

The clamped edge requires

$$w = 0; \qquad \frac{\partial w}{\partial\rho} = 0, \qquad \text{when} \qquad \rho = 1. \tag{A.6.10}$$

The problem (A.6.8) and (A.6.10) is an eigenvalue problem for the determination of λ_{cr}. For its solution we have three methods:

(1) an 'exact' method, due to Mossakowski [A9],

(2) the method of expansion into a series of eigenfunctions,

(3) Rayleigh's method.

For the application of the first method we refer to the literature. Here we shall only apply the methods 2 and 3, the general theory of which has been developed in § A.3.

The eigenfunction—method starts with the determination of the eigenfunctions of the equation (A.3.11), which in this case has the form

$$\left(\frac{d^2}{dr^2} + \frac{1}{r}\frac{d}{dr}\right)^2\psi_k - \lambda_k^4\psi_k = 0. \tag{A.6.11}$$

The solutions of (A.6.11) can be written as

$$\psi_k = A_k J_0(\lambda_k\rho) + B_k I_0(\lambda_k\rho), \tag{A.6.12}$$

where A_k, B_k and λ_k are constants to be determined with the help of the boundary conditions (A.6.10). In the expression (A.6.12), $J_0(\lambda_k\rho)$ and $I_0(\lambda_k\rho)$

are respectively the Bessel function, and the modified Bessel function of the first kind and zero order. We shall require that all eigenfunctions satisfy (A.6.10). Then we have

$$\psi_k = C_k \left(\frac{J_0(\lambda_k \rho)}{J_0(\lambda_k)} - \frac{I_0(\lambda_k \rho)}{I_0(\lambda_k)} \right), \tag{A.6.13}$$

where λ_k is determined by

$$\frac{J_1(\lambda_k)}{J_0(\lambda_k)} + \frac{I_1(\lambda_k)}{I_0(\lambda_k)} = 0. \tag{A.6.14}$$

In the derivation of (A.6.14) the well—known relations

$$J_0'(z) = -J_1(z); \qquad I_0'(z) = +I_1(z)$$

have been used.

The constants C_k may be used to normalize the set of eigenfunctions ψ_k. If we require

$$2\pi \int_0^1 \psi_k^2 \rho d\rho = 1,$$

we obtain the formula

$$C_k = \frac{1}{\sqrt{\pi \left[2 + \dfrac{J_1^2(\lambda_k)}{J_0^2(\lambda_k)} - \dfrac{I_1^2(\lambda_k)}{I_0^2(\lambda_k)} \right]}} \tag{A.6.15}$$

In the derivation of (A.6.15) some identities for Bessel functions have been used. They are

$$\int_0^1 J_0^2(\lambda_k \rho) \rho d\rho = \tfrac{1}{2}(J_0^2(\lambda_k) + J_1^2(\lambda_k)),$$

$$\int_0^1 I_0^2(\lambda_k \rho) \rho d\rho = \tfrac{1}{2}(I_0^2(\lambda_k) - I_1^2(\lambda_k)),$$

and

$$\int\limits_0^1 J_0(\lambda_k\rho)I_0(\lambda_k\rho)\,\rho d\rho = \frac{1}{2\lambda_k}\,[J_1(\lambda_k)I_0(\lambda_k) + J_0(\lambda_k)I_1(\lambda_k)] = 0.$$

We proceed, according to the general theory of § A.3, to expand the deflection w into a series of eigenfunctions ψ_k

$$w = \sum_{k=1}^\infty a_k\psi_k. \tag{A.6.16}$$

For the coefficients α_k we have the following infinite set of algebraic equations

$$a_k = \frac{\lambda}{\lambda_k^4}\sum_{l=1}^\infty a_l b_{lk}, \quad (k = 1, 2, \ldots) \tag{A.6.17}$$

where b_{lk} is determined by

$$b_{lk} = 2\pi\int\limits_0^1 \psi_k\left[\log\rho\left(\frac{1}{\rho}\frac{d}{d\rho}\rho\frac{d\psi_l}{d\rho}\right) + \frac{1}{\rho}\frac{d\psi_l}{d\rho}\right]\rho d\rho =$$

$$= -2\pi\int\limits_0^1 \frac{d\psi_k}{d\rho}\frac{d\psi_l}{d\rho}\cdot\log\rho\,\rho d\rho. \tag{A.6.18}$$

We may find an approximate solution for the least eigenvalue λ, by replacing the infinite system (A.6.17) by a finite one. A very crude approximation may be obtained so by using only one equation. We then have

$$\lambda \approx \frac{\lambda_1^4}{b_{11}}. \tag{A.6.19}$$

By considering more equations we may improve the approximation.

Another method for the approximate determination of the least eigenvalue of the system (A.6.19) is based on the method of Rayleigh.

As we have found in § A.3, the least eigenvalue is given by the formula

$$\lambda = \frac{\frac{1}{2}\int\limits_0^1 2\pi M_{ij}w_{,ij}\rho d\rho}{\frac{1}{2}\int\limits_0^1 2\pi N_{ij}^{(0)}w_{,i}w_{,i}\rho d\rho}. \tag{A.6.20}$$

For this problem the expression (A.6.20) has the form

$$\lambda = -\frac{\int_0^1 \left\{ (1-\nu) \left[(w'')^2 + \frac{1}{\rho^2}(w')^2 \right] + \nu(w'' + \frac{1}{\rho}w')^2 \right\} \rho \, d\rho}{\int_0^1 \log \rho \, (w')^2 \, \rho \, d\rho}$$

$$= -\frac{\int_0^1 \left\{ (w'')^2 + \frac{1}{\rho^2}(w')^2 + 2\nu \frac{1}{\rho} w''w' \right\} \rho \, d\rho}{\int_0^1 \log \rho \, (w')^2 \, \rho \, d\rho} \qquad (A.6.21)$$

The equation (A.6.21) produces the exact value of λ, if the exact form w is substituted. As w is an unknown, we have to make use of the property (A.3.22); in practice we determine the least value of the expression (A.6.21), defined on a class of test functions, which satisfy the boundary conditions. If the class contains the exact eigenfunction, we find the exact eigenvalue, otherwise we find only an approximation. If we extend the class, a better approximation may be found.

In the case under consideration we first take the test function

$$w = 1 - 3\rho^2 + 2\rho^3,$$

which satisfies the conditions (A.6.10). We find that $\lambda = 24.32$. The exact value lies between 20.00 and 20.20. A better approximation may be found by taking

$$w = 1 - 5.44\rho^2 + 7.48\rho^3 - 3.64\rho^4 + 0.60\rho^5.$$

We now obtain

$$\lambda = 20.27.$$

with an error of about 1%.

BIBLIOGRAPHY

1. Abduevskii, V.S. et al., Foundations of Heat Transfer in Aeronautics and Rocket Technology [in Russian], Oborongiz, Moscow, 1960.
2. Afanassjewa–Ehrenfest, T.A., Irreversibility, unidirectionality, and the second law of thermodynamics [in Russian], Zhurn. Prikl. Fiz., Vol. 5, No. 3, 1928.
3. Bazarov, I.P., Thermodynamics, Translated by F. Immirzi, Pergamon Press, 1964.
4. Vashchenko–Zakharchenko, M.E., Symbolic Calculus and Its Application to the Integration of Linear Differential Equations [in Russian], Kiev, 1862.
5. Gatewood, B.E., Thermal Stresses; with applications to airplanes, missiles, turbines, and nuclear reactors [Russian trans.], McGraw–Hill, 1957.
6. Gol'denveizer, A.L., Theory of Elastic Thin Shells [English translation], Pergamon Press, 1961.
7. Gray, A. and Mathews, G.B., A Treatise on Bessel Functions and Their Applications to Physics [Russian translation], Macmillan, 1931.
8. Danilovskaya, V.I., Thermal stresses in an elastic half–space arising after a sudden heating of its boundary [in Russian], Prikl. Math. Mekh., Vol. 14, No. 3, 1950.
9. Danilovskaya, V.I., On a dynamic problem of thermoelasticity [in Russian], Prikl. Math. Mekh. Vol. 16, No. 3, 1952.
10. DeGroot, S.R., Thermodynamics of Irreversible Processes [Russian trans.], Interscience Publishers, New York, 1952.
11. Dinnik, A.N., Application of Bessel functions to elasticity problems, Part 2, Chapter VI, Thermal stresses in a cylinder [in Russian], Izv. Ekaterinosl. gorn. in–ta, 1915.
12. Kantorovich, Z.B., Basic Design of Chemical Machines and Apparatus [in Russian], Mashgiz, Moscow, 1952.
13. Kantorovich, L.V. and Krylov, V.I., Approximate Methods of Higher Analysis [in Russian], Fizmatgiz, Moscow–Leningrad, 1962. English trans. Noordhoff.
14. Kovalenko, A.D., Plates and Shells in Turbine Rotors [in Russian], Izd–vo AN Ukranian SSR, Kiev, 1955.
15. Kovalenko, A.D., Circular Plates of Variable Thickness [in Russian], Fizmatgiz, Moscow, 1959.

16. Kovalenko, A.D., Grigorenko, Ya.M., and Il'in, L.A., Theory of Thin Conical Shells and Their Application in Machine Construction, AN Ukranian SSR Press, Kiev, 1963.

17. Kovalenko, A.D., Exact analytical solution for shells of revolution [in Ukranian], Prikl. Mekh., Vol. 10, No. 3, 1964.

18. Kochin, N.E., Vector Analysis and Introduction to Tensor Calculus [in Russian], AN SSSR Press, Moscow, 1961.

19. Koyalovich, B.M., Study of infinite systems of linear equations [in Russian], Izvestiya FT Steklov Institute, Vol. 3, 1931.

20. Landau, L.D., and Lifshitz, E.M., Mechanics [English translation], Course in Theoretical Physics, Vol. VII, Pergamon Press, 1960.

21. Lebedev, N.N., Thermal Stresses in the Theory of Elasticity, [in Russian], ONTI, Moscow—Leningrad, 1937.

22. Lebedev, N.N., Special Functions and Their Applications [in Russian], Gostekhizdat, Moscow, 1958.

23. Leibenson, L.S., Theory of Elasticity [in Russian], Collected Works, Vol. 1, AN SSSR Press, Moscow, 1951.

24. Leontovich, M.A., Introduction to Thermodynamics [in Russian], Gostekhizdat, Moscow—Leningrad, 1951.

25. Lur'e, A.I., Statics of Thin—walled Elastic Shells [in Russian], Gostekhizdat, Moscow, 1947.

26. Lur'e, A.I., Three—dimensional Problems in the Theory of Elasticity [English translation], Interscience, 1965.

27. Lykov, A.V., Theory of Heat Conduction [in Russian], Gostekhizdat, Moscow, 1962.

28. Madelung, E., Die mathematischen Hilfsmittel des Physikers, [Russian trans.] Grundlagen der mathematischen Wissenschaften, Bd. 4, 6. Auflage, Springer, Berlin, 1957.

29. Maizel', V.M., Generalization of the Betti—Maxwell theorem to the case of thermal stresses and some applications [in Russian]. DAN SSSR, Vol. 30, No. 2, 1941.

30. Maizel', V.M., The Thermal Problem in the Theory of Elasticity [in Russian], AN Ukranian SSR, Kiev, 1951.

31. Melan, P., Parkus, H., Wärmespannungen infolge stationärer Temperaturfelder [Russian translation], Springer—Verlag, Wien, 1953.

32. Motovilovets', I.O., Unsteady Heat Conduction in a Cylinder of Finite Length [in Ukranian]. In book: Problems of thermoelasticity in Energy Producing Machines, AN Ukranian SSR, Kiev, 1960.

33. Muskhelishvili, N.I., On thermal stresses in the plane problem of elasticity [in Russian], Izv. Elektrotekhn. in—ta Prg., Vol. 13, 1916.

34. Muskhelishvili, N.I., Some Basic Problems of the Mathematical Theory of Elasticity [English trans.], Noordhoff, Groningen, 1953.

35. Nowacki, W., Thermoelasticy [English trans.], Pergamon Press, 1962.

36. Novozhilov, V.V., Theory of Elasticity [in Russian], Sudpromgiz, Leningrad, 1958.

37. Novozhilov, V.V., Theory of Thin Shells [English trans.], Noordhoff, Groningen, 1959, 1964.

38. Papkovich, P.F., Expression for the General Integral of the Basic Equations of the Theory of Elasticity in Terms of Harmonic Functions [in Russian], Izvestiya AN SSSR, ser. math. i estestv. nauk, Vol. 10, 1932.

39. Papkovich, P.F., On the general integral for thermal stresses (in connection with an article of Lebedev) [in Russian], PMM Vol. 1, No. 2, 1937.

40. Papkovich, P.F., Theory of Elasticity [in Russian], Oborongiz, Leningrad—Mo cow, 1939.

41. Parkus, H., Instationäre Wärmespannungen [Russian trans.], Springer—Verlag, Wien, 1959.

42. Pidstrigach, Ya.S. and Yarema, S.Ya., Thermal Stresses in Shells [in Ukranian], AN Ukranian SSR, Kiev, 1961.

43. Polozhii, G.N., Equations of Mathematical Physics [in Russian], Vysshaya Shkola Press, Moscow, 1964.

44. Prager, W., Introduction to Mechanics of Continua [Russian trans.], Ginn and Co., 1961.

45. Sedov, L.I., Foundations of the Non—linear Mechanics of Continua [English trans.], Pergamon Press, 1966.

46. Sobolev, S.L., Equations of Mathematical Physics [in Russian], Gostekhizdat, Moscow—Leningrad, 1947.

47. Timoshenko, S.P., Theory of Elasticity [Russian trans.], McGraw—Hill, 1951.

48. Timoshenko, S.P. and Woinowski—Krieger, S., Theory of Plates and Shells [Russian trans.], McGraw—Hill, 1959.

49. Tikhonov, A.N. and Samarskii, A.A., Equations of Mathematical Physics [English trans.], Internation Series of Monographs on Pure and Applied Mathematics, Vol. 39, Pergamon Press.

50. Shiller, N.N., On the Second Law of Thermodynamics and a New Formulation of It [in Russian], Kiev, Univ, izv., 1898.

51. Shiller, N.N., Experimental data and results concerning the second law of

thermodynamics, Kiev, univ. izv., Vol. 3, 1900.

52. Biot, M.A., Thermoelasticity and irreversible thermodynamics. J. Appl. Phys., 1956, 27, 3, pp. 240–253.

53. Boley, B.A. and Barber, A.D., Dynamic response of beams and plates to rapid heating. J. Appl. Mech., 1957, 24, No. 3, p. 413.

54. Boley, B.A. and Weiner, H.J., Theory of thermal stresses, John Wiley, New York–London, 1960.

55. Buchdahl, H.A., On the unrestricted theorem of Carathéodory and its application in the treatment of the second law of thermodynamics. Amer. J. Phys., 1949, 17, 4, p. 212.

56. Carathéodory, C., Untersuchungen über die Grundlagen der Thermodynamik. Math. Ann. 1909, 67.

57. Carslaw, H.S. and Jaeger, J.C., Conduction of heat in solids. Ed. 1. Clarendon Press. Oxford. 1947.

58. Chadwick, P. and Sneddon, I.N., Plane waves in an elastic solid conducting heat. J. Mech. a. Phys. Solids, 1958, 6, No. 3, p. 223,

59. Deresiewics, H., Solution of the equations of thermoelasticity. Proc. 3rd Nat. Congr. Appl. Mech. ASME, 1958, June, p. 257.

60. Afanassjewa–Ehrenfest, T., Zur Axiomatisierung des zweiten Hauptsatzes der Thermodynamik. Zs. Phys., 1925, 33.

61. Goodier, I.N., On the integration of the thermoelastic equations. Phil. Mag., 1937, 7, 23.

62. Hemp, W.S., Fundamental principles and theorems of thermoelasticity. Aeronaut. Quart., 1956, 7, Aug.

63. Lorentz, R., Temperaturspannungen in Hohlzylinder. Z.V.D.I. 1907, 51, 743.

64. Michell, J.H., On the direct determination of stress in an elastic solid, with application to the theory of plates. Proc. Ld. Math. Soc., 1899, 31.

65. Nowacki, W., Thermoelasticity. Pergamon Press, Oxford–London–New York–Paris, 1962.

66. Trostel, R., Instationäre Wärmespannungen in einer Hohlkugel. Ing. Arch., 1956, 24.

67. Trostel, R., Instationäre Wärmespannungen im Hohlzylinder mit Kreisringquerschnitt, Ing. Arch., 1956, 24, 1.

68. Warren, W.E., A transient axisymmetric thermoelastic problem for the hollow sphere. A.I.A.A.J., 1963, 1, 11.

69. Weiner, J.H., A uniqueness theorem for the coupled thermoelastic problem. Quart. Appl. Math., 1957, 15, 1, pp. 102–105.

References

Sokolnikoff, I.S., Mathematical theory of elasticity, McGraw Hill, New York, 1956. [A1]

Melan, E. and H. Parkus, Wärmespannungen, Springer, Wien, 1953. [A2]

Parkus, H., Instationäre Wärmespannungen, Springer, Wien, 1959. [A3]

Novozhilov, V.V., Foundations of the nonlinear theory of elasticity, Graylock Press, Rochester, 1953. [A4]

Green, A.E. and J.E. Adkins, Large elastic deformations, Oxford, 1960. [A5]

Pearson, C.E., Theoretical elasticity, Harvard University Press, Cambridge, Mass., 1959. [A6]

Nowacki, W., Thermoelasticity, Pergamon, Oxford, 1962. [A7]

Perron, O., Algebra II, W. de Gruyter, Berlin, 1951. [A8]

Mossakowski, J., Arch. Mech. Stos. 16, 1023, (1964). [A9]